1976

TERRACIDE

America's Destruction
of Her Living Environment

TERRACIDE

America's Destruction
of Her Living Environment

by Ron M. Linton

Little, Brown and Company Boston-Toronto

LIBRARY OF CONGRESS CATALOG CARD NO. 75-99905

FIRST EDITION

The author wishes to thank Prentice-Hall, Inc.,
for permission to reprint a brief passage from
Crisis in Our Cities by Lewis Herber.

Published simultaneously in Canada
by Little, Brown & Company (Canada) Limited

PRINTED IN THE UNITED STATES OF AMERICA

To Nancy

CONTENTS

CONTENTS

[viii]

TERRACIDE

America's Destruction
of Her Living Environment

PROLOGUE

It was 12:08 P.M. John left his desk, glanced out the window, then walked hurriedly across his office and stepped into the corridor. He was amazed to see that no more than a dozen people stood waiting for the elevator; usually there were twice as many people and a considerable wait before he got down from the seventy-fifth floor. Today he knew a few faces, and one or two names, but he said nothing. It didn't seem long ago to John that he had worked in a building where he had known everyone on the floor, and known them well enough to have had something worthwhile to say to each of them. But these days, conversation was hard to come by, and what greetings were exchanged between individuals were embarrassingly stiff. Occasionally someone would shout at John, "There he is," or "Everything okay." But almost everyone tried to avoid recognition. And this was the way things were getting to be nearly everywhere.

Down below on the street, as John emerged from the building a few minutes later, he was struck by the intensity of the eye sting. He pushed up against the face of the building in order

[3]

to avoid being bumped into by the solid phalanx of pedestrians, and he put on the dark glasses he had absentmindedly left in his pocket. Filth covering the building left a greasy smudge on his suit.

The already dull daylight seemed dimmer from behind dark glasses. Today's was a particularly bad smog, and the streetlights, which in summer normally didn't go on until about four o'clock, were already on. But even so, it was hard to see. The lights just did not penetrate the murky haze of smog. Just before stepping away from the building John took a deep breath, and then — even though the putrid river smell of the air he inhaled somewhat dampened his appetite for lunch — moved to merge into the flowing crowd of pedestrians.

The usual all-day bustle on the street was intensified now by the noontime press of clerks, typists, secretaries, stockboys and messengers, whose lunch hour allowed them no spare time. The mechanical sidewalks moved too slowly for them, and the crowds were so dense that they could not weave. Even though they may have wanted to rush, they simply were not able to, and so they moved ahead as fast as possible in a determined slow motion. Not too long ago it had seemed that time could be made by moving along the street near the curbs. But now the crowds weaved in and out of the traffic in the streets, some moving with the traffic, some cutting across it. Vehicles — mostly delivery trucks and taxis — moved as slowly as the people. Private cars usually stayed on the fringe of the commercial sections of town, but even so there were intense traffic jams in the heart of the city.

John, whose executive lunch hour allowed him leeway, moved along the mechanical sidewalk. As he passed a newspaper vending machine and quickly grabbed a paper, he reflected that his motion had become automatic to tuck it under his arm so that it wouldn't be ripped from his hands. Strange, he thought, how people could move so slowly but with such persistence that they could knock you down.

At last John came to the square he was heading for, and he turned and crossed the street, glad to be turning away also from a construction site on the corner which was thundering a variety of deafening sounds.

When he arrived at his luncheon restaurant there already was a long line and he had twenty minutes of being pushed and jostled by passing pedestrians before he could get inside. Once he was inside it was another forty minutes before he was able to get a table — this was an old restaurant and amazingly its sit-down table service still survived. It was now 1:53 P.M. — he would be back at the office at three. This was the leisure society — a six-hour day and a thirty-hour week, plus three hours to get to and from lunch.

I

PEOPLE

1

LIFE IN A CROWD

In the cities it has become impossible to say who is "normal" and who isn't. The word "normal" for all practical purposes is obsolete. Standards of conduct cannot be measured against those of a decade ago, let alone fifty years ago. Living conditions have so changed social behavior that sociologists and psychologists have stopped using "norms" or "means" to describe people and just lump humans into several categories. Among males, the two largest categories are the homosexuals and those who no longer bother with the marriage ceremony but move from mate to mate as time changes their tastes.

What once was considered sexual deviation is no longer thought a social problem; it is commonplace. The jamming of people against one another has so altered social attitudes over the years that those males who still maintain a single female mate and go nearly every day to their homes comprise one of the smallest groups of males. Even fewer are those who maintain one and the same mate for most of their adult lives. Home life is a burden. Even those women with permanent mates and children at home seldom have much room and the disorder

[9]

in what space they do have generally reflects the chaos of the society around them. Home life is intolerable; there is no such thing as cleanliness.

Many rooms are littered with boxes of junk. Windows are dirty. Curtains waiting to be hung often are left lying on windowsills; those that are up often are dirty. Dishes are left neglected beside dishwashers. Food sits rancid on tables; dust accumulates everywhere. It is just too much trouble to clean up, and no one cares.

Most women are totally disinterested in maintaining living conditions that will attract the male. Few men ever enter the homes of their female associates or friends. Even among married couples, most husbands maintain separate living quarters close to their work.

This all began some years ago as it has become increasingly difficult to reach one's place of work from one's home within a reasonable period of time. Slowly it has become the accepted habit for a man to maintain quarters near his work and other quarters for his wife and children. As time passes, more and more men, regardless of station in life, begin to maintain the two dwellings. And they spend less and less time in the one where their wives and children live.

It has become unusual to find even those *casually* married living together in the same home. Giant all-male apartment complexes have developed. Here those who engage in homosexual activity are not looked upon as being strange, although those who lack sexual control and engage in rapacious activities are considered a threat, and efforts are made to bring them under control.

The male which society considers the most unusual makes up a third category, one of substantial numbers. This is the withdrawn male. He goes out of his dwelling almost exclusively when others are not about. He handles his business by telephone

[10]

and message carrier and appears on the streets when most of the community is asleep. But even at these times, there are many persons moving about. This is the confused society, in which crowding and density have reached enormous levels. One can see people everywhere. They move but it is hard to tell that; from a distance the mass is so dense it reminds one of a horde of ants. Close up, you can see the stream along the sidewalks, in the streets, in and out of doorways. Inside, elevators fill and empty. Corridors in buildings remain constantly crowded. Office reception rooms are seldom large enough.

There are some places where solitude still is possible, but these are limited by the economics of the day to the upper-income few. Even in offices, space economics has limited privacy to the top executives and to those particular specialists who need to be alone to work.

But while offices can be tolerated, stores are impossible, and restaurants are an improvement on one's own home only in that they are cleaner, not less crowded. And so in the office, on the street, in shops and restaurants as well as at home, it is nearly impossible in the course of a normal day to be out of sight of another person.

The female is no less affected than the male by living conditions. The collapse of homemaking is but one aspect. Far more significant is the change in the female's role as man's mate. Women seem not to care about personal relationships with men; they will live with anyone. And it is no longer unusual to find a group of women living in a single dwelling, and cared for by one man.

Maternal functions have also changed greatly. The rates of miscarriages and stillbirths have grown in the decades since 1970, and there have been increasing numbers of incidents of mothers deserting their homes and children. More and more, children are being cared for by whoever has a notion to take them in. The many children wandering the streets, even as young as six or seven, disturb few adults. In many households, infants are nursed by whatever mother happens to be nearby when the child is hungry.

If there is a motivational norm, it can best be described as "escape." Since more than 95 percent of the population live in dense urban centers where dimensions go up rather than out, escape is a must. But the parks and open spaces within the urban centers are always jammed. And it is nearly impossible to escape by physically leaving the city since outlying areas are in turn so heavily crowded by others escaping that the amount of human contact is seldom reduced.

There really is no place to escape. Most of those who do escape do so psychologically. They block out, and mentally shield themselves from contact with their fellowman. As people go about their business or do their work, they perceive that things are going on, but they avoid involvement. Behavior has become rote and attitudes so flat and blasé that one does not initiate activities that will elicit reactions from others. The escapists often look the best; they appear the healthiest and dress the most attractively. But they are nearly withdrawn from the social milieu. They do not engage in courtship or sexual activity. This is particularly true of the males, who never bother. They are just like leaves blowing in the wind as far as other people are concerned; other people to them are objects as dull as sticks and stones. For many, the noninvolvement occurs only from time to time and for short periods. But for a growing number it has become permanent. For these latter it is about the only means of survival.

Moving through the corridors of office buildings, one sees the results of intense interaction. It is not unusual for people to walk down the corridor with their faces down or turned toward the wall to avoid seeing their fellow workers. They know few of them well enough to say anything meaningful. But they know all of them just enough to be expected to say something. It has become unbearable to say "Hi" or "How are you?" or "What's new?" so all avoid saying anything. Maintaining occupational productivity, a great problem during the twentieth century, is the least problem. Most individuals still do some semblance of work, even while avoiding every other positive activity. Normal routine takes the individual through the minimal effort required if the job is not too complex. But those institutions depending upon voluntary involvement are evaporating: churches are closing; civic groups are smaller and smaller. The myriad of events that compose a full and active society are disappearing. No one is interested. It has just become too difficult to perform.

The change in the nation's urban areas appears chaotic indeed to country people cast suddenly upon the scene. They are rare, and the few from outlying areas are horror-struck to discover what the city man has come to accept as commonplace.

———

This description of future life in a crowd is not entirely imaginary. It takes its root from a study conducted by Dr. John B. Calhoun, of the National Institute of Mental Health, on the social pathology of Norway rats under intense population density conditions. Dr. Calhoun wanted to learn the effects on the social behavior of a species of rat as population growth and density reached excessive levels. By the end of the first 27 months of his experimentation, his Norway rats had become stabilized at a population of 150 adults. Yet he recorded an adult mortality so low that 5,000 adults, not 150, might have been expected from the observed reproductive rate. The reason this larger population did not materialize was that infant mortality

[13]

was so high. Even with only 150 adults in the enclosure, stress from the social interaction led to such disruption of maternal behavior that few young survived.

In later experiments Dr. Calhoun observed that behavioral pathology was most apparent among the females. Many were unable to carry pregnancy to full term; others were unable to survive delivery of their litters. A greater number after having given birth, performed their maternal functions inadequately. Among the males the behavior disturbances ranged from sexual deviation to cannibalism and from frantic overactivity to a pathological withdrawal by some rats, who would emerge to eat, drink and move about only when other members of the community were asleep.

The social organization of the animals showed similar disruption. Sex ratios were drastically changed. The rats divided themselves into groups. One group might have consisted of six or seven females and one male; another might have had twenty males and only ten females. Eating and other biological functions were transformed into social activities; some rats would rarely eat except in the company of other rats. This togetherness tended to disrupt the normal conduct of other vital behavior, such as the courting of sex partners, the building of nests and the nursing and care of the young. Infant mortality ran as high as 96 percent among the most disoriented groups. In others the infant mortality was as high as 80 percent.

Calhoun used physical habits as an index of the effect of density. As male rats approach adulthood they achieve status by the number of fights which they initiate and win. The more they win the more likely they are to establish a position of dominance. However, more than half the adult males in each of Dr. Calhoun's experiments gave up the struggle for status after a while, and in the most crowded pens no individuals occupied the top position permanently. At regular intervals

[14]

during the course of their waking hours, the top ranking males engaged in free-for-alls in between which came periods of relative calm. The aggressive, dominant animals were the most normal males in the population. They seldom bothered either the females or the juveniles. Yet even they exhibited occasional signs of pathology — going berserk, attacking females, juveniles and the less active males.

Below the dominant males on the status scale, and less active, were the pansexuals. These animals apparently were not able to distinguish between an appropriate and an inappropriate sex partner; they made sexual advances to males, juveniles and females not in estrus. The males, including the dominants as well as other pansexuals, usually accepted their attentions.

Two other types of males emerged, both resigned from the struggle for dominance. However, they were at opposite poles as far as their activities were concerned. The first group of rats were completely passive and moved through the community like somnambulists, ignoring all the other rats of both sexes and being ignored by them. Even when the females were in estrus the passive animals made no advances to them. And only rarely did other males attack them or approach them for any kind of play. They were the healthiest and most attractive members of the community, fat and sleek and showing no fighting scars. But their social disorientation was nearly complete.

The second of these two groups of non-dominant males, called the "probers," were perhaps the strangest of all the types that emerged among the males. They always lived in the middle pens and took no part in the status struggle. Nevertheless, they were the most constantly active of all the males in the experimental population, and they persisted in their activities despite attacks by the dominant animals. In addition to being hyperactive, the "probers" were both hypersexual and homosexual. And in time many of them became cannibalistic.

They were always on the alert for females in estrus, and they conducted their pursuit of females in abnormal ways. When they were not in their own pens they would lie in wait for long periods atop the ramps leading to the brood pens and peer down into them.

Research on the lower orders gives us enlightening insights and information on behavioral patterns. And the Norway rats are not our only guide as we consider population density. Hudson Hoagland, in an article in the February 1964 *Bulletin of the Atomic Scientists,* pointed out several other examples of animal response to population density. Under crowded conditions, the flower beetles turn to cannibalism. In one species of flower beetle egg production drops off and the female tends to puncture what eggs are produced. In another there is an increase of glandular gas production under dense population conditions which acts both to diminish sexual activity and to kill the larvae.

Minnesota jack rabbits demonstrate a cyclical variation in population even without changes in natural conditions such as food, disease, weather, or natural enemies. When the population cycle is on the decrease the rabbits exhibit symptoms of acute stress and glandular overactivity. They die in thrashing convulsive fits and the signs of death include liver and heart disease, hypertension, and damage to the adrenal glands.

Rats crowded together under stress conditions during the winter display decreased sexual activity, increased vulnerability to disease, premature births, cannibalism, and increased male aggressiveness. In birds, when the population goes above a critical density level the mortality rate among the young is greatly increased. In many cases the chicks are killed and eaten by the older birds, often the males.

Forty years ago a pair of deer were put on a small island. For years the deer and their descendants thrived upon this

150-acre island in the Chesapeake Bay. When the population on the island reached one deer per acre, however, the signs of glandular overactivity and acute stress appeared and despite favorable food and weather conditions the deer began to die off. Then there is the oft-told story of the Norwegian lemmings who would get the urge periodically to commit mass suicide, or, as other stories tell it, seek to return to their ancient home in some lost continent now under the ocean. The lemmings are not led by some mythical Pied Piper, however; their migration from Scandinavian mountains to the sea occurs every few years, whenever their population becomes too great. At these times physical and psychotic changes occur and the animals develop lethal brain and glandular destruction associated with the changes under stress conditions, and exhibit patterns of mass psychosis.

Intense population density and the resulting pathology such as described in Calhoun's study of rats creates added burdens when humans are involved. When people interact too frequently, they, like rats, become frustrated. As frustration mounts, one of two things happens: either behavior becomes more unusual or the individual withdraws and avoids contacts that will frustrate him. Through withdrawal, a human being tries to get to where others are not. As that becomes more and more difficult he achieves withdrawal by psychologically blocking out from the scene. But humans have verbal as well as physical and visual contact with each other, and communication involvement increases even more sharply than other factors as population density grows.

And there occurs what psychiatrist Leonard J. Duhl calls "input overload," which simply amounts to too much incoming information for a person to handle. When this happens the individual may suffer a breakdown, and the breakdown can take a wide range of forms: biological pathology, psychological

[17]

abnormalities or socially unacceptable behavior. Duhl says that findings in animal research support what has been learned about human input overload.

But the nation's most eminent environmental scientist, René Dubos of Rockefeller University, cautions against too readily translating the animal pathology resulting from overcrowding into human pathology under similar conditions. Dubos sees two obstacles to applying to human living the information learned from animal research. One is that man very readily adapts to potentially dangerous situations. The second is that man's reaction to crowding is conditioned by social and cultural determinants. Thus the problems involved are much more complex with humans than with animals. Little is known concerning the level of population density or stimulation intensity which man can take physically or mentally. For example, the minimum living, sleeping, and working space required per individual varies from culture to culture. Dubos notes also that many unproven assumptions underlie the belief that the goal of technology, including medicine, should be to provide man with a sheltered environment in which he is protected as completely as possible from any form of traumatic experience. This assumption is dangerous, Dubos says, because certain important traits of man's nature cannot develop normally or remain in a healthy state without constant stimulation and challenge.

Man's ability to use his social structure to prevent excessive harm to himself through the altering of his physical surroundings, his institutions, and his activities is the predominant reason human pathology is unlikely ever to reach the excessive levels described in the beginning of this chapter. Unlike the rat, man is able to institute far-reaching changes in his environment. Dr. Dubos is quite right, then, in pointing to man's physiological, biological and mental ability to adapt to extreme changes in his natural habitat.

But modern man has the opportunity to prevent extreme changes in his habitat only if he recognizes and understands their advent well ahead of crisis point. Thus, while it is unlikely that we will ever see the extreme conditions among the Norway rats occurring in human life, our well-being can't be taken for granted. Unfortunately, man also has the unique habit of failing to use his social organization to prevent extreme pathology until well after considerable evidence of trouble has begun to emerge and create disturbances within society. Man must be aware that the path to the confused society is ignorance of its occurrence.

Over the past decade or so, man has begun to understand that the natural habitat consisting of air, water and soil can be spoiled by the way he uses it. He has also begun to learn that this spoiling of the physical environment will affect both his health and his welfare. But the element of living space is as important to humans in a physical environment as are air, water and soil. The latter three are polluted by the dumping of refuse, waste or effluents. Living space is polluted by the way man lives with other men. The good places to live become fewer and fewer, for man seems unable to use his physical surroundings without spoiling them. Though complaints reach a shattering crescendo through the irritability of people jamming together, jam they do.

People are shocked to learn that neither air, nor water nor soil is free — that it costs to dump wastes into water or onto land and to spew effluents into air. Soon there will be a similar shock when people become aware of the high price they pay when living space is used unwisely, for it, like air, water and land, is not free.

[19]

Without translating the social pathology of animals and insects as a result of overcrowding directly into similar pathology for human beings, we can nevertheless see disturbing parallels. In a section of Washington, D.C., known as Trinidad I visited an ugly brick building with most of its windows broken. The six apartments on three floors housed a fluctuating and undetermined number of people. "They move in and out too fast to know who's there," a resident of six months' duration noted. In this woman's apartment, one flight up a cold, iron-railed staircase with brick interior walls, six persons were living in two rooms.

The brick building smelled. There was trash all about, so much that it created a crowded feeling. There was a feeling of tension; doorways were opened only slits and muted faces studied me a long while before beginning to speak. The sidewalk leading to the building was full of children; so were the stairs and stairwell. They formed small groups, each seemingly unaware of the others. "They are afraid," I was told. "There's so much violence. There's so much fighting; everyone's got to see who is the toughest and the girls is always got to be tested."

The observation was not made by a social scientist. Nor was it studied or tested. But it was real, and it was from someone who had never read Calhoun. Life in that building was just plain miserable. The residents were poor and Negro. But those two factors only served to speed up the condition of crowding; it makes no difference how rich one is or of what color if the living space isn't available.

The woman visited had not always lived there. Only six months before, her family had had a house normal-size for the four children and two adults. Then her husband had been injured on the job, and their income had declined sharply. Now it was difficult for them to fit into the new quarters. Everyone got under everyone else's feet, and so the husband began coming home less and less and the mother going out less and less. The children stayed home too because of the fighting and violence outside. The mother developed a nervous condition and later had to be hospitalized. The family had no friends among the neighbors, because people moved in and out too frequently and didn't trust one another. The noise was described as unbearable, making it almost impossible to sleep. There were guns being shot and dogs barking, and the people "were harsh and messy." Each said he felt the walls were closing in on him and wanted "to just kick 'em out."

A few blocks away in an apartment in a row house where five and sometimes six people lived in three and one-half rooms, the scene was similar, with things piled around and a closed-in feeling. But this family had been there for ten years. The husband "didn't spend much time here," nor did the children. The mother admitted that it was hard to keep a small, crowded place clean but didn't seem to care. She talked while watching television, without turning to look at her visitors. And she made clear that nothing in her living condition was unusual to her. She left the impression that she long before had ceased to feel that she was crowded. She had blocked out the condition, while her neighbor a few streets away felt it intensely every moment.

Neither of these cases is a scientific study. But both types of situation occur many times over. Whether a family of six with plenty of money but limited to two rooms would suffer a pathology similar to that of the poor may be subject to scientific debate. There is some evidence that money and color make no difference. In Washington, D.C., schools, conflict among students increases sharply where enrollment runs 20 to 40 percent over capacity. In heavy traffic, tempers flare; there is little politeness on a crowded elevator.

Yet one can also find an opposing example. Professor Richard

Meyer of the University of California found in a series of studies done in Hong Kong that none of the pathology symptoms identified with the rats in the Calhoun study occurred among the Chinese living in intense densities in Hong Kong. Space is at a very high premium there, of course. Yet Meyer found that the Chinese more and more were moving into dwellings in which space per person was reduced by the increasing number of people arriving. Densities were up to five times greater than in New York City. And the poorest kept on renting and renting out space until they were living in about twenty-four square feet per person. They were living in twenty-story buildings in which elevators made only three stops.

Perhaps the "Kessler phenomenon" helps to explain this situation. Starting with a large number of mice in a small space, Dr. Alexander Kessler began an experiment on the relationship of population growth to the survival of animals with differing genetic backgrounds. Other scientists who had done rat experiments had found that in comparable areas the population had stopped growing at somewhere between forty and eighty rats. But when Dr. Kessler terminated his experiment he had eight hundred mice in one pen and one thousand mice in another, this mouse population having gone over ten times the maximum observed by anyone else.

Female mice were conceiving and giving birth. They were nursing young, although not necessarily their own: there were pups everywhere, and whenever a female stopped moving, a pup could latch on long enough to get some milk. There was relatively little strife; there was some withdrawal.

Calhoun, noting that his interpretation was "purely speculative," suggested that the Kessler phenomenon may indicate that when mice are put into a society where they can never be out of the presence of at least one other mouse, they never identify with anything outside their own skin. If a mouse never knows anything other than his condition of life, he adjusts to it.

And so you have a situation where the personality and the ego are confined to the physical perimeter of the body. As a result, there is no involvement with other animals, no reason for argument or testing or exploring. No tension builds up. The mice are too accustomed to everything that happens to them. So the animals just keep on reproducing.

Analogously, in a place where there are so many human beings that one never gets away from other persons, one individual has no personalized space, conceptual or physical. He is completely blasé about life, but not withdrawn.

But there is insufficient evidence on which to base any definitive answer as to the role social stress might play in decreasing the growth rate of human populations. Some evidence does show, however, that the human pituitary-adrenal system responds under stress in the same way as that of other animals.

While we do not have available the information to make a direct causal relationship between environmental stress and death or disease, we do know that there are increased levels of mental disorder and neurotic behavior in our crowded urban areas. The effects of stress upon the population are often masked by the improvements in medical services in other areas and by the ability of a chemical-oriented society to alleviate symptoms with pills or drugs. Before social problems such as juvenile delinquency and street gangs can be related to the stress produced by overcrowded slums, a great deal more investigative work must be carried out.

Edward T. Hall notes in his book *The Hidden Dimension* that the concentration of ethnic groups, or the ethnic enclave, in the city once had a beneficial purpose. These concentrations acted as half-way houses in which the ethnic generations were able to learn the skills, attitudes, and actions necessary to be able to leave the enclave later and make the transition from foreign immigrant to American city-dweller. Today the ghettos are not transitional staging areas but more like permanent confinements. The residents of the urban ghetto don't believe that they, or even their children, will get out of the ghetto.

With outside pressures to contain the ghetto and not let its blight spread, the density of a particular area increases. This creates the condition known as a "sink," in which common behavioral patterns collect people or animals together in large concentrations. In the sink all kinds of deviant social pathology are amplified. New York City's Harlem district, with its densely packed Negro and Puerto Rican populations, is an example of a "sink." While the worse effects of sink conditions can be avoided in animals through keeping them well fed and clean and creating the illusion that they are alone by blocking their vision of other animals, the animals become mentally dull.

Paul Chombard de Lauwe, in a study published in Paris in 1959, collected the first statistical data on the consequences of crowding in urban housing. Finding no correlation between the number of persons per dwelling unit and social expression, he used instead the number of square meters per person per unit as an index. When the space available was below eight to ten square meters per person, social and physical pathologies doubled. There was a definite link with illness and crime. When the space available was greater than fourteen square meters per person, pathology increased as well, but less markedly.

An explanation for the latter finding was that families in this category in the housing units studied were usually intent on raising their standard of living and paid little attention to their children; the figures are relevant only for the particular group under study at that particular time. The investigation implies, however, that there is indeed a relationship between crowding and social pathology.

Crowding also helps destroy the illusions that children build about other people. The kinds of positive or negative images which they have of others help to determine their own goals, and there seems to be a point at which contact becomes excessive and affects the construction of illusions. In crowding, people surpass that point, being seen too often, and soon are viewed as they *are* rather than as they would wish to be. As an example, there are boys who won't follow in their fathers' footsteps. While many of these youths come from families representing the least-advantaged groups, suggesting that they do look to other lines of work as a means of escaping their economic background, there are also many instances in middle- and upper-income families where children rebel against following their fathers' careers. The reason can be that the child knows the father too well and doesn't want to be the same kind of person.

Crowding also prevents the development of illusions about sex. Sexual activity is a natural biological action for reproduction, but in most human cultures it is used also as a means of expressing a unique emotional relationship that becomes the heart of a marriage. Between the ages of seven and ten, children ordinarily begin to be aware of the sexual relationship between men and women. But their first awareness is of the physical aspect of the sexual involvement, not the emotional. This is particularly true in crowded families, whose records are filled with cases of children viewing sexual activities to which they can give no other connotation than that of physical gratification. These children may never form more than physical attitudes about sex, and may never learn its relationship to affection and love. Overcrowding thus threatens to change cultural patterns where sexual relationships are involved.

[25]

In defensive response to the mental effects of crowding, people build walls to protect their egos from being harmed. The maintenance of these defense mechanisms creates another strain. The inability to relax or escape the crowd not only results in attitudes of defeat and negativism — only partially relieved by irritable outbursts or temper tantrums — but in addition creates the fatigue phenomenon.

Dr. Dubos takes another view. He says man is a gregarious animal who generally tends to accept crowded environments and even to seek them. But, he cautions, while this attitude has social advantages, it may have pathological counterparts if acceptance of crowding is carried too far.

There also have been reports which indicate that crowding results in an increased secretion of various hormones. Greater activity of the adrenal cortex is of particular importance here because it affects the whole human physiology. Adequate secretion of adrenal hormones is essential for well-being, but an excessive secretion has deleterious effects.

Lewis Herber, in *Crisis in Our Cities*, captures the scene that plays havoc with the secretion of adrenal hormones: "To stand in a fettered subway car often in a preposterously contorted position, staring blankly into space, is undeniably a stress-generating experience. To be pushed about pell-mell by inrushing excited crowds, to scurry rudely for a seat or a choice standing location is a distinct insult to the nervous system as well as to the dignity of the urban dweller."

It is not very different using an automobile. Waiting impatiently to edge from a side street into a heavy flow of traffic is undeniably a stress-generating experience. So is being cut off by a car swerving from one lane to another in the interminable wait at a traffic light.

The factors involved in crowding and density which affect mental and social well-being go beyond the quantitative contact with other people — the living density within dwellings, the distribution and arrangement of rooms, and the disturbance by noise and smell. In addition, there are qualitative factors which must be considered: provision of basic services — fire and police protection, sewage and trash removal; transportation systems; recreational opportunities; all the material conditions of physical and mental well-being.

At the same time that investigators are concerned with discovering the correlations between environmental conditions and certain diseases they are aware that the environment, while often not directly producing a specific malady, can help set the mental and emotional stage which determines moods, attitudes, and the ability to respond to various situations. Thus, while diseases which have a genetic factor are spread more uniformly over all areas, crowded ghettos have high incidences of alcoholism, juvenile crime, schizophrenia and general social maladies. A question still to be answered is whether the slum areas attract the weak and keep them from leaving. From evidence gathered in individual studies, it appears to be a complex combination of all factors.

For single young men, the crowded urban areas can be more devastating than for whole families. Often cut off from attachments, ties, and the stabilizing factors of family, religion, and other familiar social institutions, the young man must fight alone for the right kind of dwelling, for some measure of social prestige, and for a job whose wage will allow escape. Rather than elevation, the result is too often mental disorder, suicide, alcoholism, and crime.

This is a limited review of the areas which connect stress from urban crowding. Community mental health programs are aimed at alleviating and correcting the conditions of mental strain within the individual. But it is the planner and the environmentalist who can provide the physical surrounding

[27]

that will lay the groundwork for the most effective control of mental strain.

Sometimes planning for one goal can unexpectedly turn out to solve another problem. For instance, architects in Geneva recently used variety in color to reduce the mental strain of living in a large housing unit. The information book for new residents took advantage of the colors and instructed each tenant to "note the color of the story where you live — it will help you find your way home."

In a similar housing unit in Bergen, Norway, nothing at all was planned to alleviate the mental strain of finding home. There, it is explained, in new fifteen-story blocks of flats in a city of about 120,000 people, mothers of small children place their own photographs on the doors of the flats so that the children know where to come home.

For the scientist, evidence is far from conclusive that emotional stress is directly related to disease and death. The effect of crowding on disease and death is largely circumstantial. Yet information on the body's chemical reaction to stress increasingly is suggesting an explanation of how tension may worsen or cause a chronic disease.

The relationship between an acute attack of some physical disorder and a severe emotional experience has been known by the medical profession for years. Ever since the time of Hippocrates, the correlation between emotional stress and stomach disorders has been recognized, and the ubiquitous peptic ulcer is associated in our present society with a life of tension and anxiety. Under stress, the nerves carry a message to the intestinal tract, the stomach produces too much acid, and the muscles in the gastrointestinal tract constrict. Too much stress, too many messages, too much acid, too many tense muscles, and there is the good possibility there will be an ulcer.

Evidence of a more recent date brings many other diseases,

[28]

including rheumatoid arthritis, allergies, disorders of the blood vessels, skin diseases and quite possibly cancer, within the scope of a broad new science of mind-body relationships called psychosomatic medicine. Few doctors claim that emotional stress is the sole cause of these disorders, but most have good reason for suspecting that it contributes to their occurrence.

The San Francisco Mount Zion study examined the effects of psycho-stress on the blood and cholesterol counts of two groups of accountants, one composed of tax accountants and the other of corporate accountants. The results of the study were startling. Average blood and cholesterol levels increased approximately 26 percent during periods of high stress, and clotting time nearly was halved. According to the researchers, there appeared to be an extreme sensitivity of the blood cholesterol to the occurrence of emotional duress of a particular type described as socioeconomic stress. The possible effects of weight changes and dietary and exercise habits were followed closely and found not to vary significantly from a period of stress to one of respite. It was concluded therefore that the stress was the primary cause of the observed cholesterol changes.

In his studies of the mortality of captive animals and birds at the Philadelphia Zoological Garden, Dr. Herbert L. Radcliffe found a correlation between overcrowding and damage to the coronary arteries. Whereas autopsies of birds and mammals from 1916 to 1931 disclosed vascular damage, hardening of the arteries, and coronary lesions in only a small number of older animals who had died from other causes, later studies, made when the zoo population density had increased and the average animal ages had decreased, showed a vastly increasing rate of arteriosclerosis. Dr. Radcliffe concluded that even in young animals the stresses of confinement and crowding were more responsible for the increased arterial disease than were age or changes in diet.

[29]

With cardiovascular disease — diseases of the heart and blood vessels — being the major cause of death in the United States, much research has been directed by heart specialists toward finding the possible causes. So far, the major portion of this research has been focused on the relationships to heart disease of cigarette smoking, food, stress, and exercise. While there is no unanimity of opinion arising from these investigations, it is known from statistical studies that the highest death rates from cardiovascular disease are in the cities. As one moves from the city to the suburbs and to the rural areas of the United States, the rate declines. In some sections of the country the rate in men is two to three times greater in the city than in rural areas.

One doctor who feels that emotional stress is causally related to cardiovascular disease is Dr. Henry I. Russek of New York City's U.S. Public Health Service Hospital. Dr. Russek instituted a series of surveys of professional men whose jobs had varying degrees of exposure to stress situations. In his first study, Dr. Russek compared the more stress-producing occupation of the anesthetist with that of the dermatologist. The results showed that the anesthetists had a greater incidence of heart disease than the dermatologists, ranging from two and one-half times greater to four times greater, depending upon the selected age group.

When Dr. Russek expanded his studies to include other professional groups exposed to varying degrees of stress, such as general practitioners, dentists, surgeons, and different types of lawyers, he again found that the incidence of heart disease varied according to the stress level of the occupation.

The effect of emotional stress on physical and mental health is amplified by the demands of modern urban life. These demands can cause massive emotional injuries. Too many urbanized Americans live on the brink of sheer hysteria. They are insecure in their jobs, degraded by the herd-like congestion of public transit and large retail stores, packed into overcrowded dwellings, assailed by the uproar of vehicles and machines, and frozen in sedentary jobs. These urban dwellers too often reach outright psychosis. They appear bitter and tight-lipped, barely concealing the ever-increasing emotional pressure within.

New stresses are being added to old ones. Countless irritations of a petty nature now plague the urban dweller, each adding its own bit of distress to a mounting pile of strains and vexations. Consider the daily ordeal of looking for a parking space in congested residential and business quarters, the irritation of clawing for a seat at a packed luncheon counter, the bustle of shopping in congested retail stores, the interminable waiting that permeates nearly every aspect of urban life from entering a subway to paying for a purchase in a mammoth food market.

During the 1950s, a team of investigators led by Dr. Thomas A. C. Rennie, before his death in 1956, conducted a study of New York City's Yorkville district in Manhattan to look into the effects of city life upon mental health. Their report, issued in 1962, indicated that 80 percent of the people interviewed had symptoms of psychiatric disorders and about 25 percent had neuroses which could disrupt their daily life. According to Herber, again in *Crisis in Our Cities*, the appalling figures of Rennie's study probably reflect less than the true extent of serious mental illness in mid-town New York, since a significant number of people in particular groups were omitted from the sampling. Transients, college students, those in the service or in jail, people in nursing homes, hospitals, and other institutions were not included. These groups, Herber suggests, would probably have raised the study's figures.

As might have been expected, the poor suffer more than the well-off. According to the Rennie Study of Yorkville, they are under greater stress and strain and suffer more emotional upsets.

At the time of the study, almost one out of every two adults trying to live on less than $2800 per year was severely disturbed psychologically. If one was able to earn more than $6000 a year, his chances of being emotionally disturbed decreased to one in eight. However, the largest group in this section of New York at this time had a family income of $3000 — $6000; they were able to have a tolerable standard of income, but were not able to put aside money for emergency or reserve use.

Particularly among our older citizens, life expectancies are higher in the smaller cities of the northern and western United States than in large cities in these regions. In older age groups this difference may be as much as 15 percent. Also of interest are the differences between the most prevalent causes of death in large and small cities of the North and the West. While the large cities list cancer, heart disease, tuberculosis, diabetes, ulcers and suicide as important causes of death, small cities have lower rates for these ailments and list instead pneumonia and the flu, appendicitis, kidney infection, brain lesions and intestinal blockages.

This information gives some indication that the principal health advantage of the large cities is the immediate accessibility of superior services for the treatment of acute diseases and childbirth, whereas the populations of these large urban centers are more vulnerable to the long-term accumulative environmental hazards.

Comparative studies of two orders of monks in Holland revealed that although differences in their diets reflected themselves in an increased level of blood cholesterol in one group of monks, there was no difference in the incidence of heart or other cardiovascular diseases between the two monasteries. Furthermore, the two monasteries' common rate of heart disease was much less than the general rate among males living in Holland.

[32]

Medical tests were made twice on a newspaper editor who was suffering from hypertension and high blood pressure, once shortly after he had met a deadline and gone through all the pressures of the efforts to meet that deadline and again after he had driven through town in the rush-hour traffic to reach the downtown area. The physical tests showed that the editor's blood pressure and hypertension were substantially greater as a result of the driving than they were as a result of meeting the deadline for the newspaper.

The pressures and anxiety resulting from social and professional competitions, the effects of crowding, and the complexities in general of urban living in light of all this must be considered factors that play a part in the cause of vascular diseases.

Modern man has been fairly successful in his battle against the ravages of weather, famine, epidemics, and predatory animals. However, he has continually been building new threats to his health and well-being, and now mechanization, crowding and pollution are exacting a more subtle toll.

The reaction of the human being to mounting numbers of stress situations has several stages. Upon recognizing the intrusion the body reacts in alarm to set up its defenses. Then this defensive posture must be maintained. All stress situations initiate the same general effect. The body is called to react and protect as long as this stress is applied; if the stress is applied for a significant length of time and is sufficiently forceful, there will be a state of exhaustion. As with any alarm or defense mechanism, if one's body is mobilized too often or taxed too long it will break down. The response may be too large or too small, too soon or too late.

Man suffers indirect as well as direct results from polluting living space with excess population. Too many people living inappropriately in a given space produce social pathology. Too many people coming into contact inappropriately within a given space produces a health pathology. Likewise, too many people using a space inappropriately produces an economic pathology that results in the degradation of the other resources or habitats of man: air, water, and soil. The concentration of man in an urban area requires an increasing degree of economic activity.

The industrialization process requires the generation of power. The power produced has a side effect of dispensing into air the effluence from the combustion of fuel used to produce the power. Thus the more people that jam into a space, the more power required; the more power required, the more effluence is spewed into the air, polluting it and harming the health of the people living in the area.

The same thing can be said of the use of the water resources in an area. People consume, in the consuming there is waste and the waste must be disposed of. We dispose of liquid wastes by discharging them into surrounding bodies of water. Even with advanced treatment methods now available to society, the volume of effluence being discharged into the waters surrounding limited geographical areas is such as to lower the quality of that water for any future use.

A third problem caused by crowding is the disposal of solid wastes: wastes which cannot be carried away by water or be burned and discharged as an effluence into the air. As the number of people in an area multiplies, the waste of this nature increases. And as it increases, its disposal must be handled in one of several not always satisfactory ways: either by landfill in existing water areas (which reduces the amount of water available and increases the amount of land upon which people can settle, further increasing the density or population growth); by burial (which can increase the nitrogen and phosphate compounds in the soil and thus change the nature of the soil and its runoff into waters, further aggravating water pollution); or by piling it up in composts (further reducing the amount of space available to people already crowded).

Our cities are great cities. The incidence of disease is low, and the standard of living is the highest in history. Culture and commerce bloom in the cities. They provide unprecedented opportunities for education and entertainment; millions find they offer new ways of life, far more attractive than the ones from which they escaped. Certainly the city has problems. Its economic problems are enormous and its harsh and often confusing physical environment aggravates social and personal problems. Much of this is from the stress imposed by the city; it's the noise and polluted air, the rush and the push, the irritations that go beyond the limits of comfort or even of tolerance. But the problems of the physical environment of the cities can be controlled.

Technology can be used to affect pollution of air, water and land. Technology and public policy combined can affect the pollution of space and bring about relief from the stresses imposed by the crowding and congestion of the city.

It will be difficult to define when and where over-population exists. It will also be difficult to develop and implement a rational plan of population and space control. But over-population must be adjusted by relating the use of space to human needs. If this is done, rush-hour driving in the morning, and rush-hour driving in the evening, which now result in long lines of cars bumper-to-bumper, may possibly be eliminated. If this is done perhaps the freeways, now the major means of egress from downtown to the suburban areas, may be able to move cars at generally planned paces. Even auto lines may then be able to move at fifty to sixty miles an hour, with movement in and out of lanes and the proximities of one car to another automatically controlled so as not to leave the driver extremely tense, angry, and frustrated.

Maybe in the city which provides the proper relationship between man and space, public transportation will be on time and there will be enough clean and comfortable room to eliminate the frustrations which now accompany riding public transit systems. Maybe uncongested city office buildings can be designed to reduce the tension of waiting for elevators and jamming into them and fighting out of them. Maybe then it will also be possible to be waited on in a store or a restaurant without the pressure of "hurry, the next person's waiting."

In the city which provides for the control of space pollution, maybe the houses will be built, the streets laid out, parks created and commerce and industry conducted with concern for the effects of demographic intensity.

Maybe the lakes will then be worth living beside.

2

BREATHING

In the fall of 1805, the Lewis and Clark Expedition, searching for a water route to the West, crossed the Bitterroot Range on the western side of the Rocky Mountains and followed the course of the Clearwater River in five canoes. In a narrow little valley some seven hundred feet above sea level, on what is now the Washington-Idaho border, Meriwether Lewis and William Clark met the Snake River, navigated it south to where it joins with the Clearwater River, and turned abruptly west on the final leg of their journey westward to join the Columbia River — west to the Pacific Ocean.

Today, the twin cities of Clarkston, Washington, and Lewiston, Idaho, nestle in this narrow valley formed by the confluence of the Snake and Clearwater rivers in the western foothills of the Rockies and together they are the center of commerce and trading for a population of more than 100,000. In this valley center, there are about 30,000 people: 12,700 reside in Lewiston; another 10,000 in a community known as Lewiston Orchards; 7,000 in Clarkston; and the remaining several hundred in Clarkston Heights.

This area in Idaho is popularly called the "Banana Belt," for it has the lowest elevation in Idaho and has an unusually mild climate. On the north the valley is protected from the elements by a range of mountains which rise sharply to about two thousand feet above the valley floor. To the south a slope rises more gradually to about seven hundred feet, then levels off.

The gentleness of the winter climate, the fertile land and the length of the growing season combine to make this area an important agricultural center. Near the cities, where irrigation is feasible, vegetables and fruits are grown. Further away, wheat, which is the area's principal crop, is grown in abundance. In the metropolitan area the production of forest products is the most important economic activity, employing an estimated one-third of the labor force. There are three to four lumber mills in each of the two cities. Potlatch Forests, Incorporated, in Lewiston is one of the largest white pine pulp mills in the world.

In looking to their future, the citizens of Lewiston and Clarkston are very conscious of their past. Like the namesakes of their cities, the residents hope to open a water route to the West. It now appears that this will become a reality, as dam construction and planning on the Snake and Columbia rivers are designed to permit deep draft barges. Yet another link with the Pacific Coast will be the Lewis-Clark Highway, which generally following the route of the original expedition will open up the Pacific Northwest, from the coast to Montana, to the benefits of tourism and the economic development of its resources.

In this historic area, unusual natural beauty is one of the most important resources. In the mountains to the east are dense forests, deep river canyons, high alpine meadows, lakes, and white rushing rivers. The rainbow and cutthroat trout join with the migrating ocean-going steelhead to make this country a fisherman's paradise. The mountain goats, deer, elk and moose share their territory with bear, bobcats and coyote. Over 1.2 million acres of land have been set aside as an area of primitive beauty in the Selway-Bitterroot Wilderness.

This is an area that comes as close to the frontier as any American is likely to find in his country today. There is plenty of open space. There is no particular sense of crowding. It is the Northwest, the Rocky Mountains — it is the rural, rugged United States. The scenery is breathtaking near Lewiston, Idaho, and Clarkston, Washington — but it is not just clean, crisp air that flows into the lungs with each breath.

The air inhaled in Lewiston-Clarkston includes, besides oxygen and nitrogen, sulfur oxides, nitrogen oxides, hydrocarbons, aldehydes, organic gases, ammonia, hydrogen sulfide, methyl mercaptan, dimethyl sulfide and a variety of other organic gases, as well as particulate matter. The area belies its image of being close to nature: there are mountains and streams, open spaces and scenic beauty . . . and there is air pollution.

In Lewiston-Clarkston, there are nearly ten lumber plants, an asphalt and gravel plant, stockyards, feed-grain mills, meat-packing factories, brick kilns, homes which burn coal for heat, and automobiles, all of which contribute to the degradation of the air. The largest offender, however, is a kraft paper-pulp mill producing 450 tons per day of bleached paper board and 200 tons per day of market pulp. At this paper mill logs are reduced to chips, and the chips cook for approximately three hours in a solution containing sodium sulfide and sodium hydroxide. Steam is added to the cooking process, and as this is done gases are driven off. Some of these gases are used in the process of creating the pulp, and others, which are called untreated blow or relief gases, are discharged into the atmosphere and become a major source of odor. In addition, large quantities of water vapor, which can have adverse effects upon visibility

[39]

under certain weather conditions, are emitted from the kraft mill.

Seventy-seven percent of the gas emissions in the Clarkston area come from the kraft mill. Other industrial operations in the Lewiston-Clarkston area contribute hydrocarbons and small particles, but compared with the kraft mill these sources are relatively minor. The burning of coal is an additional source of sulfur and nitrogen oxides as well as hydrocarbons and particulate matter.

The sulfide gases and other air pollutants in the Lewiston-Clarkston area tarnish and, under certain conditions, blacken lead-base house paint. While there is no conclusive evidence that there are any adverse health effects upon the residents of the area, the people there don't like the situation, particularly the stench and odor.

In a U.S. Department of Health, Education and Welfare opinion survey of the Clarkston area, 80 percent of the people interviewed felt that an air pollution problem existed. About 66 percent indicated that they were bothered by the pollution. They reported ill-effects from bad smells and nose, throat and eye irritation and excessive dust and dirt.

In Colorado, about 750 miles to the southeast of Lewiston-Clarkston, the Great Plains are abruptly halted by the rising mass of the eastern edge of the Rocky Mountains. Approaching Denver from the east, a visitor is struck by the panoramic view of the foothills just west of the "Mile-High City" forming a purple backdrop in the late afternoon sun. Sitting at the gateway to the Colorado Rockies, Denver in the 1870s and 1880s was the focal point for miners, fortune hunters, saloon keepers and a wide variety of characters from the East seeking to strike it rich in one way or another as a result of the discovery of gold, silver, and copper in the nearby hills. This era of colorful Colorado and American history is preserved in Denver in the

[40]

Cody Museum, Buffalo Bill's tomb, and the Silver Dollar Saloon as well as through the reconstruction of several ghost towns in the nearby hills.

There still is gold in the mountains around Denver, and a wide variety of characters from the East still come to Colorado in great numbers each year to seek their fortune. In this case, the gold comes in a variety of forms and colors depending upon the season, and the fortune sought is the freedom, beauty, health and awe that come from partaking of Colorado's mountain scenery and recreation facilities.

In the winter, Colorado mountain gold is the falling white snow that lures the skier through Denver to some of the finest ski facilities and conditions in the country. In the spring and summer, the gold is the lakes, fishing, hiking and mountain climbing and the increasingly rare opportunity to investigate nature's wonder and magnificence in a setting relatively unspoiled by man.

Denver is the gateway to the impressive spectacles of the Rocky Mountains and has prided itself on its respectful partnership with nature, maintaining the largest system of public parks and recreational facilities in the world. Unfortunately, in recent years Denver has not worked completely in harmony with its partner, nature, and has developed air pollution that often blankets the city in a cloud of smog, obliterating the western view of the mountains, damaging property and causing physical irritation to its residents and visitors.

In January 1964, the Senate Subcommittee on Air and Water Pollution visited Denver to listen to testimony as to the extent and nature of Denver's air pollution problem. The committee heard Colorado State Department of Health Director Dr. Roy L. Cleere explain that "until a few short years ago, air pollution was not considered an important problem in Colorado. In fact, Coloradans prided themselves on their state's clean mountain air and enjoyed viewing its natural beauty through clear, unsullied skies. As Colorado cities grew, however, and as fuel consumption, industrial production, and combustion processes multiplied even faster, our air, like that in other states, became more saturated with the wastes of progress."

The pollutants found in the Denver air have been particulate matter, oxidants, nitrogen oxides and sulfur dioxide. An estimated 40 percent of these chemical effluents come from automobiles, 30 percent from industry, and 30 percent from domestic sources such as home heating, backyard incineration, and burning dumps.

Further complicating Denver's air pollution problem is its meteorological and geographic situation. It has a dry climate with cold winters. The ground cools off very rapidly during the winter, with the early setting sun being prematurely blocked out by the mountains to the west. This produces a shallow layer of cold air on the ground with a layer of warmer air on top acting as a lid. The occurrence of this stagnant layer of trapped air is known as a temperature inversion. The layer generally lies about 300 feet high, and because the warmer air acts as a lid, all the pollutants are trapped in a shallow band.

Not only is there a temperature inversion. The normal movement of ground air — drawn by the convection currents set up by the warming action of the sun on the mountain and carrying air pollution away from Denver toward the western mountains during the day — is reversed in the late afternoon, as the mountains are first to lose the warming rays of the sun. The result is that all the day's pollution comes back into the city at ground level just at the time the temperature inversion begins, and the lid starts trapping the cumulative amount of many hours of industrial emissions in this thin layer. It may not be until late the next morning that this inversion is broken up in the Denver area by the sun warming up the ground again and causing the layers to mix.

Because of the timetable of this phenomenon, both the morning and evening rush hours occur during the period of concentration, stagnation and inversion, causing the heavy amounts of automotive pollutants to be trapped in the air.

The population of the Denver metropolitan area is expected to be found to have increased from 930,000 to 1.2 million during the decade of the sixties, with industrial growth maintaining the same pace. In that same time, however, the increase in cars and trucks is expected to go from 400,000 in 1960 to 800,000 in 1970. In 1970, the meteorological and geographic conditions will of course remain the same. The volume of air over Denver will also remain the same. The only increasing factor will be the level of emissions from automobiles.

Across the Rocky Mountains and 650 miles or so from Denver, the peak of Mt. Lemmon rises out of Arizona's rugged Santa Catalina Mountains to about nine thousand feet above sea level. A snowfall of nearly two hundred inches every year turns Mt. Lemmon into the southern-most ski area in the United States, enjoyed in winter by visitors from all over the country. In summer the Santa Catalinas and the Coronada National Forest reveal magnificent examples of nature's sculpting talents — the rock formations carved and arranged by wind, rain and time — and the remains of Indian villages and the stratified layers of rock or canyon walls provide a vivid screen upon which to project contemplations about the development and history of man, of nature, and of man and nature.

Six thousand feet lower and only several miles south of Mt. Lemmon and the Santa Catalinas the city of Tucson, Arizona, sits in the Santa Cruz River Valley basking in the dry air and warm sun. With mountain ranges on almost all sides, Tucson enjoys a desert climate that averages only eleven inches of rain per year, with a temperature twenty to thirty degrees warmer than on top of Mt. Lemmon. Because of its warm, dry climate and yet easy access to cool mountain ranges, Tucson has been a favorite resort area and a healthful place for those seeking relief from humidity, cold and smog, and a release from the strain of a crowded human environment.

In 1870 Tucson offered its three thousand residents water supplies only thirty-seven feet below the ground and a warm, dry, clean and sunny climate to make easier the worries of continuing Apache Indian raids. By 1950 the population had grown to forty-five thousand, the Indian menace had disappeared, and the water table was dropping, but the air was still warm, dry, and clean in the sunny desert climate of this part of Arizona. In 1965, it was discovered that the population had multiplied more than five times and was approaching a quarter-million people; that Indians — or at least the ancient ones and their dwellings — had become a great historical and curiosity attraction; that the water table had dropped to between three hundred and four hundred feet below the ground; and that while the sunny resort climate still had warm dry air . . . it was no longer clean. Tucson now had air pollution.

The College of Engineering of the University of Arizona at Tucson produced a report on local air pollution conditions. They defined air pollution as "the presence in the atmosphere of substances, resulting from the activities of man, in sufficient concentration to interfere with human comfort, safety, or health; or to interfere with the reasonable use and enjoyment of property." The report went on further to state, "Large scale contamination of the air is accelerated by such forces as industrialization, urbanization, and scientific development of new processes and products. It is not surprising that the air over Tucson is beginning to show signs of pollution."

[44]

The signs of air pollution that the College of Engineering found in their survey included a relatively constant level of oxidants throughout the year, sulfur dioxide transported into the Tucson Valley from smelting copper operations up to forty miles away, and particulate matter that could block out the view of the mountains.

But the major source of air pollution within Tucson was the automobile. It was estimated that 75 percent of the emissions in the metropolitan area were due to automobiles spewing hydrocarbons, carbon monoxide, nitrogen oxides, sulfur dioxide and aerosols into the air. In 1960, the approximately 108,000 cars registered in Pima County put about 320 tons of material a day into the air over Tucson. The second-greatest offender was the airplane. Twenty percent of the Tucson air pollution in 1960 was estimated to be due to the commercial and military air traffic from four airports in the area.

In areas where coal, petroleum, or wood are burned, fuel combustion is one of the major sources of pollution, but because natural gas is the predominant fuel in the Tucson area, the contribution of fuel combustion to the fouling of its air was minimal. Tucson also is not an industrial city and therefore is not subjected to the additional volume of smoke, dust, odors and gases that infect other cities. Even without two of the major sources of pollution problems in large cities, the consumption and poor combustion of sulfur fuels and the emissions from heavy industry, Tucson still has a problem with air pollution. It is caused by the automobile, the airplane and as in Denver, inversion.

While time will not alter the geology and weather that produce the inversions, projections indicate that by 1980 there will be great changes in the major sources of Tucson's air pollution. In 1980, 296,000 automobiles are expected to be registered in Pima County, three times the number in 1960, and in 1980 these automobiles will burn, based on present consumption levels, 250,000,000 gallons of gasoline. By that year these automobiles will have tripled the amount of pollutants they inject into the atmosphere if auto engines continue to be built on current engineering principles.

Wide open spaces and cowboys were not restricted to the American West. On the other side of the country, about halfway down the Florida peninsula, near Tampa, Polk County in the early 1850s was a center of the cattle-raising industry. Fifty years of work, thought, and the application of modern scientific agricultural methods had combined to produce fine herds of purebred registered Brahmas and healthy pastures for them. Besides its flourishing cattle business, Polk County had as well a growing citrus industry. As the livestock and citrus prospered off the land, so did the farmers and growers.

Between 1953 and 1964, however, an estimated 150,000 acres of cattle land were abandoned, and 25,000 acres of citrus groves in the county were damaged. Truck crops were lost, and the commercial gladiolus industry in an adjacent county was blighted. In the seven-year period between 1953 and 1960, the cattle population of Polk County dropped 30,000 head.

"Around 1953 we noticed a change in our cattle. They failed to fleshen as they normally did. We put them in our best pastures and used all known methods to fatten. Worming, mineral drenches, changing pastures did not improve the condition. We watched our cattle become gaunt and starved, their legs became deformed; they lost their teeth. Reproduction fell off and when a cow did have a calf, it was also affected by this malady or was a stillborn." Thus did a former president of the Polk County Cattlemen's Association describe the onset of a condition in his cattle that was diagnosed by veterinarians as mass fluoride poisoning. The source of this fluoride poisoning was traced to gas and dust emissions spread by the wind from

[46]

the stacks of the many phosphate-processing plants near the grazing lands and citrus groves.

Almost 75 percent of the nation's commercial supply of phosphate comes from mineral stores underneath Polk and adjacent Hillsborough County land. After World War II more than a dozen plants sprang up in this area to process the phosphate ore into triple super phosphate. High temperatures in the processing cause fluorine and/or fluorides to be released into the atmosphere, to be scattered by the winds to the forage land and the citrus groves, where they are deposited and absorbed.

In the citrus groves, the entry of fluorine into the leaves is indicated by a characteristic pattern of decoloration or a lightening of the normal dark green, which is caused by the destruction of the chlorophyll content of the leaf upsetting the metabolism of the plant. In severe attacks, the leaf is actually killed — burned to a brittle and dark brown condition. Fluorosis is characterized by the stunting of growth, the failure of the bloom to set, the dropping of fruit, delayed maturity, and lessened production.

Polk County, Florida, and Powell County, Montana, have a bond of common misery. Each once had a flourishing cattle industry and a bucolic environment. Now both have phosphate plants, fluoride gases and dust in the air, and the stains of air pollution on the land. Rocky Mountain Phosphates, Incorporated, started its operations in Garrison, Montana, in August 1963, coinciding with the first rash of citizen complaints to the Montana State Board of Health concerning smoke and fumes from the factory that had caused eye-burn, nose and throat irritations, coughing, and adverse effects on children with respiratory problems.

By August 1967, the local cattle industry faced extinction due to direct losses of cattle from fluoride poisoning and the

[47]

concomitant deterioration of the value of ranches. In addition, an interstate air pollution conference held that month in Powell County heard testimony from residents of the Garrison area with regard to damage due to the fluoride emissions to their homes, yards, and automobiles. Testimony also noted continuing eye, nose, throat and respiratory irritations. A Garrison citizen described the four years of Rocky Mountain Phosphate operation as

. . . a nightmare for me and my family. I have seen my neighbor's business destroyed. Our business is only half what it was when this outfit moved in. I have been forced to cut down some of my shade trees that were killed by the emissions from this plant. There are many more that will have to be trimmed. We have had little pleasure in our home and surroundings.

But above all has been the misery and distress to my family and myself. There has scarcely been a night when this plant ran that I haven't awakened with a burning tongue and throat, or with a headache or aching lungs. This is also true for the rest of my family. We seldom have been able to open a window, especially at night. We simply do not get proper rest and sleep.

Fluoride gases and dust in the air in Montana and Florida are only a part of the air pollution effect on agriculture. Widespread evidence of extensive plant damage throughout the United States has been shown by a number of studies. John Middleton, in a paper to the National Conference on Air Pollution in December 1962, reported evidence of plant damage from photochemical air pollution in twenty-three states and the District of Columbia. Dr. Robert Daines of Rutgers University, in a communication in July of 1964 cited foliage markings on thirty-five types of plants in New Jersey. F. W. Went, at the 1955 National Air Pollution Symposium, stated that vegetation unmistakably smog-damaged was found in or near Los Angeles, San Francisco, New York, Philadelphia and Baltimore. Damage from air pollution has also been noted in white pine, in shade grown tobacco, and in a variety of truck crops.

George H. Hepting, a research scientist with the U.S. Forest Service, reported in a paper in 1964 that in recent years the ozone in Los Angeles smog has been considered partly responsible for destroying ponderosa pine in the mountains east of that city. He noted that until a few years before damage to forests from air pollution had consisted mainly of localized but very severe cases of growth loss and mortality due to oxides of sulfur or to fluorides associated with ore reduction.

Air pollution also has been determined as the cause of the long known needle blight of eastern white pine, and evidence is accumulating that the eastern white pine disease known as chlorotic dwarf may be caused by air pollution. The loss of eastern pine has been occurring within a twenty-mile radii of power plants consuming large quantities of soft coal. Hepting reported that while some particularly susceptible white pine, exposed for seven months in industrial east Tennessee, suffered uniformly severe damage, other less susceptible but similarly exposed trees were not injured. Susceptible trees kept out of the affected area remained healthy.

Hepting's work indicates that much crop damage, including damage to trees, appears to be the result of air pollution, a product of our enormous urban development. Industrial plants are using fossil fuels at rates far beyond those of only fifteen years ago. In the past, the principal pollutants have been sulfur oxides, from industrial sources, and fluorine, mainly from ore reduction. Today, many additional elements in polluted air contribute to plant damage, particularly ozone and peroxide compounds, including one called PAN, or peroxyacyl nitrate. Ozone and PAN are the main elements of Los Angeles–type smog that are toxic to plants and animals. They result from photochemical reactions between oxides of nitrogen and organic vapors mostly derived from the incomplete combustion of petroleum. Plant damage has been caused by sulfur dioxide as well as by these pollutants.

Virtually all of the principal types of agricultural crops have suffered important damage from air pollution. Alfalfa, cotton and lettuce have been easily injured by sulfur dioxide at ground level. Gladiolus, azaleas, and baccinium are among those plants most sensitive to fluorine. Tobacco is weather-flecked by ozone. Orchard blooms are ruined by ethylene. A recent report of the University of California states that the photochemical smog in Los Angeles has reduced the production of fruit in the main citrus area south of that city by 20 to 25 percent in the past fifteen years.

Destruction of individual shade trees is seldom connected with air pollution unless a direct relation to the source of the pollutant is apparent. But there are cases of death obviously related to such sources, including the blighting of trees in close proximity to automobile exhaust, toxic gas leaks, waste burners or burning municipal dumps. No one knows how many city and highway trees are lost from urban smogs. When such data become available undoubtedly they will show that many of our tree species have a low tolerance to urban air.

New Jersey, generally considered an industrial state, supports extensive truck farming, and while air pollution damage to its vegetation dates back about one hundred years, the problem did not become acute until the late years of World War II. Before that time, air pollution damage was believed to be limited to that produced by sulfur dioxide, illuminating gas and ethylene. In 1944, an unusual pattern of foliage injury was noticed in many cultivated crops and other vegetation in two areas of New Jersey along the Delaware River. This injury often was followed by partial or complete defoliation of many

[50]

deciduous and coniferous plants. Gladiolus and tulip plants showed considerable injury, corn developed a characteristic mottling, peach growers reported early fruit drop and foliage injury and defoliation as causes of considerable loss in the crop.

Then Robert H. Daines, Ida A. Leone, and Eileen Brennan of Rutgers University discovered that industrial expansion and the development of new processes in connection with the war effort had introduced new pollutants.

Air pollution is not a new problem — it has existed for centuries, born in the flames of the first creation. The gases of decaying vegetative and animal matter, the products of forest fires, dust and sand storms, and volcanic eruptions have all unleashed particulate matter and gases and prevented the existence of a truly unpolluted atmosphere.

With the social and technological development of man, however, the range, extent and variety of atmospheric pollution began to grow and expand. Man the social animal founded communities, and man the technician developed the purposeful use of fire. As man developed early civilization with the aid of combustion, so he developed the first public air pollution; for along with the light and the heat, simple combustion produced smoke, ash, sulfur dioxide, and other gaseous products that fouled the air. In medieval European towns, primitive society added the gaseous odors of decaying rubbish and the vapors of the tanning trade to their wood smoke.

If effluents from automobiles, homes, industrial fires and refineries bring health problems to people, damage to crops in rural areas and problems to farmers, the effect there is far less serious than their effect on the human being in the urban area. Our urban areas today require tremendous quantities of continuous power to run factories, to illuminate buildings and streets, to heat homes, to drive buses, trucks and automobiles.

To do all this, industry looks for the least expensive fuel and the least expensive way to get rid of the waste products of combustion. The least expensive fuel generally has the highest sulfur content, and the least expensive way of getting rid of the waste products is to dump them into the most convenient dumping ground, in this case the immediate atmosphere. New York City is an example of this in the extreme. Most of the electric power for the city is produced by nine fossil-fuel-burning plants located right in the heart of the city, and the waste combustion products of these plants goes right into the atmosphere above the city. New York automotive vehicles consume one billion gallons of gasoline a year; seventy million gallons of this amount are discharged into the atmosphere as waste products known as unburned hydrocarbons.

This pollution problem is shared by New Jersey. Anyone who has driven the New Jersey Turnpike with the windows open on a hot June afternoon knows the smell of the country-side and the haze of the pollution rising from the industrial complex across the Hudson from New York City. A federally called interstate air pollution conference on the New York–New Jersey metropolitan area learned from the New Jersey Turnpike Authority that air pollution was contributing to reduced visibility endangering the safety of traffic. Representatives of the Airline Pilots Association, the Air Transport Association of America and the Federal Aviation Agency showed that decreased visibility due to air pollution demanded special measures to insure the safety of aircraft operations. But the problem went far beyond safety. The conference participants concluded unanimously that there is interstate air pollution endangering the health and welfare of persons in New York and New Jersey.

There was extensive meteorological and photographic evidence that pollution originating in New Jersey blew into New

York, and that pollution originating in New York found its way into New Jersey. In addition to the effect on health, widespread damage to materials was reported, including those of historical and architectural value. A representative of the Metropolitan Museum of Art described irrevocable losses to works of art caused by air pollution, and he detailed different aspects future damage may take. It was indicated in the report that the annual cost of air pollution in the 17-county New York–New Jersey area was $3 billion. This would be an average of $200 per person per year.

The air in the New York–New Jersey area is saturated with sulfur dioxide from space heating units in private residences, with a variety of sulfur compounds from the miscellaneous industrial processes underway in the area with carbon monoxide from automobiles and industrial sources, and with a variety of suspended and particulate matter that find its way into too many human bodies.

Evidence before the air pollution conference indicated that some 40 percent of the toxic corrosive sulfur dioxide in the atmosphere of the 17-county New York–New Jersey area came from steam and electric power-generating plants, and that 50 percent came from the use of sulfur-rich fuels for home heating. Ninety-five percent of the carbon monoxide in the New York area air comes from motor vehicles, with only two significant industrial sources contributing carbon monoxide: the Hess Oil Company and the California Oil Company. In 1967 the Hess Oil Company was discharging 79,000 tons of carbon monoxide annually, and the California Company 75,000 tons.

Norman Cousins, chairman of the Task Force on Air Pollution for the mayor of New York and editor of the *Saturday Review*, testified before the Senate Subcommittee on Air and Water Pollution in 1966 that ". . . more poisons per square

[53]

mile are pumped into the air in New York than anywhere else in the United States." He went on to identify the sources for these poisons:

They come from New York City's eleven municipal refuse disposal stations. They come from the city's own Housing Authority projects with 2,600 incinerators and 2,500 heating furnaces. They come from the privately owned apartment houses and office buildings. They come from 600,000 private residences using fuel oil and heating furnaces, for the most part. They come from Consolidated Edison's 11 power generating stations inside the city. Power stations that burn in the neighborhood of 10 billion pounds of coal each year and 800,000 gallons of oil. They come from the 8,500 industrial manufacturing establishments. They come from demolition and construction dust. Ordinary street dirt from the 13,000 lunchrooms and restaurants and from 1.5 million automobiles, buses and trucks. They come from 400,000 take-off and landing operations of jet aircraft at New York airports each year, and from some 25,000 steamship operations in New York.

Cousins reported that 230,000 tons a year of particulate matter, soot and fly ash, 597,000 tons a year of sulfur dioxide, 298,000 tons a year of nitrogen oxide, and 567,000 tons a year of hydrocarbons were poured into the New York air. Finally, the emissions of carbon monoxide totaled 1,536,000 tons a year. All of this was equivalent to about 730 pounds of dirt and poison per person a year in New York City.

The nation's capital, lying by the Potomac River, has attracted attention for some years because of the contamination of water supplies for drinking and recreation. The city has been noticeably free of industrial development, its main economic activity being dependent upon government and government-supported services, and it is not particularly known for its Los Angeles–smog type of weather. Nor does it have the population density of New York and New Jersey. For a major city it seems an unlikely place for emergence of a severe air pollution problem. Yet as long ago as June 1959, the area experienced a four-day episode of eye irritation as severe as anything that had been recorded in Los Angeles. It was photochemical smog: It was a Los Angeles smog.

In the past several years the Washington area has experienced an increased amount of photochemical smog that has caused reduced visibility, eye irritation and damage to vegetation, and this has occurred even without major industrialization. The pollutants have been identified as sulfur oxides, nitrogen oxides, carbon monoxide particulate and hydrocarbons. They come from stationary fuel combustion sources and refuse burning, and they come from automobiles: fully 75 percent of the pollution emitted into the Washington atmosphere comes from the exhaust of gasoline and diesel vehicles.

Aircraft pilots have complained about decreased visibility and are concerned about air safety. Vegetation is damaged extensively, and materials deteriorate and suffer damage and destruction. The Library of Congress has reported the deterioration of books and manuscripts by atmospheric pollution, and the National Gallery of Art has indicated that permanent and irreparable damage from air pollution has been suffered by art masterpieces. The National Park Service has said severe maintenance problems are encountered as a result of air pollution's effects on the memorials and statues in the area.

Detroit, Michigan, is the third-largest industrial city in the nation, ranking just behind New York and Chicago. As the world's leading automobile manufacturing center, Detroit sends products all over the country and throughout the world. In addition to its manufacture of automobiles and other products in the industrial complexes along the Detroit and Rouge rivers, Detroit produces great amounts of air pollution for local and international consumption, ranking it among the most polluted cities in the country.

A study of pollution in the atmosphere of the Detroit River area, made by the International Joint Commission (United States and Canada), identified the largest source of solid particulate matter in the air as the blast furnaces, steel mills and foundries. These auto-associated operations put great amounts of iron, zinc, lead and other non-ferrous oxides into the air along with the gases from the combustion of fossil fuels, especially coal. Not only is Detroit polluted by the manufacture of automobiles, but its air is filled also with the gaseous oxides and organics emitted by the final gas-consuming product as it travels over Detroit's streets and highways.

The International Commission also indicated that Canada (in particular Windsor, Ontario, located just across the Detroit River from the "Motor City") is the recipient of gratuitous gifts of United States air pollution as the prevailing winds carry the polluted American air across the river. During the early part of September 1952 Windsor shared with Detroit a three-day period of air stagnation and high pollution levels. The smog soon produced eye irritations and respiratory complaints. A later study of the Windsor Medical Care Plan records and area mortality records for this period showed a statistical relationship between the increased level of air pollution and the distinct rise in mortality of infants and of adults with malignant disease.

In the latter half of the nineteenth century rich deposits of iron, coal and limestone were uncovered in Alabama at the southern end of the Appalachian Mountain range. During the Civil War, these mineral resources were turned into cannonballs and rifles for the Confederacy, and afterwards, with the development of the railroad and steel industry, they provided the impetus for the founding of the city of Birmingham in 1871.

In the latter part of the twentieth century, heavy deposits of minerals and chemicals were discovered in this area in the air above Jones Valley. In the years since its founding, the city has fed on the coal and iron deposits nearby, becoming the "Pittsburgh of the South," the largest city in Alabama, the southern center for iron and steel manufacturing and other industry, and a city with foul and dirty air.

At the same time that the flames from Birmingham's steel furnaces are making dramatic figures in the nighttime sky, they are also throwing a large amount of particulate matter into the air. A study of Birmingham air made during and after a steel strike showed that pollution increased significantly when the strike was over and the industrial activity resumed. The high concentrations of manganese, lead, tin, iron and titanium particulate matter in the Birmingham sky have been found to exceed the levels in other major industrial cities such as Chicago and Detroit.

A few hours straight north of Birmingham lies Nashville, Tennessee. The capital city of Tennessee has long had a history of air pollution, particularly smoke problems and the attendant smog. In 1935, the U.S. Weather Bureau reported that "Few cities in the United States have a greater smoke nuisance to contend with during the winter months than Nashville, Tennessee. It has been so dense on occasions that the visibility was reduced to zero, the sun's disc invisible from street level, and street and automobile lights kept burning until after 10:00 A.M., although at the same time just outside the smoke area, the sky was brilliantly clear."

Aggravated by poor meteorological conditions which fail to disperse and ventilate pollutants, Nashville's air problem has long been associated with the combustion of soft coal in the home and for industry. The soft coal gives off large amounts of smoke, small-sized particles, and sulfur dioxide when it is burned. As recently as 1965, soft coal was still the major contributor to Nashville's air problems, being responsible for

[57]

a good 85 percent of the sulfur dioxide in the air and the majority of solid particulate matter, according to the U.S. Public Health Service. The Public Health Service also cautioned that the reduction of soft coal consumption and replacement by oil or natural gas may not result in much cleaner air, since the steadily rising number of motor vehicles is producing and spewing another group of pollutants into the air, primarily the hydrocarbons, nitrogen oxide, and carbon monoxide. This increase may produce a deterioration of quality that far overcomes any improvements realized through the elimination of soft coal combustion.

The problem of air pollution and smoke obscuring visibility is not merely a nuisance or inconvenience. The National Center for Air Pollution Control investigated the extent and effect of air pollution upon visibility in the vicinity of Kansas City Municipal and Fairfax airports. This study concluded that reduced visibility around the two airports due to air pollution caused reduction of visibility and hazardous flight and traffic control conditions at both airports. It was found that twenty-one industrial operations accounted for very nearly 85 percent of the total particulate emissions in the survey area, an estimated 55 million pounds of solid matter thrown into the air to block visibility around the airports.

In addition to the generalized decrease in aircraft safety that occurs when large areas are subjected to smoke, smog and haze, individual stack emissions from sources close to the airport can result in specific problems for both the aircraft pilot and the airport control tower operator. The horizon, tower, runway, landmarks, and other aircraft can be obscured from the pilot. The tower can lose sight of activities in a portion of the flight pattern or on the ground.

For two weeks during the study of air pollution around Kansas City airports, special hourly observations were made of visibility conditions at the Fairfax Airport. The following re-marks recorded along with the observations for one day are indicative of the extent and effect of the air pollution on air-port operations: "0700 — Heavy smoke all directions causing a partial obscuration west, north and east. Very hazardous conditions at north end of field. 0730 — A Bonanza made a touch and go runway 35 and then quit because of very bad smoke condition; north and northwest of airport visibility near zero. 1000 — Heavy smoke in all directions. Smoke is lying right in airport valley."

Around Fairfax Airport at the time of the study, Owens-Corning Fiberglas Corporation was sending up a dense gray continuous plume of smoke, frequently obscuring aircraft in the traffic patterns for the most often used runway. Gustin-Bacon Manufacturing Company contributed significantly to general smoky conditions, around Fairfax particularly during low wind periods. The Doepke Disposal Service, operating a dump at the north end of the airport, sent up black clouds of smoke which could adversely affect six different traffic patterns at the airport and block the view of approaching aircraft from pilots waiting on the ground for takeoff. The dump as observed from the airport control tower once was described this way: "At approximately 1930 on May 23, 1966, a column of dense black smoke arose from a point just north of the General Motors Assembly Plant. The wind at Fairfax was north at 10 to 20. Smoke covered the entire airport making it impossible to see traffic in the pattern. This condition existed to a lesser degree for about one hour."

With the coming of the Industrial Revolution and with sub-stantial and continuing technological innovations and more sophisticated means of combustion, air pollution made a big step towards its present state. The use of coal for domestic heating, as a municipal and industrial power source, and as a

[59]

major factor in the manufacturing process, so increased the level of air pollution as to make it a matter of public concern. As society and industry have become larger and more complex, so have the effluents which are put into the atmosphere. Not only are the products of simple combustion of conventional fuels spewed to the air, but industrial wastes of increasing amount, diversity and complexity as well.

Long considered as a nuisance, air pollution is now being recognized as an extremely costly nuisance. For many, there is the conviction that air pollution is a menace to human health, in addition to causing economic loss and aesthetic discomfort. Eye, nose and throat irritations, as well as soiling and property damage, are associated with air pollution. Several serious air pollution episodes have been recorded in recent history (in the Meuse Valley and London in Europe; in Donora, Pennsylvania, and New York City in the United States) that suggest that increased deaths during these periods were due to air pollution. Some contemporary research has indicated a relationship between chronic exposure to a polluted atmosphere and diseases such as acute bronchitis and primary lung cancer.

Air pollutants generally can be classified into two groups. First there are the airborne particulates consisting of solid and liquid particles. Second there are the gases or vapors. For a long time, air pollution was thought of in terms of soot and sulfur. The eye and the nose acted as detection equipment. More sophisticated technology has now identified over one hundred substances arising from the varied activities of man that contaminate the air, and there are many more products that are still unknown. The chemical culprits run from acids and aldehydes to peracylnitrites and organic free radicals.

Nearly half of America's present air pollution is attributable to the automobile and the by-products of other internal combustion engines. This type of pollution is essentially carbon monoxide, hydrocarbons and the oxides of nitrogen. When these compounds are released into the air, in which an extremely large number of substances may already be present, the ultraviolet rays of the sun act upon them to produce a photosynthetic reaction and a whole new range of air pollutants still not understood by science enters the air.

In addition to the direct by-products of internal combustion engines and their photosynthetic offspring, tetraethyl lead is being explored as a contributing factor to car-related air pollution. René Dubos, in *Man Adapting*, reports an ever-increasing exposure to lead in the industrial and urban environment. He says, "there seems to be no doubt that the concentration of lead is increasing rapidly in the air, water and food and that the chief source of contamination is alkyl lead." Dubos reports blood levels of lead to be highest in auto mechanics and second highest in traffic policemen. Dubos also suggests that unknown or unrecognized sources of air pollution due to vehicular traffic may include highly pulverized rubber and asphalt, which are liberated by the abrasion of tires upon the streets.

While science probes further into the identification of pollutants — where they come from, how they interact with each other and what they do — the debate rages on as to their effects upon human health. In a Washington, D.C., symposium in 1967, Dr. P. J. Lawther, Director of Air Pollution Research at St. Bartholomew's Hospital, Medical College, London, claimed that, on the basis of a fifteen-year study of the problem of air pollution, "We have found that emphysema, bronchitis, and other respiratory diseases are not caused by increased air pollution, but simply because people are living longer."

A counterview is offered by Dr. Benjamin G. Ferris and Dr. James L. Whittenberger. Writing in the December 22, 1966, issue of the *New England Journal of Medicine*, they claimed that increased levels of air pollution have been demon-

[61]

strated to have had an effect upon the health of human beings in a variety of countries at different age groups. Most of these effects, they reported, had been related to pollution characterized by increased levels of sulfur oxide equivalents and particulates.

Herber, again in *Crisis in Our Cities,* states that we can now say with complete confidence that the conditions for many illnesses are directly prepared by airborne contaminants. He claims that an impressive amount of statistical evidence implicates air pollution as well as smoking in the rising incidence of lung cancer.

Pollutants that injure plants and erode stone are likely to have an ill effect on humans as well. Carbon monoxide is lethal under certain intensities. One hour's exposure to 1,500 parts of carbon monoxide per million can endanger a person's life, and in concentrations of it as small as 120 parts per million for an hour there can be an effect on equilibrium. Carbon monoxide concentrations of 100 parts per million have been found in a number of tunnels and garages and on some city streets. Sulfur oxides can irritate the skin, eyes and upper respiratory tract. Extreme exposure in some instances can do irreparable damage to the lungs and even attack the enamel on teeth. Ozone produces eye irritation, coughing and chest soreness. Carbon particles blacken the lungs and carry gases which have been absorbed into their surfaces. Particles of arsenic, beryllium, cadmium, lead, chromium and possibly manganese, discharged into the atmosphere by a variety of man-made processes, also contribute to cancer and heart disease.

In terms of scientific study it has been but a short time since the first substantial amount of research on community air pollution and respiratory disease has been undertaken. For only ten years have scientific studies on air pollution and

[62]

human health been conducted. The period is too short to permit detailed exploration of all aspects of so complex a problem. Nevertheless, former Secretary of Health, Education and Welfare John W. Gardner, appearing before the Senate Subcommittee on Air and Water Pollution in 1966, said, "There is no doubt that air pollution is a contributing factor to the rising incidence of chronic respiratory diseases — lung cancer, emphysema, bronchitis and asthma."

In the ten years since the beginning of substantial work on the connection between air pollution and respiratory disease, a number of studies have been undertaken on illness and death from respiratory disease and on impairment of respiratory function in relation to air pollution. This research has produced a substantial body of factual information concerning the ways in which exposure to community air pollution affects the human respiratory system.

In a memorandum supplementing Gardner's testimony, the Public Health Service said, "The main thrust of the evidence is clear and conclusive — the types and levels of air pollution which are now commonplace in American communities are an important factor in the occurrence and worsening of chronic respiratory diseases and may even be a factor in producing heightened human susceptibility of upper respiratory infections, including the common cold."

Chronic diseases, as indicated by their name, develop slowly over long periods of time. Unlike infectious diseases, the chronic disease comes after a series of assaults on the body rather than from a single event. This makes it quite difficult to satisfy the traditional scientific preference for concrete evidence of a direct and demonstrable cause-and-effect relationship between such factors as air pollution and such effects as the development of chronic respiratory disease.

[63]

But the scientific argument notwithstanding, the Surgeon General, addressing the National Conference of Air Pollution in 1962, succinctly summed up the meaning of debate when he said

I submit that much of the speculation and controversy of whether or not air pollution causes disease is irrelevant to the significance of air pollution as a public health hazard. That there is frequently a simple association between an infectious disease agent and the acute disease reaction which it provokes was once a startling revelation. And in Public Health it has served us well and continues to serve us well. But we have learned that it is not the master key that unlocks all the secrets of disease and health. The idea that one factor is wholly responsible for any one illness is patently too simple to provide all the answers we need to deal with the chronic diseases which are on the rise today. Chronic bronchitis, which in Great Britain is established as a specific disease entity, is a good example. It develops over a long period of time and can become crippling through a combination of many factors. Air pollution, smoking, repeated and recurring bouts with infectious agents, occupational exposures — all affected perhaps by an hereditary predisposition. What then is the cause of chronic bronchitis? The answer is obvious. There is probably no single cause, but there is sufficient evidence that air pollution can and does contribute to its development. This is what really matters, whether we choose to consider it the cause, one of several causes, or simply a contributing factor.

If air pollution is a contributing factor to increased respiratory diseases, then it stands to reason that the adverse effects of air pollution on health are most serious in those urban communities which have the greatest concentration of air pollution sources and people. But the health hazards of air pollution are not limited to cities above a certain size; many small communities suffer to some extent from air pollution problems. These problems may differ in degree from those experienced by larger cities and may be less complex, but they are still likely

[64]

to produce adverse health effects on the people exposed to them.

A 1966 Public Health Service memorandum assessed the relationship of air pollution to several diseases as follows: Deaths from cancer of the lung, especially among males, have been increasing rapidly in recent years, with a striking urban-rural differential in mortality. As quoted in the memorandum Dr. Paul Kotin, Director of Environmental Science Services of the National Institutes of Health, stated: "The most satisfactory explanation for the consistent observation of an increased incidence of lung cancer in urban populations is exposure to polluted air." The Public Health Service memorandum notes that cancer of the lung is believed to reflect the interaction of a number of factors and that it is considered unlikely that a single factor can bring about lung cancer.

At present, available evidence of the role air pollution plays in lung cancer is based on findings of several research projects. Independent studies have indicated that individuals migrating from areas of low air pollution to areas of higher air pollution suffered a higher rate of lung cancer than did those who remained behind; and that the rate of deaths from lung cancer in the largest metropolitan areas in the United States is nearly twice that in the rural areas. A contrast continues even after full allowance is made for differences in smoking patterns. (But while air pollution can be considered partially responsible for an increase in lung cancer, or at least be called an aggravating factor, most scientific opinion considers cigarette smoking to be a much more significant factor.)

In Great Britain nearly 10 percent of all deaths and more than 10 percent of all industrial absences due to illness are caused by chronic bronchitis, and study and investigation now indicate that a similar condition exists in the United States. Cigarette smoking and air pollution are now accepted in Great

Britain as distinct causes of chronic bronchitis, and the same is beginning to be accepted in the United States. Observation of individuals known to suffer from chronic bronchitis have shown a worsening of their symptoms on days of higher air pollution.

Illness and death from pulmonary emphysema are increasing rapidly in the United States. Between 1950 and 1959, deaths of males from this disease rose from fewer than 1.5 per hundred thousand population to nearly 8 per hundred thousand. A study of patients suffering from pulmonary emphysema showed they improved when protected from irritant air pollution. Patients in a room in which the outdoor air of a smoggy Los Angeles day had been purified by electrostatic precipitation and charcoal filtration showed relief and improvement after twenty-four hours.

It is harder to breathe when the air is polluted. Studies show that when the levels of irritant air pollution are beyond certain levels in the urban environment there is constriction in the air passages. While healthy persons may not notice the extra breathing efforts imposed by airway constriction, this added burden may become unbearable for persons whose lungs or hearts are already functioning marginally because of respiratory disease.

Indications are that bronchial asthma is another condition often made worse by air pollution. Because there is a long list of materials which are capable of triggering asthmatic attacks, it is difficult to ascertain the precise role of air pollutants. The Donora, Pennsylvania, catastrophe in 1948 provided a striking example of local aggravation of asthmatics. In New Orleans, epidemic outbreaks of asthmatic attacks have been shown to have been associated with air pollution.

The Public Health Service indicates that colds and other infections of the upper respiratory tract occur more frequently in areas with high air pollution levels. This was indicated in a study in a small Maryland city as long ago as 1950, and has since been confirmed by studies in Great Britain, Japan and the Soviet Union. A study of air pollution in the Detroit, Michigan–Windsor, Ontario, area indicated that people living in the two high-pollution areas of Detroit reported themselves afflicted with more symptoms of illness than people living in the two low-pollution areas. This was particularly true in regard to the prevalence of coughing and colds.

A twelve-year study on the causes of death completed in 1960 in Nashville, Tennessee, showed that the sections of the city subjected to the heaviest air pollution were areas of maximum deaths from all respiratory diseases. The mortality ratios were correlated with air pollution levels in the ambient air. Similar findings were made in a study conducted in the area of Buffalo, New York.

Moments of significant history often go unrecognized by those immediately affected. The participants and spectators are usually too busy coping with the immediate situation to reflect upon the broader implications of the event. Thus a newspaper on September 8, 1943, reported: "Thousands of eyes smarted; many wept, sneezed, and coughed. Throughout the downtown area and into the foothills, the fumes spread their irritations . . ." As the haze settled over the city, cut down the visibility, and invited a variety of citizen wheezes and tears, it is doubtful that Los Angeles realized that it was embarking upon a career as the smog capital of the world, a reputation that was to be subsequently investigated by experts, promulgated by comedians and castigated by its residents.

Smog had been experienced in Los Angeles previous to 1943. But September 8 is cited as the genesis of an air pollution condition that is known as "Los Angeles smog." The term smog is a combination of the words smoke and fog, and was historically used to describe the condition in London when coal smoke and soot combined with the famous London fogs to cause the thick impenetrable throat-wracking soup. Smog was also the name for pollution in Pittsburgh and St. Louis composed of smoke and soot from inefficient coal furnaces during the fall and winter months.

Los Angeles smog occurs on bright sunshiny days when there is no natural fog in the air, and is the result of invisible gases rather than smoke and soot from coal. The primary substances responsible for the smog are certain hydrocarbons and oxides of nitrogen. When these chemical ingredients are mixed together in the presence of ultraviolet light from the sun, a reaction takes place, and Los Angeles smog, or more exactly photochemical smog, is created. Adding to this mixture their own special flavor and flair are the sulfur compounds generated by the combustion of sulfur-containing fuels in power plants, from petroleum factories, and from industry. Together they have made Los Angeles unique in air pollution.

Three factors have been ascribed as the cause of Los Angeles smog: meteorology; the tremendous population growth since World War II; and the particular mode of housing, industry and transportation. The meteorology is unique to the Los Angeles Basin. The second two forces have corollaries in many other cities and regions in the country and the world.

The Los Angeles Basin geographically and meteorologically has a very limited air supply in which it can dump its effluents. Ringed by mountains on three sides and controlled by an inversion phenomenon centered over the Hawaiian Islands, the basin sometimes has an air supply less than 300 feet high in which to dilute all its contaminants (whereas in Chicago or New York the air supply mixing bowl is 3,000 feet high). In addition, Los Angeles has an average annual wind speed of only 6.2 miles per hour (compared with 10.1 for Chicago and

12.5 for Boston). Thus the inversion condition, a layer of warm air effectively putting a lid on the colder, denser air below, and the lack of a sufficient wind force to ventilate and disperse contaminated air, restrict Los Angeles to a limited air supply.

Into this fixed air supply Los Angeles has introduced the wastes produced by a population growing tremendously rapidly. In 1937 the population of the Los Angeles area was less than 3 million and there were about 1 million automobiles consuming less than 2 million gallons of gasoline daily, and there were also only 6,000 industrial units. In 1967 the population had more than doubled to 7.2 million, 3.84 million automobiles used 7.85 million gallons of gasoline daily, and there were approximately 18,500 manufacturing units. But the volume of air has remained the same. Projections to 1980 forecast 6 million cars on the Los Angeles freeways; the volume of air will remain the same.

Not only has the automobile molded the social character of Los Angeles, it has physically affected the area as well. The automobile has created a very decentralized city with industry dispersed uniformly throughout. Also dispersed throughout are the wastes from these autos, which are the largest source of hydrocarbon contamination and nitrogen oxides and the chief cause of photochemical smog which irritates the eyes and damages plant life. Today the automobile is the primary reason for the gray veil which hangs over the metropolitan area, contributing 90 percent of the effluents which pollute the air.

In 1947, the Los Angeles County Air Pollution Control District was formed to attack the smog and effluents in the Los Angeles Basin atmosphere. This pioneer effort has been praised as a model air pollution control system and copied and set up as an example for other governmental units. In 1967, the Los Angeles County Air Pollution Control District prevented 5,180 tons of pollution from entering the air by regulation of the

[69]

18,500 stationary sources in the area. It was estimated that this level of control represented the expenditure of almost three-quarters of a billion dollars, including the cost to industry for equipment, and the amounts spent by the Control District for research and operational expenses. Another 1,140 tons of air pollutants were controlled in 1967 by the installation of crankcase and exhaust control devices on motor vehicles, making the total amount controlled some 6,320 tons, after twenty years of work and the expenditure of millions of dollars.

Yet in 1967, 14,000 tons of material entered the Los Angeles atmosphere. Of this amount, 1,330 tons came from all stationary sources including industry, domestic heating, and cooking. The remaining 12,465 tons came from automobile exhaust pipes. As Louis J. Fuller, Air Pollution Control Officer for Los Angeles County, summarized the twenty years of the nation's best air pollution control program,

Today, pollution from rubbish disposal has been eliminated, pollution from industry has been reduced almost to the practicable minimum, but pollution from motor vehicles has been controlled only slightly. In the meantime, the number of motor vehicles has more than doubled, and there is more than twice as much pollution from this source as there was when the control program began. . . . That is the balance sheet: 6,320 tons controlled; 14,000 tons uncontrolled. That which can be controlled from nonmoving sources has been almost completely controlled; that which can be controlled from automotive sources has been scarcely touched and makes up 90 percent of our problem.

The present level of control of the stationary sources of pollution is about 80 percent efficient. This has been achieved by rules and regulations of the Control District governing smoke, nuisance, particulate matter, sulfur compounds, combustion contaminants, storage of petroleum products, oil effluent–water separators, dusts and fumes, open fires, incinerator burning, gasoline loading, sulfur content of fuels, gasoline composition, solvents and animal reduction processes.

These rules and regulations have applied controls to incinerators, rendering cookers, coffee roasters, asphalt plants, open hearth furnaces, electric furnaces, restaurants, crematoriums, housing tract developers — from the smelting of metal to the production of dog food. Electric precipitators, baghouses, afterburners, separators, scrubbers, absorbers, and vapor collection equipment have been installed to prevent the air from becoming contaminated. The result of this diligent activity is that after twenty years, 10 percent of the air pollution can be controlled with an 80 percent efficiency.

Meanwhile, in Los Angeles, the population increases, the industries and manufacturing units multiply, the automobile sales rise, the consumption of gasoline grows, the ratio of air volume per person decreases, the exhausts spew forth, the sun shines, the cauldron bubbles, and Los Angeles coughs. And all cities are Los Angeles.

3

SMELLING

Each morning for more than ten years the quiet little town of Selbyville, Delaware, awoke fearful that a south wind would blow across the state line from Maryland. The residents needed no sophisticated meteorological reports from the weather bureau, no radio announcements, not even a wet finger poised in the air to confirm or dispel their fear of another day of nausea, vomiting, headaches, and emotional strain. All that was required was a tentative nasal probe of the air — a sniff or two to determine the quality of Selbyville life for that day. For if the wind was from the south it was announced by an overpowering stench so strong that it permeated every nook and cranny of every home, school, church and business establishment in Selbyville as well as many other nearby communities.

The cause of this malodorous siege of Selbyville has been known ever since the day in 1955 that the Bishop Processing Plant in Bishop, Maryland, went into operation. This reduction and rendering plant processes animal wastes, particularly that of poultry — the skins, the bones, the blood, the offal and the feathers — and the process releases the foul gases that ride the south wind to envelop the region of Selbyville.

The plant operations were restricted for a short time in 1957 by the Circuit Court of Worcester County, Maryland, but this brief respite for Delaware residents was ended by the simple payment of a fine, and the Maryland courts failed to act further. The reduction and rendering operations resumed, the stacks billowed their noxious charge, Selbyville noses quivered, and the unrelenting complaints and anguished pleas began again.

Representative of the complaints received from Selbyville residents are those which are directed to its government officials. Says former Mayor William Ringler:

Every year since being elected mayor of Selbyville to the present day, especially in the spring, summer, and fall, I have had numerous complaints on the odors from Bishop Processing Company . . . One Town Council meeting was interrupted by a citizen of our town walking in and saying, "That smell from Bishop Processing Plant is awful tonight. For God's sake, isn't there something you can do about it?" I saw the look on this citizen's face. It was a wearied, disgusted look of anger due to the foul odor. . . . In one instance a citizen was complaining with tears running down her face, saying she had not slept the night before, couldn't eat her breakfast, and that her husband did not retain his breakfast, she couldn't afford air conditioning, and now "I am trying to put in a day's work."

The complaints record the pervasive effects of the stench upon all the activities in the town. The education of Selbyville students once was interrupted when schoolrooms had to be sealed, the recruitment of teaching staff has been hampered when prospective members have been exposed to the odors, and a high school graduation exercise had to be conducted under extremely oppressive conditions, necessitating inadequate apologies to the speaker and other nauseated guests.

[73]

Selbyville's churches offered no sanctuary for worshippers. The pastor of the Salem Methodist Church, the Reverend David W. Baker, cited lowered attendance and the conducting of weddings and other services under the most difficult of circumstances due to the polluted air. "On several occasions when a wedding or worship service is being conducted, with attendance anywhere from 125 to 300, the odor has descended upon us, making it necessary to close all windows; and because of the outside air being contaminated, we have not been able to use the fresh air fan system we recently installed."

From the mid-fifties Selbyville began economically deteriorating. Through the sixties it was losing business establishments and population. Unemployment was rising. And new customers and businesses declined to come there.

At the Tally-Ho Cocktail Bar and Restaurant, according to its proprietor, William P. Penza, "Patrons have even gone so far as to walk out of the dining room without finishing their meal, and some come in with the intention of dining, but cannot because of the smell."

The owner of the J. Conn Scott furniture store was told by customers from out of town that they had become physically ill upon entering Selbyville and had left without doing business because they had not been able to tolerate the odor. Another out-of-town businessman stated that he almost had an accident while attempting to flee Selbyville and its smell.

Dentists, realtors, insurance men, proprietors of nurseries and clothing and jewelry stores — all testified to losing sales and failing to introduce new employment opportunities into the town. Property values and the total economy growth were stunted by the odor.

Long-time residents were forced to move, and invitations to new residents were declined. The comment of T. Harry Baylis indicates the situation prospective homeowners experienced:

[74]

"When I retired on January 1, 1965, we immediately made plans to move to Selbyville. Until we decided whether we wanted to buy or build, we have rented a home here. After this past summer, we are indeed glad that we have not invested money in real estate in Selbyville. . . . We were unable to use our air conditioner at night in order to sleep because an open window was an open invitation to the most obnoxious odor I have ever encountered."

The residents and officials of Selbyville were not concerned with the physical and economic deterioration of their community alone. They were aware also of deleterious effects upon their health:

"We have been awakened in the night by the offensive odors. We could not sleep, consequently we have been tired and suffered headaches due to this condition."

"It was in the early morning hours on August 19, 1965, the winds were of southeast direction. I was awakened with nausea and odor—the nausea lasted during the remainder of the day. I was not able to perform any household duties for the day."

"The stench that overwhelms us when the wind is from the south seems to aggravate my condition; and on several occasions, I have had to resort to oxygen therapy to get relief."

"As a registered nurse, I also know the hardship this odor causes among the people who suffer any respiratory ailment."

"Other nights it will wake you up in the middle of the night, and I have been sick to my stomach. After two nights of this you can imagine how one feels and I have gotten up and cried, it has gotten on my nerves so bad."

The Selbyville residents' complaints and concern were reinforced by the physicians in the town. Dr. Jack C. Lewis, in addressing the mayor and council, said he felt that the fumes from the Bishop Processing Plant not only worsened already existing diseases, but actually caused illness and impaired the health of citizens otherwise free from sickness. Dr. Lewis empha-sized his medical opinion that "this constitutes a serious threat to the local citizen's health" by referring to his patient files. He indicated a causal relationship between this polluted odiferous air and eye irritations, infections, and allergic con-ditions. When the stench is swallowed or inhaled, nausea and vomiting occur which worsens preexisting conditions such as pregnancy, peptic ulcer, and coronary insufficiency and others. Respiratory ailments, bronchitis, emphysema and asthma may be caused or aggravated by the polluted air, according to Lewis, placing an added burden on the heart and increasing the danger to cardiac patients.

In addition to the physical impairment noted by Dr. Lewis in his experience with Selbyville residents, he emphasized ". . . the more intangible but certainly very real effect that air pollution has on the emotional health of affected persons. Any attempt to categorize impairment of mental well-being is fraught with difficulties, but even the most dubious skeptic must certainly admit that when local citizens are so affected by the stench as to be moved through a gamut of emotions ranging from actual tears to threats, then this is certainly not an ideal community situation."

The mayor of Selbyville, Asher B. Carey, Jr., was a physician as well, and he concurred with the conclusions Dr. Lewis and other Selbyville residents made about the relationship between community health and the rotten gases:

With obnoxious odors present from Bishop Processing, persons in ill health have an added struggle to obtain comfort; those with an allergy problem find it almost impossible to live here; the more fortunate citizens who normally enjoy good health are affected by nausea and vomiting which no longer classifies them "in good health" because if one cannot eat or sleep, he cannot remain in good health. . . . These odors do jeopardize health, as well as create much unhappiness, and certainly you are deprived of peace of mind.

In 1965, Selbyville residents, because they had exhausted the local and state abatement remedies and because the problem was an interstate matter, solicited the federal government for its assistance under the authority of the Clean Air Act. In 1967, after two hearings in which testimony was received from all the interested parties — the town of Selbyville, the Bishop Processing Company, agencies of the two states involved, and representatives of the U.S. Department of Health, Education and Welfare — orders were issued to the Bishop Processing Company to correct and control the odors issuing from its plant in Bishop, Maryland, which were fouling the air and endangering the health and welfare of Selbyville, Delaware, and adjacent areas in two states. Even after the hearings and the 1967 orders to cease the discharge of odorous pollutants into the air and across the state line into Delaware, the Bishop Processing Company failed to comply. The continued resistance on the part of the company resulted in a series of court battles with the U.S. Department of Justice over the enforcement of provisions of the Clean Air Act, and eventually over a U.S. District court order to cease all manufacturing and processing operations.

While the legal issues and orders were being aired and appealed in various federal courts in 1969, the smelly emissions riding south winds still had the residents of Selbyville holding their noses. With these specific legal actions, however, odor has gained official recognition as an environmental problem equivalent to the air pollution caused by chemicals or particulate matter coming from industrial establishments.

Odor created by man's activity has long been a problem. For the most part it has been considered only as an aesthetic

[77]

matter. The smells that have emanated from industrial activities have been accepted as the price one pays for jobs and economic activity. They irritate; they bother; people complain, fuss and fume. But little thought has been given to whether it is necessary for human beings to live with an unappealing odor. Freedom from stench is a luxury. Those affected by foul industrial smells are usually employed by the source industry, forced to live within close range of their place of employment and are, therefore, relatively powerless to complain or escape from the discomfort. The health relationship with odor has not generally been considered, much less known.

In the case of Selbyville, however, it was determined that odor had adverse effects upon health and deleterious effects upon welfare. The official findings of the hearing board give governmental language and recognition to the physiological and psychological burden imposed upon the citizens of Selbyville for over ten years. For an understanding of the human thoughts and feelings of those who were forced to bear this burden, one might consider the statement of an anguished resident of Selbyville, Mrs. Maxine Simpler:

We in Selbyville have as much right to a good life here as people in other states and towns. We contribute to the welfare of our country. We obey its laws and pay our way. There is no reason for us to be burdened with this awful situation. The olfactory senses and nerves being what they are, it is just as necessary that we have clean air to breathe and smell as it is to see, or hear, or feel. And we feel pretty angry about our nice little town being ruined, just ruined. We are greatly embarrassed and chagrined that our beautiful section of Delaware has been allowed to become such a stinkpot.

An outraged sense of smell and indignation over the odors emanating from rendering plants are not limited to small towns or to the average American citizen. The Hopfenmaier Rendering Company has been cooking a malodorous brew of animal fat, bone, scraps and grease for over eighty years right under the noses of some of the country's leading social and political figures who live in the exclusive Georgetown section of Washington, D.C. This company processes the bone and scraps from supermarkets and restaurants within a 75-mile radius of Washington. Operating six and sometimes seven days a week in an around-the-clock operation that handles over twelve thousand pounds of product daily, the company spreads its putrid odors throughout this neighborhood of expensive houses and sensitive noses.

One of the offended noses belongs to Senator Stuart Symington of Missouri, who vented his personal anger on the floor of the United States Senate in 1967. That day in March, odors became a momentary matter of ranking legislative concern, as Senator Symington explained the situation:

Those of us who live in or around Georgetown have first-hand knowledge of this disgraceful condition in our nation's capital because for many years, without success, we have tried to have something done about the almost unbelievable smells which come from the Hopfenmaier Rendering Company, at 3300 K Street NW any day or night the wind blows the odor over Georgetown.

The Hopfenmaier people cook old horses, bone scraps, grease — anything to obtain the desired residual and a profit — to the point where the smell is so unbearable that some people have left the neighborhood and others have been "rendered" ill. The smell is so bad that the plant next to the Hopfenmaier plant has a sign on it: "The objectionable odors you may notice in this area do not originate in this plant."

Rendering plants producing putrid gases and the stench of rotting animal matter are but one industrial source of offensive odor. An equally obnoxious aroma is associated with the manufacture of paper.

The town of Lincoln, Maine, is situated upon the east bank

of the Penobscot River, and its approximately 4,500 residents take pride in their long Yankee tradition of hardiness, independence, and ingenuity. In 1958 a pulp and paper mill in Lincoln was purchased by the Standard Packaging Company, who installed a new kraft paper process. It became Lincoln's major industry, employing about 400 people within the town, and proceeded to emit a rank combination of gases — hydrogen sulfide, methyl mercaptan, methyl sulfide, dimethyl sulfide, and other sulfur-containing gases. This soon caused the residents of Lincoln to become concerned about their health, the effects and damage to their property, the increasing business losses, and the resultant environmental blight which made life in Lincoln miserable.

Although the company provided the major employment for the town, it soon became apparent to the Yankee mind of Lincoln that good neighbors keep their odors on their side of the fence. In 1964 the Lincoln Town Council sent attorney Peter Briola before the Subcommittee on Air and Water Pollution of the United States Senate Public Works Committee to report the conditions which had existed in Lincoln for the six years that Standard Packaging Company had been spewing their noisome product into the air.

Briola related to the subcommittee the history of his town from its incorporation in 1829 up through 1957. This was a description of beautiful clear-water lakes, rolling countryside, postcard scenery, fishing, clean air, and a prospering mercantile business which drew many out-of-town customers. As Briola reported of this period, "The people prospered and healthwise lived to enjoy what Mother Nature so graciously and bountifully provided."

In 1958, as Standard Packaging Company started contaminating the air with its fumes, this appealing environmental picture began to change. Attorney Briola observed the evidence

[80]

of deterioration and degradation as a result of this odorous insult. Street after street of houses painted white and light shades became discolored. The paint and chrome on Lincoln's automobiles became pitted and marred. Vegetation was damaged, and the postcard nature of Lincoln faded.

Briola also noticed a decline, beginning in 1958, in the good health heretofore enjoyed by Lincoln residents. They experienced watering and irritation of the eyes, sinus difficulties, nosebleed and breathing problems. Local doctors noticed increased incidences of respiratory ailments and linked these to the fumes and odor of the mill.

The attorney testified to frequently being awakened from a sound sleep choked up and unable to breathe and nauseated because of the intensity of the odor. He likened this experience to ". . . a thief in the night slipping into your house and grabbing you by the throat in an effort to choke you to death."

Lincoln's plea to the subcommittee, as expressed by the respected Briola, was direct. He stated: "All in all we have a very serious situation and respectfully plead with this Senate committee to help us, for ourselves and our children's sake, to again enjoy what God gave us — clean air uncontaminated with the injurious chemicals and nauseating odors now puffing out of the stacks of Standard Packaging Company at Lincoln."

This appeal to the federal government had to remain unanswered, since as subcommittee chairman Senator Edmund S. Muskie of Maine explained, the Clean Air Act cannot operate until a state confers jurisdiction. Even though the hearings brought out that governmental action at the local, state and federal levels was restricted in the Lincoln situation, it was pointed out that technical control of these particular sulfurous odors maligning Lincoln were both possible and economically feasible within the kraft paper industry.

A report to the U.S. Public Health Service indicated that

a completely odorless kraft mill was technically possible if management was willing to pay the price, which, the report suggested, would be neither excessive nor a pure additional expense without industrial operation benefits.

A second report, this one by a representative of the kraft mill industry, Weyerhaeuser Company, reaffirmed the Public Health Service conclusion that odor control was feasible. The report related the actual implementation and operation of such an odor-free plant in the Weyerhaeuser kraft pulp and container board mill in Springfield, Oregon. In this instance, the public outcry of Springfield citizens (the most effective of which were Valentines to the Weyerhaeuser Company with the affectionate message "You Stink") resulted in a long but eventually effective program and investment by the company to reduce the kraft odors.

In Springfield, Oregon, management paid the price and felt proud of their progress. In Lincoln, Maine, the town residents had to pay a price in property damage, environmental degradation, business decline, and impairment in good health. This physical investment was without return, as Standard Packaging Company closed down the plant in the spring of 1968.

Odor pollution problems are not always so easily identifiable or specific as the rotten stench of a rendering plant or the sulfurous emissions of a kraft mill. In the spring of 1964, the people of Terre Haute, Indiana, accustomed to occasional foul odors, suddenly discovered that they were under an olfactory siege. The reports began to come in to City Hall of strong, objectionable odors, numerous complaints of illness, and darkening of paint. In Terre Haute, the question was first — what was it? Then — where was it coming from?

The mayor of Terre Haute, concerned primarily about the health effects upon the city's residents, inaugurated a study of the problem. Within a day or so he realized that he needed

[82]

more assistance than could be obtained at the city level and sought the aid of state health officials and the U.S. Public Health Service. Together they determined that the offender was hydrogen sulfide, a gas characterized by its odor of rotten eggs and its darkening effect on lead-base paints.

Reports of adverse health effects and odor complaints were investigated, and medical records such as mortality data and emergency room records were studied. A medical evaluation of the data did not reveal a medical disaster, but it did show conditions of health impairment greater than what is termed a nuisance. While no lasting health effects and no deaths could be accurately ascribed to the stench, the health of the residents was found to be affected by nausea, loss of sleep and abrupt awakening, shortness of breath and headaches.

The investigating team discovered four operations with the potential for creating hydrogen sulfide problems: a septic-tank dump, lagoons used by the Commercial Solvents Corporation for industrial wastes, the spray waste area used by the Weston Paper Company, and the Indiana Gas and Chemical Corporation. The culprit soon was discovered to be gaseous emissions of hydrogen sulfide from the Commercial Solvents Corporation lagoon, which because of meteorological conditions were concentrating in high volume in a shallow valley and causing property damage, discomfort and adverse health reactions.

The identification of the specific odor, the determination of the extent of health effects, the exact source of the malodorous gas, and the eventual attempt to control the problem all involved the cooperative efforts of a vast number of people, professions and organizations. Three levels of government were involved as well as physicians, engineers, firemen, policemen, Purdue University, the news media, industry, the weather bureau, sociologists, chemists, and residents whose health and property were threatened by the stench. Total

[83]

community recognition was given to the seriousness of odor pollution.

A dictionary definition of odor is "that characteristic of a substance which makes it perceptible to the sense of smell." The sense of smell is "that one of the five senses of the body by which a substance is perceived through the chemical stimulation of nerves (olfactory nerves) in the nasal cavity by particles given off by that substance." Within the human nasal cavity is a tiny area yellowish-brown in color, covered with mucous, and containing the nerve endings of olfaction or the sense of smell. When minute particles in the air dissolved in the mucous stimulate the nerve fibers of the olfactory organ, a message that an odor has been detected is transmitted by the olfactory nerve to the brain. The olfactory sense is able to receive an unlimited number of dissimilar odor stimuli, sometimes from very great distances and in diluted concentrations as weak as one part per billion of air.

One of the branches of the trigiminal nerve also ends in the nasal mucosa, and it plays a specific role in the perception of quality in odor, rather than mere sensation. This nerve can perceive and transmit the sensations of irritation, acridity and pungency. From the nerve endings the stimulus is transmitted to the brain where a quantitative report is made regarding strength and a qualitative judgment is made as to type of odor and its value.

The measurement of odors by mechanical or instrumental means requires the measurement of some physical or chemical property of the substance to be analyzed; therefore, to measure odor instrumentally it is necessary to measure some property which is characteristic of odor. However, there is no known measurable property that is characteristic of odor. Instruments are available for detecting specific odors by mechanical means;

they measure some known characteristic property of that specific substance to ascertain its presence. Since odor is present in concentrations as small as one part per billion parts of air, however, even these specific odor instruments can't sense diluted concentrations or detect mixed or unknown odors.

The most effective method of detecting the strength of an odor is through organoleptic measurements. This is the term embarrassed scientists use to describe the best instrument developed so far to measure odor strength — the human nose. This limited method is complicated by the variations among individuals' abilities to smell and by fluctuations in sensitivity in every individual.

Qualitative odor judgments are even more bound to the human response. They are a subjective matter, although there is common agreement as to which smells are bad or disagreeable.

Numerous attempts have been made to classify odors into groups by using general descriptive terms such as fruity, aromatic, spicy, balsamic, or alliaceous as a basis for comparison. General classifications which are judged by odor analysts to be objectionable are empyreamatic or burnt odors, caprylic or goaty odors, and fetid or putrid odors. Most of these classifications, however, are distinguishable only by expert "sniffers" and are without scientific validity. The detection and qualitative judgment of odors in the general environment still depend upon individual human sensitivity and shared community reaction.

The most objectionable common community odors, as measured by complaints to city bureaus, are animal odors, odors from combustion and food processes, odors from the paint, chemical and foundry gases, and odors of decomposition and sewage smells.

Of all the odors reported, the most frequent complaints

are about meat-packing and rendering plant odors, automobile exhausts, coffee-roasting odors, paint lacquer and varnish plant smells and coke-oven or coal gas odors.

Community sensibilities have been upset also by the odors of putrefication and oxidation from organic wastes; burning rubber; hydrogen sulfide; food-processing plants which use fish oils; bakeries; manufacturers of asphalt; plastic, and fertilizer; and poultry raisers and processors.

Not the least numerous of the complaints to municipal authorities have been about municipal incinerators and city sewers.

Complaints about offensive odors have been increasing for several reasons. With a rising standard of living, people are becoming more concerned about the quality of their environment, have more time to enjoy their property and outdoor recreation, and have more varied employment opportunity. What had previously been ignored is now vocally labeled offensive, and the fears of repercussion if one speaks his complaint have been reduced. Furthermore, as a concomitant of increased living standards, concern about health has increased. The public is becoming more aware of the health implications of odors, more willing to express their opinions on health matters and to press for an abatement of that which they feel causes damage to their person and their property.

The industrial and manufacturing activities in this country have expanded greatly. This expansion and the resultant emission of odors have occurred within a fixed volume of air. The great dilutions previously existent are not to be found as easily in industrial areas as each establishment adds its pollutants to a single local atmosphere.

The quantitative expansion in industry and manufacturing has been accompanied by both a qualitative expansion of varieties of processes and of products, and a qualitative shift in emphasis. The modern world of manufacturing and industry concentrates on new and complex chemicals, exotic compounds created by science for specific needs, many times without consideration of the full effects of either their manufacture or their disposal. An industrial example of this lack of foresight is in the field of plastics where the rush toward production has overlooked the odor problems created by solvents needed for manufacture and the complex gaseous compounds given off when the plastics are disposed of by burning.

Odor complaints have also been on the increase because of the rapid development of land. The industry or business that produces unacceptable odors once was able to pollute a relatively isolated region some distance from either residential or commercial areas. Now, increased population and rapid suburban expansion has put industry within olfactory distance of human concentrations unwilling to bear the aesthetic, physical, or emotional insult of foul odors.

The complexity of dealing with odor pollution in a populated area which includes a large number and variety of industrial odor sources began to be recognized soon after the end of World War II, at a time when odor pollution was more often than not the municipal responsibility of the Bureau of Smoke Inspection, or some similar office. In 1952, in Cincinnati, Ohio, 231 chemical products were being produced within the metropolitan area. These chemicals included industrial chemicals; drugs and medicines; soaps and glycerin; cleaning solvents; paints, varnishes and pigments; fertilizers; and vegetable and animal oils. Cincinnati's air was the repository of odors coming not only from chemical products but from six coffee-roasting plants; twenty-four meat-packing plants; eighteen plants producing petroleum and coal products, roofing felts and paving compounds; eight rubber-products plants; three tanneries; six breweries; one distillery. The local ordinance declared that strong and obnoxious odors should be treated as a nuisance, but the legal proof necessary to prove odor intensity and foul quality was difficult to obtain.

The public protection from the odiferous insults of the nearly 300 emission sources in the area was in the hands of the Chief Smoke Inspector. The inspector, whose prime duty consisted of comparing the colors of smokestack emissions, expressed a growing awareness of the problem of odor control, and an attitude that this control was a very complex matter, when he said "It is harder to analyze the [odor] situation than to pick out the shell that covers the pea at the carnival."

Several sources of Cincinnati's odor problems in 1952, however, were neither difficult to locate nor complex in their nature. And the people in the affected neighborhoods were willing to bear the odiferous intrusion no longer. One neighborhood refused to accept the putrid stench emanating from a clinical laboratory which failed to effectively incinerate its pathological wastes, the bodies of dogs and monkeys; their complaints to city officials resulted in action against the laboratory. Another neighborhood distinguished between the occasional savor of freshly roasted coffee and the stench of a nearby plant processing thousands of pounds of coffee an hour.

A chemical plant producing printing inks, lacquers, dyes and pharmaceuticals had started operations in the country, but the city had grown out around it. The plant grew too, and during and under the demands of World War II the neighbors remained tolerant. When hostilities ended, however, the neighborhood circulated petitions, complained of seventeen different odors including "rotten fish," "moth balls," "rotten eggs," "glue factory," and "polecat," and demanded abatement action. This reaction was paralleled in a Cincinnati neighborhood where a twenty-five-year-old plant processed animal feed from brewery wastes. When an unvented grain dryer was installed and began to spew the odor of scorched fat into the area, its neighbors sounded the alarm and flooded the city Bureau of Smoke Inspection with complaints. Even changing the odor from scorched fat to popcorn was not totally satisfactory.

An increasingly more militant public concerned about odor pollution from long existent sources is not peculiar to Cincinnati. The complaints have been heard around the country, by public officials and the press, and have in some instances received the legal recognition of the courts. In Saddle Brook, New Jersey, the Sommers Rendering Company established their plant soon after the turn of the century when the township was rural and sparsely settled. As the population grew and the township turned residential, the rendering company cooked and processed their butcher shop wastes and dead animal stock just as they always had. The odors which the plant produced were described as "very vile," "sickening," and "nauseating." They produced extreme discomfort to nearby residents, caused some to become ill, spoiled meals and made normal life impossible. The only relief was obtained when the plant was not operating.

In 1961 the New Jersey appellate court upheld a lower court decision finding the plant a nuisance and hazardous to health and enjoining its further operation. In the case of *State ex rel Board of Health v. Sommers Rendering Company*, (N. J. Super. Ct. App. Div. 1961) 169 A.2.d. 165, the court held that "carrying on an offensive trade for 20 or more years in a place remote from buildings and public roads does not entitle the owner to continue in the same place after houses have been built and roads laid out, if such continuance is a nuisance to the residents in those houses and to travellers on the roads."

After years of operation in a plant in Mt. Vernon, New York, production expansion necessitated movement of Mrs. Kornberg's Chicken Liver Paste to a larger plant. The logical sites for the new plant were in the neighboring towns of heavily suburban Westchester County, New York. The towns wanted nothing to do with Mrs. Kornberg's bad breath — odors arising from the slow roasting of sliced onions in chicken fat, a key step in the production of the liver paste. Only when a catalytic air pollution control unit was introduced into the production process to trigger flameless oxidation of combustible gases and vapors and eliminate the highly odiferous organic compounds, did Mrs. Kornberg's become a welcome neighbor in an expanded plant in North White Plains.

In St. Louis, a soap company had been located in a quiet, semi-residential neighborhood for years. When the company expanded and changed their production, neighboring householders began complaining of a fish-like odor which permeated homes and persisted in its deleterious effects for days. This odor deadened the sense of smell at high concentrations and clung to hair, skin, clothing, and automobiles. Public hearings by the Health Commissioner of St. Louis and the city's aldermen forced the company to research and change their process.

E. I. du Pont de Nemours and Company had no odor difficulties with their neoprene plants until they opened up a new one at Montague, Michigan, a semi-resort area located in the western part of the state near the shore of Lake Michigan. There, the local residents made it quite apparent to company officials that what was good enough for du Pont was not good enough for them. An inadequate waste burner, which allowed by-product chemicals to escape into the atmosphere uncombusted, was replaced, and other modifications made as well.

When the city of Austin, Texas, provided a three-million-gallon covered municipal sewage holding tank to act as a reservoir for untreated sewage during periods in the day when the flow exceeded treatment capacity, they found it necessary, particularly in the summer months, to provide catalytic treatment of the vented gases to avoid contamination of an adjacent residential area with a mixture of complex hydrocarbons, mercaptans, amines and other organics released by the stored sewage.

The Pacific Adhesives Company in Beaverton, Oregon, was told by an aroused citizenry and a court order either to clean up their odorous air or get out of town. The heating of dried blood for the manufacture of glue used in plywood production created a by-product which made the presence of this plant unacceptable to the residents. Rather than leave Beaverton, the company spent $4,000 on equipment and made municipal peace.

The indignation of citizens over odor conditions which sap energies, inhibit a full enjoyment of life, and make certain municipal areas unbearable, has caused a growing governmental awareness and sensitivity to noxious smells.

Chicago long had considered the odiferous conditions associated with the famous stockyards an indication of the industrial progress of the city, a sign of its prosperity and a necessary evil that had to be tolerated if prosperity was to continue. As complaints to City Hall increased — pointing an accusatory finger at postal zone number nine and its meat packers, rendering plants, and animal-hair processors — and as the larger packing plants began to relocate out of the stockyard's area, the city took another look at the district and their ideas about progressive economy indicators.

What was found in the stockyards were not complex and highly technical chemical processes at work but rather appalling conditions of poor sanitation and housekeeping, putrefaction and rotting which broadcast a stench across Chicago. Oil drippings had so completely saturated the wooden timbers in old plants that they reeked with rancid odors. Large quantities of scraps, offal, and bones lay in the yards in the open sun and air after having fallen off trucks and railroad cars. Plant catch basins were filled with organic matter. Many companies were found to recirculate contaminated condensor water through roof-top cooling towers, depositing decomposing odiferous solids on cooling tower slats.

Thousands of animals in the animal holding pens, the hog house and cattle pens created far-reaching and voluminous odors. Manure piles were common around the pens; periodically, manure was collected in one large pile in one corner of the yard. Loaded railroad gondolas filled with manure waited uncovered on sidetracks for days before being removed.

These were the "signs of prosperity" which caused the city of Chicago to instigate a control program aimed at eliminating the odors coming from the stockyards.

Recognizing the need for odor control in the central industrial district of Kansas City, Missouri, and Kansas City, Kansas, the "stockyards" district of this metropolitan area, but realizing the necessity of having factual ammunition to elicit abatement action, the City Manager of Kansas City, Missouri, in 1963 wrote to the U.S. Public Health Service to request assistance in determining the type and general level of odors in this district. As a result, an odor survey was made of the two Kansas Cities using the staff of twenty-seven fire stations in Kansas and Missouri to systematically observe and chart the range and intensity of odors. As expected, the stockyard odors were the most frequently observed. The firemen also reported the incidences of smoke and transportation odors at a level very close to the stockyard smells.

In this survey over fifty different odor types were detected in the area of the two Kansas Cities. The general categories of these odors, besides the stockyards, smoke and transportation, were foods, sewer, soap, chemical and industrial, unpleasant, miscellaneous and pleasant. Of the fifty or more odor types detected, only four were considered by the firemen surveyors to be pleasant. In many parts of the metropolitan area combinations of one or more of the different unpleasant odors could be found with varying intensity and frequency.

A similar detailed odor survey, sponsored by eleven governmental and civic units, was conducted in St. Louis, Missouri. This study determined which areas of St. Louis had odor problems, the types of odors, which ones were most undesirable, when odors were prevalent, what meteorological conditions aggravated the odors, where the potential sources were located, and the jurisdictional and interstate problems involved.

These studies indicate a recognition of odors as a municipal concern. Rather than waiting for critical outbreaks of epidemic type proportions some cities are adopting an anticipatory attitude and express a strong desire to eliminate existing odors as well as prevent new smells in the future. This philosophy of planning as well as enforcement indicates a serious concern about odor problems, a public awareness of the dangers of odor pollution to expanding concepts of environmental good health.

The future with its growing and geographically expanding population and its development of new processes and new chemical raw materials will require even greater awareness and vigilance on the part of the public, the government, and business. There is some indication that the inclusion of odor control in industrial planning is recognized by businessmen as an essential cost of progress if they are to maintain a position of civic leadership and have the cooperation of their neighbors.

Perhaps of most importance in this society, at a time of increased mental stress and strain, is the knowledge that odors can provoke psychic disorders and produce emotional disturbance. Odors provoke irritability, anger, and anxiety. They can alter dispositions and may become the provocations for

[93]

community hysteria. The range of physical and emotional reactions due to exposure to repulsive odor pollution surely must require consideration of this problem from a health standpoint and will not allow odor disturbances to be characterized as mere nuisance problems per se, or an unfortunate inconvenience.

More than a hundred years ago, Samuel Coleridge described the town of Cologne in this way: "I counted two-and-seventy stenches, all well defined, and several stinks." The catalog of bad odors in American towns and cities has grown far beyond that. And environmental quality, enjoyment of outdoor activities, and a good and healthy atmosphere will require that we do more than just count the smells. Rather, we must follow our noses to a program of action.

4

HEARING

On December 18, 1967, the Plaza of New York City's Lincoln Center for the Performing Arts, one of the nation's artistic and cultural showpieces, was the stage for a most unusual performance. The program was a solo concert; the featured instrument was the jackhammer. The percussive noise of construction equipment was being introduced as an art form. This concert was neither pop art nor frivolous entertainment — it was a deadly serious effort to demonstrate that the American people *can* live in a sane acoustic environment. The producer of this bizarre performance, who in his normal pursuits is a Broadway theatrical manager of note, rapidly is becoming known as one of the nation's leading lay experts on the problem of noise.

Alex Baron had never thought about noise as a human problem until several years before the concert. It was in the spring of 1964 that the city of New York first began to shout in his ears. The first loud noise boomed out of a New York Transit Authority project designed to extend the Sixth Avenue subway from Fifty-second Street up to Fifty-eighth Street — directly below the apartment in which Baron and his family lived. The new subway started as an open cut seven blocks long, covered with timber so that traffic could proceed on top as workmen labored underneath. The resulting tube acted as a resonating chamber and amplified the constant booming sounds produced by the construction equipment and by the traffic crossing the poorly seated timbers. Baron recalls the night traffic's repetitious boom, boom, boom and the cacophonous chorus at seven in the morning of compressors, jackhammers, and bulldozers. The noise and the vibration were incredible.

It soon became apparent to Baron that the neighborhood was becoming unusually upset and seemed to be in a state of chronic tension. Within his own family, the noise was having an effect on his young daughter, who on occasion required sedation in order to be able to take daytime naps during the unrelenting bombardment of noise from below. At the start of the construction Baron was managing a Broadway show and was exposed to the noise for only a few hours of his day. But after the show closed, Baron's days and nights at home were subjected to the unceasing barrage. It got to be too much, and he decided that something had to be done to lift the siege that was making life unbearable for his family, his neighbors, and himself.

So Baron set off on his own. He talked to the police; he talked to city officials; he searched everywhere for help in fighting this intrusion on his normal life. The only response he ever got was "This is the price of progress." He found that the Health Department had no facility for noise control and, in fact, had very little to do with noise.

He discovered that the administrative code in New York prohibits "unnecessary construction" between 6:00 P.M. and 7:00 A.M. and also prohibits "unnecessary noise" throughout the day. But construction noise is apparently considered "necessary" noise. So in the daytime anything goes. Furthermore, a special permit can be obtained for construction after 6:00 P.M. And there is no prohibition against "necessary" nighttime noise, such as the grinding and roaring of a garbage truck at two or three in the morning.

Baron covered as many agencies of the city of New York as he could and found that there was simply no municipal recognition of noise as a problem. It was accepted that construction makes noise and you just take it, period. He searched on the state level for assistance to control noise. The state of New York showed no interest and had no information. He went to Washington and visited the U.S. Public Health Service. He found that although there was technical knowledge about noise in PHS, there was no budget and there were no programs. PHS at that time was uninterested in noise as a community problem. Essentially, the advice Alex Baron received in Washington was — "Go home and keep up the good work."

So he returned to New York and continued his quest for information and assistance. This search led him to the discovery of the British Noise Abatement Society. He joined this group and learned that his particular problem was neither unique nor unusual in Europe. Across the Atlantic, at least, people had organized to focus attention on particular noise crises and to try to promote abatement action. So Baron gathered a group of his New York neighbors, and together they formed the Upper Sixth Avenue Noise Abatement Association. This informal group realized that direct action such as a lawsuit or an appeal to city officials would accomplish little, so they decided instead to learn as much as possible about the legislative and the technological aspects of noise.

As the head of the Upper Sixth Avenue Noise Abatement Association, Baron accepted an invitation to attend the Fourth International Congress for Noise Abatement in Baden Baden, Germany, in May 1966. Here he joined with doctors, lawyers,

[97]

engineers, government officials, scientists, and industry representatives from twenty nations. He not only discovered a sophisticated and respected group interested in the problem of noise, but also was exposed to the sizable existing body of noise technology. The impact of this experience on him was enormous.

When he returned to New York, Baron continued to read and study all he could about noise and its technology and abatement. He joined the Acoustical Society of America, the professional society for noise control engineers and scientists. He learned about sound dampening, and he learned how to treat metal products so that they did not clang and reverberate. And Alex Baron talked about noise. He talked about general noise, construction noise, home noise, appliance noise, airport noise, industrial noise, and transportation noise. He gave professional papers before the Acoustical Society of America and before the American Public Health Association in which he pointed out that the membership of both these professional groups was neglecting the health problems growing out of everyday environmental noise.

Alex Baron realized at that point that the problems of noise were far more extensive than acknowledged in the specific focus of the Upper Sixth Avenue Noise Abatement Association, the subway construction project. As a result of his travels, his experiences, his studies and his conversations, his larger concern was the total range of everyday environmental noise excesses. And so, with the assistance of a number of New York's leading citizens who had backgrounds in law, medicine, sociology and science, Baron formed the Citizens for a Quieter City, Incorporated. The stated objectives of this group were: "To advance knowledge about the deleterious effects of noise; to advance the development of information about methods useful in controlling and reducing the noise assault on urban man in all of his environments; to educate and alert the general public about the injurious effects of noise; and to inform the public about methods of controlling, reducing and abating noise and noise exposure."

Demonstration had become one of the objectives of the organization: to demonstrate to the public quieter equipment and noise abatement techniques. As Baron explained, "I am a pragmatist too. I believe that first we must develop a philosophy about the environment, which would include the idea of an ideal acoustical environment, and I also believe at the same time you are going to have to go after the nuts and bolts of it; you are going to have to demonstrate that it can be done."

One day Baron asked a member of the Technical Committee of Citizens for a Quieter City to investigate a quieter air compressor that had been developed in England and to obtain a model of it for demonstration purposes. Baron's representative came back from England with the information that Holman Brothers, a manufacturer of construction equipment, not only produced a silenced air compressor, but also a jackhammer with a built-in muffler.

The jackhammer, which can destroy tranquility for a block and a half to a dozen blocks from the point where it is operating, was to Alex Baron and his associates the symbol of an environmental problem. And so, Citizens for a Quieter City sponsored a public demonstration of a jackhammer with a built-in muffler and a silenced air compressor on the Plaza of Lincoln Center for the Performing Arts.

Baron notes that he could have found an empty lot on which to hold the demonstration, for that is the place usually used to test such equipment. But he wanted to do more than demonstrate that jackhammers and air compressors don't necessarily have to make the kind of noise which most people begrudgingly accept. He also wanted to exemplify the contrast between the ugliness and barbaric nature of the tools used in the 1960s and the beauty of man's cultural achievements, such as those presented at Philharmonic Hall and the Metropolitan Opera. "I wanted that contrast because I thought that somehow or other it would make a statement without our having to say anything," Baron said.

The demonstration was held, and those who attended were indeed impressed — impressed enough so that a few months later Ingersoll-Rand announced the development of a silenced air compressor.

Alex Baron continued to talk, to study and to demonstrate. One of those who listened was James H. Botsford, a noise control engineer for the Bethlehem Steel Company. Baron asked whether Botsford could design a clang-proof metal garbage can. After some skeptical questioning from his employer and then eventual consent, Botsford went into the laboratory and shop. He pin-pointed the areas of vibration on the can and lid; applied several strategically placed bands of sound-absorbing material consisting of asphalt, felt and rubber; coated the bottom with a gummy material, and put six rubber legs on the can.

On April 18, 1968, in front of the assembled press and television cameras at the Equitable Life Assurance Building Plaza in New York City, several middle-aged men and an attractive woman proceeded to kick, hit, and drop two twenty-gallon metal garbage cans around the plaza. One of the cans continued to clang and reverberate each time it was kicked or dropped. The other made only a dull thud. Botsford's "dull thud" garbage can went on sale to the public in the summer of 1968. The price of a little less noise, a little more sleep in the morning, and a lot less annoyance was approximately $1.50 more per can.

To Baron the noise from the garbage can is but the background accompaniment to the main performer, the garbage truck. This, he said, is something people have been complaining about for decades.

During a trip to Germany and England, Baron found that quieter garbage trucks did exist in Europe. And his reaction was typically American — if they can make them, so can we. About this time he was advised that the city of New York was preparing to order four hundred new garbage trucks. Thereupon Baron sent a long letter to the mayor with copies to the Department of Sanitation and the Department of Purchases strongly urging them to take advantage of this big order to include noise specifications in the purchase contract.

The time was right. The mayor recently had created a Task Force on Noise Control, and Baron's suggestion was adopted as their first order of business. The mayor's task force learned that General Motors had been experimenting with a quieter truck and sent the company an order for trucks, including specifications to fit New York's particular noise problems. General Motors designed a quieter truck engine in a less noisy, more compact body which additionally added less pollution to the air. Baron called the equipment quieter than anything that had been produced up to that time. The cost of eliminating a major source of sleep-disturbing nighttime racket proved to be approximately $100 per truck engine.

The bane of Robert Alex Baron's life has become noise. The explosive percussions of jackhammers, air compressors, pile drivers, air conditioners, vacuum cleaners, toilets, diesel trucks, garbage trucks, garbage cans, airplanes, helicopters and motorcycles now cause Alex Baron to lose sleep at night not involuntarily listening to noises but planning the next phase of a campaign to make New York City and the nation a more healthful and productive environment in which to work and to live through the abatement of noise.

[101]

Baron and the Citizens for a Quieter City operate out of a small room one flight of stairs up from the last elevator stop at the nineteenth floor of a mid-Manhattan office building. One window in the room looks over the construction site of yet another New York skyscraper; if Baron opens that window he can hear the noise of the air compressors across the street. The apartment into which Baron moved after leaving Sixth Avenue was the fruit of a very careful search for peace and quiet. Ironically, this apartment building is now directly under the flight path of a helicopter route and is near the site proposed for the world's first short takeoff and landing strip. Baron could leave the city, but he doesn't intend to abandon New York. Instead, he intends to mobilize public support for noise abatement, first at the local level, and eventually, nationwide.

The general definition of noise used by most experts is quite simple: noise is "unwanted sound." It has been described also as a sound without agreeable musical quality or an undesirable sound.

The decibel is the term used to measure the intensity of sound. It is a unit of gradation measured against a reference level. One decibel is the lowest sound that can be detected by a keen human ear under very quiet conditions. The decibel scale reflects the increase of the pressure against the ear. But the scale is logarithmic — that is, an increase from zero decibels to 120 decibels represents an increase of 10 to the 12th power, or a million million increase.

There is no simple measuring device for general community noise, because it is made up of so many variables. There are, however, some generally accepted noise levels that the public is exposed to on a regular basis. Dr. Vern O. Knudsen, physicist and former Chancellor of the University of California at Los Angeles, developed a basis for grading noises by their decibel levels, based on short-term average readings rather than on long-term averages. This provides a reference for common noises and common exposures.

A quiet suburban family residence, for example, measured between 20 and 30 decibels. A fifth-floor apartment in Paris on a relatively unbusy street measured 40 decibels. A ninth-floor hotel room in New York City at 1:00 A.M. measured 55 decibels. Traffic noise in a hospital one hundred feet from the street, 55 decibels. The rear of the nave at Notre Dame Cathedral, 60 decibels. A fourth-floor hotel room in Dallas, fifty-three feet from a streetcar, 65 decibels. A two-engine airplane at a distance of four thousand feet, 70 decibels. An average factory, 75 decibels. Inside a sedan going 75 miles per hour, 80 decibels. A four-engine transport plane at two thousand feet, 85 decibels. A honking automobile at thirty feet, 98 decibels. The New York subway, 105 decibels. A riveter thirty-five feet away, 110 decibels. A noisy electric generating substation, 120 decibels. A large jet engine seventy-five feet away, 125 decibels.

Some other typical noise levels measured as average sound pressure levels were: A whisper registers 20 decibels. Street noises range from 40 to 70 decibels, and the tick of a watch is 30 decibels. A sports car will roar at 80 to 95 decibels, and average conversation is about 60 decibels.

The commonly accepted threshold level for occupational hearing damage is 85 decibels or above continuously for five hours a day. The level of sound found in an office with tabulating machinery or at a distance of twenty-five to fifty feet away from heavy traffic is 85 decibels.

Physicians and acoustic experts warn against the danger of noise pollution. The effects of noise are generally separated into four categories — annoyance, disruption of activity, loss of hearing and physical and mental deterioration. Individuals react to most noise in a highly subjective manner. The response

[103]

is dependent upon the situation and the person. High-pitched sounds and intermittent noises are usually most annoying. By masking speech communication, noise can upset activities. A noise may blot out all conversation for its duration, or make key words and phrases indistinguishable.

Each year as technology and population in this country increase, so does the noise. We use more machines, the machines get more powerful, and the din gets louder and louder. No section of this country is immune.

In 1907 Dr. Robert Koch, renowned bacteriologist and Nobel Laureate, warned: "The day will come when man will have to fight merciless noise as the worst enemy of his health." In 1937 the American Medical Association cautioned that "the multiple and insidious ill effects of noise constitute an inadequately recognized baneful influence on lives of millions of persons throughout the country." In 1968 Dr. Samuel Rosen, Clinical Professor (Emeritus) of Otology of the Mount Sinai School of Medicine in New York City, declared, "In the United States today, jet and helicopter transport have raised noise pollution to a new peak, and tomorrow the supersonic plane will lift it further. . . . Physicians and acoustics experts warn against the dangers of noise pollution, and some solutions must be sought before the acceleration of noise becomes too great for effective control." Dr. Knudsen explained the situation simply and candidly when he stated, "Noise is one of the chief drawbacks to the enjoyment of modern urban living."

Few people, it seems, have heard the messages. To most people, noise is a nuisance — a disagreeable irritant. They have been told that it is the price of progress — the price one has to pay in order to achieve a better world — but have not been informed of the full impact of noise upon general health and well-being.

Legally, as well as medically, intense and steady noise is

recognized as a cause of occupational disease that can inflict irreversible physical damage in the form of neural hearing loss, and so most of the work and the concern over noise has been in the occupational field. Nineteen years ago, a federal court awarded compensation to a drop-forge-worker who developed occupational presbycusis, or neural deafness. As a result, larger industries now protect their employees against chronic noise levels in the dangerous range, noises exceeding 85 to 90 decibels. Even so, Dr. George Bugliarello, chairman of the bio-technology program at Carnegie-Mellon University in Pittsburgh estimated that some 34 million workers are employed in positions where the noise level regularly exceeds 85 decibels, and that upwards to 14 million of these workers have suffered hearing loss. Other estimates for workers exposed to hazardous noise in industry range from 6 to 16 million. Thus the number of workers exposed to excessive factory noise is still considerable, and the noise problem has gone beyond its occupational concern. It is now a problem of the entire community.

According to Dr. Rosen, many city noises approach, and some exceed, the limits of noise allowed in factories. And even though these last a shorter period of time than factory noises, still they produce a crescendo of unwanted noise against which we are helpless, yet to which we think we are accustomed.

Sources of present-day noise are diverse and without limit. Noise comes from traffic, particularly trucks, scooters, motor-cycles, and sports cars — not to mention the horns of these vehicles. Noise comes from private planes and helicopters; it comes from commercial and military aircraft, from motorboats, sirens, garbage trucks and garbage pails; noise comes from power lawn mowers and snow shovelers and leaf rakers. It comes from outside air conditioners. Noise is created by con-struction equipment such as jackhammers, air compressors, riveters and pile-drivers; gunfire adds to the din. Household appliances such as dishwashers, blenders, garbage disposals, vacuum cleaners, radio and television sets — all contribute noise to the environment.

In work situations efficiency losses, reduction in employee production, and increased accident rates have all been causally related to interference in audible communication. A Colgate University study estimates that the average worker has to expend one-fifth of his energy to overcome noise.

Neural deafness is commonly associated only with industrial conditions. Recent studies, however, link hearing loss in advancing age to life-time exposure to noise at the community level. Drs. Dougherty and Welsh, writing in the *New England Journal of Medicine*, Vol. 275, No. 19, acknowledge the well-accepted proposition that severe noise exposure causes socially incapacitating hearing loss. What has never been noted, however, is that in many communities the noise levels exceed standards found to be injurious in industry.

Population studies in the United States indicate that progressive loss of hearing increases with age. This type of hearing loss is comparable to that associated with moderate or severe industrial noise exposure. The studies do not indicate what loss might be attributed to age and what loss to work-created or general community-created noise. The studies also show that the greatest changes occur in males. This has been explained by the heavier noise exposure experienced by males and the consequent increased susceptibility.

Exposure to intense noise above 85 decibels will cause partial and temporary hearing losses. These losses may last for only several minutes or for several hours. If this level of exposure is experienced continually, partial and permanent deafness may occur. Shocks, blasts, and explosive reports such as gunfire can produce similar effects. Blast waves, or any other cause of quickly occurring large-pressure variations, such as changes in altitude, can rupture the eardrum.

The effect of noise exposure upon the individual is not limited to hearing loss. Dr. Knudsen reports that research at many universities shows that exposure to noise at 90 decibels or more can flush the skin, constrict stomach muscles and shorten tempers. He stated that some doctors suspect that noise can be a hidden factor in heart and artery diseases, nervousness and even mental health.

Dr. Samuel Rosen also points out,

It is known that loud noises cause effects which the recipient cannot control. The blood vessels constrict, the skin pales, the muscles tense and adrenal hormone is suddenly injected into the blood stream, which increases tension and nervousness. . . . Noise can cause enough emotional response to make a person feel nervous, irritable and anxious. Rest, relaxation and peaceful sleep are interrupted and often denied to those suffering from illness. . . .

In 1960, Dr. Rosen and a team of investigators began a series of studies among the Mabaans, a tribe living in a virtually noise-free environment in Southeast Sudan. The village in which the tribesmen lived had a normal background noise level under 40 decibels. On rare festival occasions the level reached 110 decibels for short periods. At age seventy-five the Mabaans' hearing was still acute. Dr. Rosen's study indicated that the capillary blood flow, restricted after loud, unexpected noises, reestablished itself much more rapidly in the Mabaan tribesman than it did in the New York businessman. "It would seem that loud noise can increase body tensions which can then affect the blood pressure, the functions of the heart and the nervous system," Dr. Rosen reported.

He added that the psychic effect of noise is also very important. Noise can produce enough emotional reaction and

[107]

frustration to make a person feel nervous, irritable and anxious. For those suffering from illness, rest, comfort and tranquil sleep are interrupted and often denied.

Dr. Rosen noted that we now have millions of people with circulatory diseases, heart problems, high blood pressure, as well as emotional illness. All these sufferers need immunity from the added burden of noise. The United States makes a great issue of suppressing visitors' noise within sickrooms, but the abrupt and continuous clatter of trucks, autos, construction work and roaring jets entering from the outside respects no such rule.

The most serious existing handicap to dealing effectively with the problems of noise is the contradictory and inconclusive evidence available from existing studies. K. D. Kryter, in his monograph *Effects of Noise on Man*, notes a number of studies on work efficiency, performance and distraction as a result of noise. Some of the experiments definitely relate noise and deleterious effects. Others show slight, inconclusive, or at best inconsistent detrimental effects from noise. Other tests noted by Kryter show that there is no marked difference in the effect on the efficiency or production of physical or mental tasks between prolonged periods of noise and a quiet setting.

In some instances, it appears that noise actually improves performance. This is explained by the fact that in complicated jobs, a man concentrates on the task and ignores the noise. Other, easier tasks soon become repetitious and automatic. In the more difficult work situation compensation occurs because of the noise both voluntarily, through the worker's increased concentration, and involuntarily, through adaption after continued exposure.

In one experiment, there was a 4.3 percent increase in typing speed when sound-absorbing material was applied, but there were the same number of errors. Another experiment indicated that noise resulted in a 5.6 percent decrease in speed and a 26.6 percent increase in errors. Both of these studies were criticized for lack of proper controls.

Alan Bell's review on noise states that while it may be hard to relate noise and efficiency, there are some deleterious effects thought to result from annoyance and interrupted communication. Human capability for adaption, however, is felt to cancel out any permanent effect on production efficiency. Noise is ignored and the worker increases his concentration in difficult tasks; in easier ones noise is not an efficiency problem. If there are unfavorable effects on performance as a result of noise, they are short-lived.

Increased efficiency was noted in a Lancashire weaving factory when the weavers wore ear plugs. A similar result was noted in Indian jute mills. Film breakage in photographic shops is notably less when the noise level is reduced. Astronauts subjected to a reproduction of 145 decibels, the sound of a jet engine at full thrust, experienced difficulty at carrying out simple arithmetic operations.

The changes in the functions of the human body which occur with the introduction of noise include vertigo, muscle tension, a decrease in the flow of saliva and gastric juices, rise in intercranial pressure, and a rise in blood pressure, breathing and heart rate. Many of these are responses to an unexpected and disturbing noise. After a time, the body adapts and the functions are again normal. Above 120 decibels sounds have been shown to generate other physiological changes. At 115 decibels turbojet engine noise and sirens produced severe but temporary hearing loss and an elevation of skin temperature.

Dr. A. Carpenter, in *The Control of Noise*, suggests that noise may be a physical stress which makes demands on the people exposed to it. Carpenter says it would be expected that this stress would be reflected in the human body by increased metabolism and muscle tension and a rise in blood pressure and heart rate and that there would be an increase in those physical illnesses associated with physical stress such as peptic ulcers.

Another physical change noticed in relation to noise is the constriction of arteries on the extremities, the hands and feet. This change has not been investigated fully, but it is of interest because it appears to be of a more permanent or long-lasting nature, and because in some people who are exposed to loud noise it could be uncomfortable or inconvenient.

For persons in normal health, their rapid adjustment to noise may prevent measurable interference with their ability to perform many mental or physical tasks, but it is not yet known what effect this rapid adjustment has upon the nervous system. For some, possible stress or injury may be minor. For others, it may constitute just the additional strain which provokes a nervous breakdown. To many sick or particularly sensitive people, noise is especially irritating, and there is some evidence that it can push people over to emotional extremes.

Carpenter says the question is whether noise by itself can increase the probability of an individual producing symptoms of any neurosis to which he is predisposed. In a comparison of the incidence of reported neurosis in naval personnel serving on aircraft carriers with a comparable population not exposed to noise, the results were negative. Anxious or neurotic patients, however, search for external causes for their problems and will, no doubt, continue to blame noise.

Knudsen kept a record of the number of times he was awakened each night by different causes. Approximately three-fourths of all awakenings were due to noise. Among the most frequent offending causes were the honking of automobile horns, the barking of dogs, the screaming of ambulance sirens and the chirping of birds. The wearing of ear plugs reduced the total number of awakenings by more than half.

Although community noise has now become an object of concern, not enough of the hubbub is due to complaints of the indignant citizens insulted by unwarranted aural invasion of their lives and concerned about the possible effects on their health.

The Surgeon General and the Public Health Service, however, are receiving a growing volume of communication from individuals inquiring about the health implications of excessive noise and from communities and governmental units requesting assistance in formulating legislation that includes noise level specifications.

In examining community noise it becomes apparent that what is disturbing to one person may not be to another. What is pleasant sound to one may not be to another, and vice versa. Yet there is growing evidence that the general levels of noise from all sources increasingly is creating mental and physical strain on the people who live within audible range.

Traffic noises usually receive the highest concern from the general public. A British survey of noise taken some years ago indicated that the sources of noise that cause the worst annoyance were inadequately silenced motorcycles and motorcars, motor horns, and other transport noises including those of aircraft. Knudson notes that these findings are consistent with those from studies made in New York, Chicago and elsewhere.

Not all noise is confined to the city. Small towns and rural areas have their noise problems as well. Although the bucolic area on the Connecticut River around Lyme, New Hampshire, is relatively sparsely populated, residents from there and from the area of North Thetford, Vermont, across the river, had been complaining for some time about an unpleasant noise. The owner of Riverbend Farm on River Road in Lyme wrote

[111]

to his Congressman about a raucous disturbance to the peaceful tranquility of his part of the country, saying: "A situation in Lyme has become so intolerable that I must seek your assistance. The noise is so great that in the eyes of several of us it constitutes a hazard to public mental health."

He went on to describe the problem. Across the river in North Thetford there was a sawmill which, unlike others in the area, used three large blowers to transport bark and sawdust a distance of about 25 to 150 feet from the mill and distribute it in piles. The pipes from these blowers were aimed at the New Hampshire shoreline of the river. The Lyme farmer indicated to his Congressman that he had contacted the local health officer, who in turn had contacted the state of New Hampshire. Subsequently, the Federal Department of Health, Education and Welfare, through its regional director and the National Center for Urban and Industrial Health, became involved. All of the officials, like the farmer, treated this noise as a health problem.

The states of New Hampshire and Vermont did a joint study of the noise levels on the New Hampshire farm as well as at the Vermont site. The surveys showed that at the farm, one-half mile from the sawmill, the noise levels were below 60 decibels. This was not thought to be a health problem, but because of the rural nature of the area, and because the sawmill noises exceeded the normal background sounds, it probably constituted a noise nuisance. Right at the mill, however, the noises were found to be at such a high level as to be clearly hazardous to the health and the hearing of exposed workers.

The source of this excess noise was the debarking unit in the air transport system used to carry chips and sawdust in the cutting area. The survey unit recommended that the noise could be dampened by using Teflon-coated saw blades to lessen

[112]

friction, directing the air transport system toward the ground rather than up into the air, and by construction of a sound barrier.

Construction noise likewise is not only an urban problem. A noise study concentrated on large earth-moving equipment was conducted in the relatively remote Central Valley of California during the summer of 1965 while work was being done to extend the Los Angeles water viaduct and reservoir system. All the equipment measured in the survey, which included scraper loaders, tractor dozers, graders, and compactors was found to exceed recognized eight-hour noise exposure criteria for safeguarding hearing. The overall noise levels for the equipment ranged from 90 to 100 decibels sound pressure level, with the scraper and dozer units being the loudest.

At the time of the survey the equipment operators wore no ear protection and received no instruction or warning about hearing conservation. They were tested for hearing loss and, when compared to a control group, were found to have suffered impairment. The survey showed excessive levels of noise exposure, evidence of temporary hearing loss at the end of a working day and hearing curves that did not correspond to the control group adjusted for age groups and length of employment. The equipment used in the survey had straight stock exhausts, unmuffled because, the operators claimed, mufflers caused significant losses in engine power. Yet there are production mufflers which do not decrease engine power. Furthermore, the equipment operators also did not have the benefit of enclosed cabs.

Farm equipment also can create noise problems. Tests conducted at the University of Nebraska on fifty-eight new tractors and twenty other types of farm machinery showed noise levels of such intensity, duration and distribution as to indicate a potential noise hazard to the hearing of the exposed operators.

[113]

Of the tractors tested at 75 percent of full load, 90 percent exceeded the recommended 85-decibel average level. Of the twenty pieces of special farm equipment tested, 65 percent exceeded the prescribed level. The average overall sound pressure levels for all models, types and operator positions was 103.5 decibels.

Dr. Knudsen also did a measurement survey of the air traffic noise inside his own study, situated six miles north of the Los Angeles International Airport. Without the presence of aircraft, the ambient noise of the study was 40 decibels. During a typical thirty-minute interval on a Sunday morning, with the doors and windows of the study open, the quiet was disrupted fourteen times by aircraft. In one instance the level reached 78 decibels; four times it exceeded 70 decibels.

At the proposed location for a theater in San Diego the noise from overhead planes passing at a distance of one and a half miles exceeded 70 decibels twenty times during a one-hour period and once reached 90 decibels. There had been levels as high as 113 decibels when stunt fliers passed over at a minimum distance of 150 feet.

In March 1968, the nation's airport operators withdrew from the industry-wide National Aircraft Noise Abatement Council, denouncing the airlines and the aircraft manufacturers for laying a "smokescreen" over the problem of jet noise. The council had been formed in 1959 and had been the industry's principal anti-noise group and chief liaison with the federal government on noise problems. In withdrawing, the airport operators said they were tired of being the scapegoats for the airlines and the manufacturers. As operators of airports they claimed they could not exercise control over types of aircraft being built for the airlines, control flight patterns, air routes, or air schedules. The operators called it a federal matter, and said the sooner necessary federal legislation were achieved the sooner the public would be assured of some noise relief.

Aircraft noise is probably the fastest-growing sound problem that people are facing. The problem exists at every major airport in the world, and it will get worse. It became aggravated in 1958 with the introduction of commercial jets and will become increasingly aggravated if commercial supersonic jets become a reality. New helicopter routes and short-takeoff landing strips bring the roar to the heart of the city, and plans are being made for the supersonic transport to send its sonic boom from one end of the country to another.

A case in point is O'Hare International Airport, in Chicago, the busiest airport in the world. O'Hare routinely handles more than twelve hundred flight operations daily. In December of 1967, before a House Subcommittee on Transportation and Aeronautics, Congressman Roman C. Pucinski of Chicago explained the situation:

> On an average day, O'Hare copes with a minimum of 1,000 jet operations. During peak travel hours, this means a jet into or out of O'Hare at the rate of one every 40 seconds. To the 23 million, five hundred thousand passengers who use the facilities at O'Hare each year, this means prompt and efficient service. To the hundreds of thousands of persons clustered in homes, hospitals and apartment buildings within a 15-mile radius of the airport it means far more. It means noise — unrelenting, unremitting, intolerable noise.

At these hearings other witnesses testified to a very real concern about the worsening noise levels that are the result of the growth of aviation. E. Thomas Burnard, Executive Vice-President of the Airport Operators' Council International, projected the growth of jet airports from 150 in 1967 to 350 in 1970 to more than 500 by 1975. To add to Congressman Pucinski's distress about the effects of O'Hare upon the residents of Chicago, one of the new jet airports being considered would be built out into Lake Michigan, four miles from downtown Chicago, and would radiate a level of noise into certain densely populated areas of the city that has been adjudged officially as intolerable for schools and hospitals and tolerable for residences only if they are equipped with special soundproofing.

An aircraft traveling faster than the speed of sound creates a continuous shock wave, or sudden change of air pressure, along its entire route. People underneath the path of a supersonic aircraft and from twenty to thirty miles on either side are exposed to this wave and hear an explosive report — a sonic boom. In this country, only military aircraft have flown supersonically, and the resultant sonic booms therefore have been rather limited and controlled. Still, in an eleven-year period extending through the middle of 1967, the United States Air Force has received over thirty-five thousand claims for damage resulting from the sonic booms of its military aircraft. About one-third of these claims have been wholly or partially satisfied.

Dr. William A. Shurcliff, a physicist in Cambridge, Massachusetts, is concerned about the expected proliferation of sonic booms which will accompany the development of the commercial supersonic transport, or SST. Heading a nationwide group called Citizens League Against the Sonic Boom, Shurcliff has been in the forefront in calling attention to the possible disastrous effects which transcontinental commercial supersonic flights may have on the minds and bodies of those exposed to their booms. With powerful commercial, political, and military interests pushing for the development of the SST, Shurcliff and the Citizens League Against the Sonic Boom point out that very little is known about the effects of sonic booms on man and that there is no body of knowledge about the role which physical variables such as weather may play in the intensity or range of sonic booms.

Dr. Alexander Cohen, Chief of National Noise Study in HEW and the chief federal government scientist working in the area of noise pollution, has written that factors which may influence a community's reaction to noise can be psychosocial in nature, as based on case histories. He says it has been demonstrated that the volume of noise and noise complaints varies with the urban, suburban or rural characteristics of the impact area and with the extent of its previous conditioning to noise or other irritants. The time of occurrence is also a significant factor, he notes, with people being less tolerant of noise in the evening than during the daytime.

Classrooms, plays and concerts, as well as many other non-work activities, are disrupted by noise. One school superintendent has reported forty to sixty noise interruptions per day in the classrooms of three schools lying near a major commercial airport. Each classroom lost ten to twenty minutes a day because of the aircraft noise intrusion, in addition to the continual break in concentration. The cumulative educational time loss in all the classrooms of the three schools was estimated at between seven and fourteen hundred minutes a day.

One of the more pleasant activities in Washington, D.C., during the summer evenings is the band concert held each night at the edge of the Potomac River next to the Lincoln Memorial. These concerts, as well as the numerous other outdoor cultural activities held in the nation's capital, are continually marred by tidal waves of sound emanating from aircraft landing or taking off at nearby National Airport.

Community noise problems posed by transportation systems can be minimized through choosing sites for these installations which take into account the existing and planned uses of the

[117]

surrounding land. For example, locating a transportation facility near large industrial and commercial areas might offer possibilities for buffering or masking the noise that may radiate from the transportation system to outlying communities. Similarly, before air installations are built in undeveloped regions, it should be required that the neighboring land be zoned for nonresidential use. If this is not done, the facility developers should buy ample land to allow not only for future expansion, but for the radiant noise, as well as for larger and noisier equipment.

There are some acute airport community noise problems which may be corrected only through purchase of extensive residential land areas. While this remedy may be extremely costly, the eventual resale of this land for more compatible usage, i.e., industrial, would offset any financial loss involved in such a transaction.

The politics of community growth and roadway development also create problems that lead to undue noise conditions in residential areas. Effective planning of roads and communities, whether for minimizing noise nuisances, easing traffic congestion, or for any other public advantage, seems to be limited by the fact that planning bodies are often extremely permissive. The private developer usually has no knowledge of or interest in control of environmental problems, and very often the adverse conditions do not materialize until a variety of developers have all added their bits to the random growth of the community.

Roadway noise control can best be effected through preventing new communities from encroaching on existing busy roads and by preventing new roads from cutting through existing residential areas. The Department of Housing and Urban Development is considering potential noise radiation as well as glare and vibration as planning factors to be included in the specifications for the 2,500 miles of urban highway still to be built as part of the Federal Interstate Highway system. Although the number of complaints regarding railroad noise seems relatively small at present, the advent of high-speed rail transportation may produce considerable noise factors requiring similar planning attention.

As long ago as 1932, Dr. LaSalle Archambault, writing in the *New York State Journal of Medicine,* appealed for action to control community noise. He wrote

It is generally held that the progress and civilization of a race or country are to be measured not only in terms of mechanical, industrial, educational and scientific advancement, but also in terms of the personality traits and behavioral characteristics of its inhabitants. Granting that this adage is correct, it is a sad commentary on the civilization of our own nation — that we are becoming noisier each year and that the conduct of a large contingent of our population rivals the primitive habits and customs of the original lords of our land — the red men of North America. The reciprocal jealousies and enmities of the various Indian tribes and the resulting war dances, howling feasts, voo doo revenges and weird ceremonials of various kinds were no more inhuman or incomprehensible than our many practices and performances tolerated in the present generation.

In speaking in that issue about the effect of noise on sleep, Dr. Archambault said

It is universally admitted that the average individual requires from six to nine hours of sleep in order to remain fit physically and mentally. The pediatrician knows that in infancy and childhood a much greater amount of sleep is absolutely necessary. Every physician has learned how important are rest and sleep in the case of expectant mothers, invalids, patients critically ill in their own homes as well as in hospitals. Finally comes the case of night workers such as nurses, printers, railway employees, night-watchmen and others, who can sleep only during the day and in whom insomnia assumes particular importance in that it not only saps their vitality but jeopardizes their ability to continue their occupations.

Dr. Archambault also reported in 1932 that studies showed conclusively that the brain is sensitive to noise and that its reaction to this potential traumatism can be measured as accurately as the blood pressure or the sugar content of the urine. He said research workers in the field of cardiovascular effects have studied intently certain groups of workers such as stenographers, bookkeepers and office clerks and have described as the direct result of noise heightened pulse rate, heightened blood pressure, and irregularities in heart rhythm, all of which simply means that the individual is attempting to overcome the distraction or obstruction by putting forth additional energy in order efficiently to acquit himself of his task.

Robert Armstrong Jones, speaking for the Noise Commission of London, stated that the commission thought that noise could produce neurosis just as in the case of shell shock. He said, "Unless something is done to check this evil we may find ourselves deprived of a capacity for sustained work, clear thinking and energetic action which is the mainstay of civilized life."

As a result of laboratory studies it is felt that the nuisance of noise increases with the volume and the pitch. Other determining factors are the characteristics of the sound and the variations of the volume and pitch. Slow repetition of the sound is more disturbing than fast repetition. In a non-laboratory setting, however, the amount of disruption is not exactly related to the properties of noise. Other physical and emotional factors such as climate or association may influence the amount of annoyance, and these factors vary with the situation and the individual. The noise of a party may be annoying to neighbors, but pleasant to the reveler.

While all of this suggests that physiological problems and

disorders grow out of excessive industrial and community noise exposures, there is no definitive evidence to causally relate such noise exposure with any non-aural health defect, mental or physical. There is much conjecture and preliminary information, but the hard data necessary to make the connection is lacking.

Yet at the rate at which noise exposure is growing, studies to monitor the health status of persons subjected to airports, expressways or noisy industries are mandatory if we are to avoid another "pollution crisis."

5

EATING

In the spring of 1967, as balmy weather chased winter away, the New York City area celebrated its renewed spirits with the usual large number of catered affairs. This particular year there was a common feature to many of these rites of spring. According to the U.S. Public Health Service, between 9,000 and 21,000 people shared the aftereffects of these celebrations and suffered food poisoning caused by *Salmonella* bacteria.

Subsequent investigation revealed that the common link between the various catered affairs and the poisonings was frozen desserts manufactured by Country Club Frozen Desserts in New York City. It was discovered that these desserts acted as the carrier for the *Salmonella*, which ultimately was traced to the nonpasteurized sugared egg yolks used in the desserts and manufactured by Manhattan Egg Company, New York. Both firms halted production, but not until thousands had been affected and products had been distributed in Massachusetts, Connecticut and Michigan.

In technological America, food, in order to be grown, packaged and supplied to 200 million people, is treated, dusted, milléd, washed, injected, separated, frozen, baked, canned, boxed, stored and shipped. All processed food that reaches the dinner table is altered from its natural state, and the process some of it passes through in this alteration is as complex as any manufacturing activity.

But about the only thing today's food industry has in common with its pretechnological antecedents is its inability to eliminate completely the occurrence of food poisoning caused by bacteriological contamination. Having learned through painful experience that certain methods of dealing with food can make it unfit for human consumption, we have passed laws intended to control food additives and handling processes. Yet for those Americans who can afford it, there is a tasteful, attractive and nearly limitless variety of food, making it appear that we are the best-fed people in the history of mankind. As a result, we are content in our nutritional ignorance.

When we buy a loaf of bread, we are attracted by the wrapper reading "Enriched Bread." If we took the trouble, we might further note in the small print below that the loaf is "made from white flour, vegetable shortening, non-fat dry milk, salt, yeast, creamery butter and water, sweetened with sugar." The wrapper probably indicates also that some calcium propionate has been added to retard spoilage and that about eleven slices of this bread will provide adults with at least some portion of the minimum daily requirements of three vitamins and a mineral.

But this description on the bread wrapper and the image it creates belie the facts. From the moment that a seed of wheat is planted in the soil until a loaf of bread reaches the grocery shelf, a great deal more goes into the product than the label indicates. The assembly of bread for human consumption is a production-line series of chemically assisted processes. The final unit, a loaf of bread, is an industrial product which, in addition to age-old basic natural baking ingredients, includes the chemical residues of a multitude of additives which the baking industry uses to make mass production easier. Except for calcium propionate, the added chemicals of production are not listed on the label.

As a sample, these include bleaching agents, such as benzoyl peroxide, chlorine, chlorine dioxide, nitrosyl chloride, and oxides of nitrogen. They include so-called "bread improvers" such as potassium bromate, potassium iodate, and calcium peroxide. Other chemical additives are the chemical leavening agents: potassium acid tartrate, monocalcium phosphate, and sodium acid pyrophosphate; the antioxidants: butylated hydroxytoluene, butylated hydroxyanisole, propyl gallate, and nordihydroquaiaretic acid; and the emulsifiers: lecithin, monoglycerides, diglycerides, and certain sorbitan and polyoxyethylene fatty esters.

But it is not by bread alone that chemicals reach the human body. Meat brings its share as well. In addition to being exposed to pesticides, hormones and antibiotics on the hoof, meat reaches the dinner table doused in one way or another with preservatives such as ascorbic acid, butylated hydroxyanisole and erythorbic acid. Sodium nitrate and nitrite are common components used to fix and hold the natural color of lunch meats, cold cuts and frankfurters. Indiscriminate use of the sodium nitrates and nitrites can result in illness and death, as they are poisons in high concentrations. Tranquilizers are sometimes used to prevent beef cattle from becoming active, and various thyroid compounds have been proposed in order to slow down the metabolism of livestock. Chemical tenderizers also may be injected prior to sale to artificially soften up an otherwise tough piece of meat.

But bread and meat are by no means isolated examples of

foodstuffs bearing the marks of chemically induced and controlled production, and if the past has brought extensive use of chemicals and new processes, it is but a taste of what the future may be. And while Food and Drug laws seemingly protect the consumer, problems still exist. Many additives are legally recognized as safe without there being tested certainty. The synergistic effect of additives — that is, what happens when two or more additives are mixed together — is an unknown. There is little knowledge about the effect of processes on food. While no imminent danger exists from chemical treatment and the manufacturing process of food, the residual toxicity that builds over a long period of time may be the greatest threat people face. Only the food faddist can find foods which are not intentionally chemically touched or tampered with during growth and processing.

Modern technology not only leaves us with unanswered questions about its effect on food but fails to give us solutions to one of the oldest health problems: food illness arising from unsanitary conditions. Chemical additives result in no immediate widespread illnesses, but the same cannot be said of unhygienic handling of food. The National Communicable Disease Center of the United States Public Health Service annually receives reports of twenty thousand cases of *Salmonella* contamination, and perhaps seventy of these result in deaths. What the Center won't receive are the reports of many times that number of similar cases of illness and death, because the reporting system, like the control system, is inadequate.

Salmonella as a food problem is not created by modern technology and new processes but rather is complicated by them. The problem is compounded by the increasing number of food handlers, the difficulty of control in large food factories, the proliferation of small operators taxing the ability of control efforts to reach all, and the far-flung distribution system which allows eggs processed in Kansas to be used by food processors anywhere in the United States.

While our ignorance about additives usually concerns their effect, the most difficult aspect of *Salmonella* is our ignorance of how it travels from origin to victim and how it works.

The group of bacteria known as *Salmonella,* named to honor the work of Dr. D. E. Salmon, are among the most widely distributed pathogenic bacteria in nature. Not only is this group found in virtually all countries, but there are over nine hundred *Salmonella* species now recognized. The most common form of salmonellosis is gastroenteritis, which is characterized by diarrhea, fever, nausea, and vomiting within twelve to eighteen hours after ingestion of contaminated food and/or drink and which is responsible for typhoid and paratyphoid. Salmonellosis has replaced botulism in the popular jargon as a term to indicate food poisoning. In this broader sense, salmonellosis must also then include the intestinal diseases caused by *Shigella, Clostridium perfringens,* and *Escherichia coli.*

The consumption of poultry, meat, eggs and egg products are the most common means by which the bacteria are transferred to humans, but the chain of infection goes back to the live cattle and poultry, and to the animal feeds that are the principal reservoirs for this ubiquitous and proliferating bacteria. Contaminated raw agricultural products carry the disease either directly or through processing to the consumer. Raw meats and poultry, frozen and dried foods, precooked frozen foods such as poultry, meat, or fish pies, prepared meals, cooked shellfish, cream pies and cakes; and precooked chilled foods all serve as vehicles for the introduction of salmonellosis into the human system.

But animal and dairy products are not alone in carrying to humans bacteria that result in salmonellosis. In 1968 a chocolate candy appeared as a possible new problem area when three major producers found *Salmonella* contamination in their finished products. Its presence was unexplained, and research projects have been launched to determine why it came and where it came from.

Baked goods have had their share of problems. In April 1967, the Johnson Pie Company of Los Angeles recalled more than one hundred thousand frozen custard and pumpkin pies. Inadequately pasteurized liquid eggs had been used uninspected by the firm.

In Chicago, approximately 20,000 pounds of prepared cake mixes had to be disposed of due to contamination with the bacteria *E. coli.*

Contamination of foods by bacteria first became recognized as a hazard to health during the latter part of the nineteenth century. It was associated with polluted drinking water and with the use of milk from dairies having polluted water supplies. But only rarely was it identified, and only rarely did it affect more than a small group of people at any one time.

During the early part of the twentieth century, industry and the various public health agencies developed many control measures that were successful in generally bringing under control the ravages of the more deadly food-borne diseases, such as botulism and typhoid fever. The pasteurization of milk, the heat-processing of canned goods, chlorination of water supplies, refrigeration of food, inspection of dairy cattle and emphasis on food sanitation all contributed to a more healthful situation. The introduction of these measures as well as the relative extinction of botulism and typhoid have made it appear that food-borne disease is under control. This, unfortunately, is an inaccurate reflection of the situation.

During the years between 1950 and 1960, even with limited reporting capabilities, the United States Public Health Service reported about 2,300 outbreaks and 100,000 cases of milk-, food- and water-borne diseases. Of these outbreaks, over 93 percent were attributed to food.

Most of the present food-borne diseases are short-term, non-fatal gastroenteritis, primarily staphylococcal food poisoning and salmonellosis. Other offenders are *Clostridum botulinum*, *Clostridum perfringens*, *Bacillus cereus*, and paracolon organisms, *Streptococci*. *Trichinella spiralis*, the virus of infectious hepatitis, and various poisonous chemicals.

As far as is known, the most effective control measure for *Salmonella* is cleanliness at each stage of processing. The substitution of processing procedures such as heat, irradiation, drying, refrigeration or prolonged freezing, can never substitute for good sanitation practices.

Thanksgiving was not a very pleasant experience in 1967 for a group of people in Asheville, North Carolina, who ate turkey dressing prepared by a local supermarket. A high buildup of *Staphylococcus* bacteria led to an outbreak of illness with the hospitalization of several persons. And *Staphylococcus* contamination, this time in cake icing, was responsible also for breaking up a birthday party in Florida, where eight celebrants had to be temporarily hospitalized.

In April 1968, the kitchens of Sara Lee recalled eight thousand dollars' worth of pastries from the New Jersey area after complaints of contamination. The pastries had been shipped in a privately owned refrigerator semi-trailer. At the first New Jersey delivery stop the driver reported noticing a slight odor when he opened the door of the trailer, but since it quickly disappeared, he didn't report it.

Contamination problems can arise almost any place. Some 54,000 pounds of shelled peanuts were seized in April 1967 at the St. Louis Terminal Warehouse Company in Berkeley, Missouri, when they were found to be adulterated by rodent urine. More than 26,000 pounds of garbanzo beans were seized in New Orleans because careless use of DDT powder had contaminated the lot in storage. In September 1967, 530 tins of frozen strawberries with no lids or markings were seized in Wilmington, Delaware, because they contained wood chips, insects, and other debris.

One of the more graphic descriptions of uncleanliness was given by Minnesota's Senator Walter Mondale when he introduced the Wholesome Poultry, Eggs and Fish Products Act of 1968. He told of the seizure of 6,000 pounds of egg whites from an egg company in Lonsdale, Minnesota. According to the Senator, the

egg whites were found to contain *Salmonella* fecal strep, and a coliform count more than ten times that of raw sewage. The FDA report on the Lonsdale Egg Company explained the reason for contaminating: flies in the breaking room; dead flies in empty cans that then were filled with eggs; cleaning equipment that was itself contaminated from a hose left lying on the floor when it was not in use; raw, whole eggs stored in a holding tank at a temperature of 65 to 67 degrees for one hour or more; employees taking sanitized empty cans from the floor and stacking them on one another.

According to reports to the Association of Food and Drug Officials, microbial food poisoning is one of the commonest forms of non-fatal illness occurring in the United States. But detection, investigation, and reporting of outbreaks are so incomplete that the actual incidence cannot be determined. Although staphylococcal enterotoxin and *Salmonella* organisms are the most frequently reported causes of food poisoning, most illnesses caused by food are of unknown origin. Reporting is so inadequate that estimates of illness range from several hundred thousand to millions of cases annually. Senator Mondale claimed that, as a conservative estimate, a quarter of a

[129]

million people suffer annually from food poisoning. Most authorities agree that the reported total of illness is about 10 percent of the actual occurrence. On this basis it means that at least 200,000 cases of illness from *Salmonella* alone occur each year, and perhaps 700 of these result in death.

The accurate reporting of these diseases is very poor at the local and state levels. Unless persons suffering from these illnesses require hospitalization, they are apparently reluctant to report digestive tract upsets or to report the instances to the local public health official. The common element of an outbreak may not be obvious since the symptoms may not appear for some time and may be similar to another condition like intestinal flu. Physicians, when consulted, may treat an individual case as common diarrhea and not probe to elicit the cause or find out if others exposed to a common source may also be ill. Public and private food institutions naturally are reluctant also to report incidents of food poisoning arising in their establishments. By no standard is digestive illness due to the bacterial contamination of food under control.

The simple age-old method of preparing food in the individual homes from staples and local produce has been replaced by complex systems of food production, manufacturing, distribution, and service. Food items available to the consumer in supermarkets number in the thousands, and more are introduced every day. Convenience foods such as precooked, prepared, and semiprepared foods make up more and more of the daily diet. Food vending machines and large commercial centers feed more and more people. Preservation of foods may involve the application of one or more methods which include high temperature, short-time processing, freezing, vacuum dehydration, or radiation from high energy sources. Partial heat sterilization requiring subsequent refrigeration has become a more

[130]

dominant method of processing than complete sterilization and canning.

The future promises to offer an even greater array of processing and preservative alternatives. Freeze-drying, dehydrofrozen, vacuum-packaged, gas-sterilized products are slowly making their appearance on the grocery shelves and among institutional staples.

As food moves less and less directly from garden to table and more and more through a manufacturing process replete with additions and colorations, winding up in cans and jars or wrapped, our concern must turn to how much we know about what we are doing to our food. There has been an almost unbelievable mechanization and process of alteration. We have looked at many individual additives and processes, but not at the "synergistic" action of two or more.

Look at the story of bread.

In its natural state, freshly milled wheat flour has a pale yellowish tint, and if allowed to age naturally it slowly will turn white and undergo an aging process that improves its baking qualities. Impatient with natural aging, mass-producers of bread discovered that this process could be accelerated through the addition of chemical oxidizing agents. To speed the production line from mill to oven, industry now adds bleaching agents to flour. Benzoyl peroxide helps make flour "whiter than white" without affecting the baking properties. Others both bleach and age the flour. To further improve the appearance of bread, if not the quality, the baking industry will add oxidizing substances. These "bread improvers" contain inorganic salts, such as ammonium and calcium phosphates, to serve as yeast food and dough conditioners. Mineral salts may be added to stabilize the gas-retaining properties of the flour gluten and cyanide or chlorinated organic compounds may be employed in fumigation of the resulting flour in storage.

Before wheat seeds are planted, they are most likely treated for plant disease protection, and the soil in which the wheat is grown is probably infused with fertilizers and no doubt contains the built-up residue of numerous complex and poisonous insecticides, pesticides, herbicides, and fungicides used on previous crops grown in the same soil. After harvest and during the storage period prior to milling, grains are subjected to another exposure to the organic poisons used to prevent plant disease or rot and insect and rodent damage. One hopes that these chemicals do not migrate with the wheat grain to the flour.

In the baking industry, a variety of chemical additives are used to produce carbon dioxide, which causes the dough to be light and porous.

The water which is added to the flour may have been chemically purified by means of alum, serta ash, copper sulfate and chlorine. Sugar or dextrose is added to the mixture, and in its refining lime, sulfur dioxide, phosphates and charcoal are used. The salt may contain iodide and agents such as calcium and magnesium carbonates to promote free running and prevent caking. The yeast used is treated and fed with ammonium salts. The shortening is a refined, bleached, deodorized product which may contain traces of nickel, be glycerinated, and contain anti-oxidants in combination with citric acids, ascorbic acid, and phosphoric acid.

The basic ingredient of bread is milled wheat flour, a grain of which is composed of three principal parts: the outer shell or husk; the endosperm or kernel; and the germ from which the grain reproduces itself. When the grain is planted, the husk protects the seed while it germinates and the endosperm — mostly carbohydrate — feeds the germ until it gets a foothold

[132]

and takes nutrients from the earth and air. When the mature grain goes to the mill to be converted to flour, the milling process removes the outer husk and the germ, leaving the endosperm. What emerges is pure starch which when mixed with water becomes an easily shaped paste-flour.

The removed bran is sold as feed for animals; the wheat germ is sold, ironically, as a food supplement for human beings and animals. These discarded parts contain the nutrients essential to human health and life. The husk is composed of minerals and vitamins, including the essential B vitamins. The wheat germ, along with its high protein and mineral content, is rich in Vitamin E and a complete Vitamin B complex.

Since the original nutrients in the wheat grain have been removed, leaving almost pure carbohydrate, there must be a reintroduction of some portion of the original vitamins and minerals if the end product, bread, is to be sold to the consumer with nutrient value. Thus the fiction of "enriched bread" and the addition of percentages of the adult daily minimum requirement of thiamine, riboflavin, niacin and iron. The milling process removes the B vitamins, several minerals, Vitamin E and protein from the wheat grain. "Enrichment" is a government requirement to replace a percentage of three discarded vitamins and one mineral.

In order to achieve the soft, spongy, foam-like texture of today's commercial white bread, large amounts of chemical emulsifying agents are employed to turn the dough into a mass of uniform tiny air bubbles glued together by the other ingredients. These emulsifiers or surface active agents make it easier for the baking industry to machine the bread dough, increase the volume to weight ratio by incorporating more air into the dough, and slow down the firming rate. None of the emulsifier chemical additives add to the nutritional qualities of the bread and in the case of polyoxyethelene fatty esters enable the baking company to reduce the amount of shortening and milk solids in a loaf of bread.

Besides using calcium propionate to extend the shelf life of bread and retard spoilage, sodium diacetate, sodium propionate, acetic acid, lactic acid and monocalcium phosphate are effective in controlling the growth of bacteria or molds.

The wrapper surrounding a loaf of bread does not list the large number of intentionally or unintentionally added chemical substances included in each slice. Terms such as "dough conditioners," "yeast nutrients," and "enriched" do not indicate the kind, the number, or purpose for these added compounds. Peek-a-boo vitamins and minerals, emulsifying agents to prevent all this and more are parts of the chemical creation of an industrial product called bread.

The majority of the chemicals used in this production and carried by the product into the human system have been added for industrial reasons exclusively. The dictates of turning the production of basic foodstuffs such as bread into a mass assembly-line process require the addition of a multitude of chemical agents to control the various production stages, to accelerate a reaction here, retard one there, or change a physical characteristic to make the production uniform, continuous and rapid. All of these added items may not be bad, but they also may not be necessary.

A corollary result of this industrialization of bread production is that vital nutrients are lost in the process and only partially replaced, and a host of extraneous chemicals, otherwise foreign to the human system, are ingested with the consumption of each slice of bread by the public. The consumer, uninformed of the extent and nature of these productional changes and chemical additions, has only taste, appearance, and price as criteria to judge the product on the grocery shelf. The wrapper label fails to indicate to the consumer that "Enriched Bread," unlike the rose, which by any other name is still the same, is not bread.

The success of turning the baking of bread into a mass assembly-line process utilizing multitudes of chemical additives for production purposes is not a singular experience in food assembly, nor is it restricted to the non-living assembly line. Beef cattle born through artificial insemination are chemically prodded and herded through life to the butcher's block and the dinner table. In the final metamorphosis to steak, roast, or hamburger, the chemical marks of this accelerated life to death race are not totally erased, and residual traces of powerful chemicals are included in the meat products consumed by humans.

One of the most powerful groups of chemicals found in meat and meat products for public consumption are the pesticides. Complex insecticides, fungicides, rodenticides, herbicides, fumigants, defoliants, nematocides, desiccants, and plant-growth regulators are intrinsic to modern agriculture. The direct and intentional contact of cattle to pesticides may only occur in the attempt to protect livestock from flies, mosquitoes and other parasites which could inhibit growth and feeding efficiency. But it is the ubiquitous nature of general pesticide usage in agriculture, the great variety of pesticides available, and the migration of slowly degrading pesticides to water and feed supplies that are indirect and therefore practically uncontrollable additions to cattle diets. After indirect contact to various pesticides through animal food, water and other environmental factors, these pesticides may not be metabolized rapidly enough in the system and as in the case of chlorinated organic pesticide such as DDT which can deposit in the fat at a rate of about 20 times the dietary intake, be stored in the animal's body. The animal metabolism may also act to change, break down and recombine various pesticides ingested through indirect sources into new toxic compounds or metabolites.

Because the extent of agricultural usage of pesticides prevents the exclusion of these poisons from animal feeds and water supplies, and because the animal metabolism is able to store pesticide residues or alter their chemical form, protection of the consumer from ingestion through meat or meat products of toxic quantities of pesticides, metabolites, or synergistic chemical compounds is dependent upon a system of adequate surveillance, control, and removal from the market. One of the difficulties of maintaining an adequate system of survey and control of an end product before it goes to market is that the prohibited residues may fluctuate greatly in level and kind.

Direct and intentional use of powerful chemicals in livestock production, traces of which may enter the human system with the meat, are of potentially greater concern to the public. Since the late 1940s nearly all beef cattle have been purposely given hormone and antibiotic treatments to achieve accelerated growth and a greater weight increase with a smaller amount of feed. One of the most popular chemicals used for this purpose is a synthetically produced compound, commonly called stilbestrol. Stilbestrol is a potent and a dangerous chemical, which cannot be purchased for human medical use without a prescription. Acting very similarly to the natural female sex hormones, this artificial estrogen has been used by the medical profession to alter the sexual hormone balance in patients. It has been used to inhibit tallness in girls, relieve the pain of prostate cancer in men and to alleviate menopausal difficulties in women by replacing the diminished supply of female sex hormones.

In the human body, primary and secondary sexual characteristics are determined by the relative amounts of male and female sex hormones present in each human, the androgens

[136]

and the estrogens. The quantities and relative proportions of these hormones will affect sexual drive and the development of sex organs, secondary sex characteristics such as breast development, quantity of facial and body hair, height, muscle development, and voice pitch. Upsetting the balance and proportions of sex hormones through the addition of the female sex hormone estrogen will result in the acquisition of more feminine characteristics.

It was the desire to change body characteristics and actions that led to the skyrocketing use of hormones in livestock and poultry production after World War II. Until 1959, over 100 million stilbestrol-treated chickens were being consumed annually. This chemical was implanted in the form of a pellet in the upper region of the bird's neck about four to eight weeks before market. As the chemical was slowly absorbed in a male bird's system, many of the masculine characteristics were altered. Combs, wattles, and reproductive organs shriveled and aggressive actions such as crowing and fighting disappeared. More fat than meat resulted, producing a bird for market that was said to be juicier, though more watery. These reactions in the male bird through the implantation of a stilbestrol pellet in the neck duplicated the costlier and more difficult process of surgical castration.

Stilbestrol given to human beings is known to greatly alter the reproductive organs and secondary sex characteristics in both men and women, old and young. It has also been implicated in the occurrence of breast cancer in women, and has been used for the deliberate introduction of cancer into laboratory animals. Experimental animals fed upon waste from stilbestrol-treated poultry became sterile and had deformed ovaries and uterine walls.

It was thought that stilbestrol given in poultry through a pellet in the neck would be completely absorbed by the time the bird went to market or would be discarded with the severed neck and that no residues of this hormone would travel with the bird to the stewpot. It was found by the Food and Drug Administration in a number of surveys that such was not the case.

The pellets oftentimes were not completely absorbed, were sometimes improperly implanted, or migrated to fleshy parts of the bird. It was also found that residues of the hormone remained stored in the chicken liver, fat, and other tissue even if the pellet was properly placed, absorbed and the neck discarded. In December 1959, the Food and Drug Administration announced that the poultry industry was discontinuing the use of stilbestrol in chickens, based upon a 1958 law that prohibited carcinogenic substances in food.

Stilbestrol is still being used to promote growth in cattle. The hormone is placed under the skin at the backside of the ear near its base. The FDA requires that all residues of this synthetic hormone be removed by the time the cattle go to market. To comply with the requirement of no detectable residues, a systematic survey and control system is needed to successfully prevent even small amounts of stilbestrol from remaining in marketed cattle. Such a system requires careful application of the pellets, strict adherence to the prescribed timetable between injection and slaughter to assure natural elimination and metabolism, and close scrutiny of slaughtered meat as it goes to the market.

The problems of controlling the residues in meat of dangerous chemicals purposefully added were pointed out by Dr. Fred J. Kingma, D. V. M., Deputy Director of the Bureau of Veterinary Medicine at the Fourth Annual Conference for Veterinarians in April 1967. Dr. Kingma explained:

The employment of simple arithmetic will emphasize the far-flung effect from the misuse of a potent drug by one individual at one of the larger beef cattle feeding establishments. Forty thousand animals on feed simultaneously at a single lot is not uncommon today. The average animals dress out conservatively at 50 percent. The total of the edible products represent 20 million pounds. If we use one-half pound as the average meat consumption per day, this represents the intake of meat for approximately one fourth to one fifth of our U.S. population. An error in the use of a potent drug or chemical in this single feed lot — resulting in residues in edible tissues — could affect from 20 to 25 percent of the people in the United States. In other words, if the 20 million pounds of beef were brought in half pound quantities, 40 million people could be affected. . . . Such a possibility did not exist a few short years ago. Everything now points to the fact that such a possibility may be even greater in the immediate future as the emphasis on large integrated establishments increases.

The wide use of antibiotics in agriculture extends to livestock. Antibiotics are used in the livestock industry to promote growth, to treat debilitating conditions therapeutically, and for preventive use. Studies have also been made to demonstrate the effectiveness of using antibiotics as a preservative to extend the shelf life of meat and meat products. The use of antibiotics in cattle has become so common and widespread, that no surface or cavity of the carcass remains untouched. Antibiotics are injected, given by mouth, mixed in feed, and spread or sprayed on every part of the body. The problems which this extensive use of antibiotics presents for humans are more than those of toxic reaction to residual traces.

About 2.7 million pounds of antibiotics are used annually in animal feeds, the prime source of these drugs for cattle. Antibiotics are introduced into feeds during the early growing period to increase weight and to ward off disease. The amount of antibiotic in the feed may vary from 20 parts per million a minimum for growth stimulation, to from 50 to 400 parts per million for prophylactic purposes. Therapeutic concentrations go as high as two thousand parts per million when necessary.

There are now approximately twenty antibiotics that are used for the treatment and prevention of infectious disease in man and animal. Whereas human usage is usually for short, concentrated periods for therapeutic purposes to aid the body in driving off bacterial infection, cattle are exposed to antibiotics for an entire lifetime.

Many of these antibiotics produce allergic or toxic reactions in human beings. The American Medical Association has reported that about 10 percent of the United States population is susceptible to becoming sensitized to some food, drug, cosmetic, or other substance during the course of a lifetime. Some of this 10 percent react upon first contact; others do not become sensitive until they have come in contact with the drug or substance several times.

Reactions in sensitive human beings can range from brief mild rashes to chronic skin conditions, from a short asthmatic attack to fatal shock. In a population approaching 200 million, this means that nearly 20 million Americans have a tendency to sensitivity, and may react adversely to antibiotics. Under a physician's care and prescription proper control can be exercised to avoid these dangerous reactions among the sensitized group. If residues are present in meat products sent to the general public, however, no such anticipation or control can be exercised.

In livestock with a lifetime exposure to antibiotic feeds, therapeutic doses, and tranquilizing shots for quiet shipping, preventing residues from being ingested by humans depends upon the proper application of control mechanisms on the farm and in the feeding lot so that the carcass is residue freed at the time of slaughter. The prevention of residues in carcasses also requires a careful, accurate, conscientious and complete system of carcass inspection by the United States Department of Agriculture. Carcass inspection is particularly important when it is understood that the meat packers and meat processors are seeking even further use of antibiotics to help preserve their meat products after slaughter and extend their shelf life in the grocery store. Should this use of the drugs be permitted, the arguments against the presence of antibiotic residues at the time of slaughter and enforcement activity would be diluted. The prevention of residues of antibiotics in animal carcasses and the pressure to use antibiotics to extend shelf life present a conflict for the Agriculture Department. Responsible for carcass inspection, the federal agency also seeks to promote the economy of the livestock industry.

In the 1950s it was discovered that milk contained significant amounts of antibiotics, particularly penicillin, to which some humans are acutely sensitive. The source of these antibiotics was the treatment of milk-producing cows suffering from mastitis with an infusion of the drugs in the udder. It was estimated that more than seventy-five tons of these drugs were used yearly to treat this common infection. While it was known that the entire amount of a given antibiotic is eliminated by regular milking over a period of three days, the failure of farmers to heed the warnings — and to discard the milk from treated cows — was largely responsible for the residues found in milk available for human consumption.

In recent years it has been discovered that in certain individual situations in certain locations with certain bacteria, it has been necessary to use very high dosages of antibiotics or a combination of antibiotics to produce any beneficial effect against infection. In some cases, there was no therapeutic response at all despite increased dosage or antibiotic combination. It was found that certain strains of bacteria and even viruses have developed which are resistant to antibiotic treatment.

Resistance to drugs in bacteria is known to develop in several ways. In mutation, those strains of a particular bacteria that are not destroyed by antibiotic treatment remain and multiply to take over the dominant role from their weaker relations. Antibiotics may also be rendered ineffective against disease through the destructive action of enzymes.

Since the fall of 1966, however, when reports of studies of drug resistance based upon investigations of *Salmonella, E. coli,* and *Shigella* cultures taken from humans were printed in the *New England Medical Journal,* the concern of American medicine has been the development of drug resistant strains of bacteria through a process known as conjugation. In conjugation, one bacterial cell is able to pass the message of drug resistance to another bacterial cell. This communication has been found not only to cause resistance to one antibiotic, but to several. It allows infectious drug resistance to be spread from one species of bacteria to another. This means that dangerous microorganisms can become resistant to a number of presently known effective antibiotics and can pass this ability to other species of pathogenic bacteria which cause infectious diseases in human beings.

Several specific drugs are now known to be involved in infectious drug resistance transferred through conjugation. They are: penicillin, ampicillin, streptomycin, chloramphenical, sulfadiazine, tetracyclines, neomycin, kanamycin, and furazolidone. Japanese scientists have found examples of antibiotic resistant dysentery-causing bacteria which could pass the resistance to *E. coli* bacteria, which, in turn, could pass the resistance to *Salmonella* bacteria. So far this transfer of infectious drug resistance has only been known to occur between certain bacteria that are found in the intestine of man and animals, such as *Salmonella, Shigella,* and *E. coli.* These bacteria, however, can cause dysentery, salmonellosis, and typhoid fever, to name several diseases.

[142]

Since certain bacteria potentially dangerous to humans are common to both human and animal intestinal tracts, the long-term use of antibiotic feeds during the lifetime of cattle may present problems of lowered human resistance to infection plus antibiotic effectiveness. Even if all traces of drug residue have been eliminated from meat and meat products before human consumption, the continuous interaction between antibiotics and bacteria in the intestines of livestock may create resistant strains of bacteria, reservoirs of disease which are not subject to antibiotic treatment.

In May, 1966, the Committee on the Veterinary Medical and Non-Medical Uses of Antibiotics reported to the U.S. Food and Drug Administration their concern about "the long-term use of antibiotics in animal feeds and the possibility of micro-organisms in animals developing resistance or of strains being selected that are resistant to antibiotics." Following this report, the FDA began a study of the long-range effects of antibiotic feed supplements to promote growth, increased their concern about drug residues remaining in the meat after slaughter, and sought to disallow the practice at that time of treating poultry, fish, and shellfish with an antibiotic dip of chlortetracycline and oxytetracycline for preservative purposes. The committee had also reported to FDA that the use of these two powerful drugs had tended to reduce sanitation in processing and had promoted resistant bacteria.

While the direct use of antibiotics as a preservative to extend display and shelf life has been discouraged in the two cases of dips for poultry, fish, and shellfish, there are still many proposed uses of a similar direct nature. Antibiotic preservation of meat and meat products has been proposed. Nisin has been suggested for use in heat-processed canned foods, pimaricin to reduce fungal spoilage in canned and non-frozen concentrated orange juice, tylosin for heat-treated mushrooms, canned dog food, and in smoked fish. All of these direct additions of anti-biotics for food preservation have been proposed with the knowledge of the possibility of human toxic sensitivity, the emergence of resistant pathogens, cross-resistance to thera-peutically important antibiotics, and the ease of substituting good manufacturing practices and sanitation with drugs.

As pressures continue for further direct use of these powerful chemicals, the indirect, yet far more massive, introduction of antibiotics continues in the daily supplementation of cattle feeds. As former FDA Commissioner Dr. James L. Goddard viewed the situation, "We are conducting our business today more on hope and faith and less on hard data."

The point is made that basically all components of food are chemicals, comprised of carbohydrates, fats, proteins, minerals, and water, and including vitamins and the natural accessory chemicals which act as antioxidants, antimyotics, buffers, thickeners, emulsifiers, colors, and flavors. It is also known that natural food stuffs contain substances that are without apparent nutritive value and which may, in fact, be harmful if ingested in amounts "larger than those encountered in normal usage of the food," in the words of the National Academy of Sciences Research Council. The chemical composition of natural food-stuffs is reasonably well known and understood and any par-ticular substance of dubious nature can be controlled by limit-ing quantity and by diet control.

With the intentional introduction of chemical additives in the production of foodstuffs the changes in food become in-credibly more complicated. Many chemicals used in food are strangers to the human diet. Many have been nonexistent until technological necessity dictated their laboratory creation. Added chemicals can replace natural components of positive nutri-tional value. Some chemical additives are in such general use that they have become a common element of the diet even though their natural role is minuscule.

In 1965 the National Research Council of the National Academy of Sciences published a 294-page document listing the chemicals used in processed foods. This list was neither complete nor an accurate reflection of the amount of each chemical that can be safely ingested by man in his diet, but it did indicate some of the chemicals used in food processing, and the reasons for their introduction.

Of the more than 1,400 chemicals listed by the National Academy of Sciences, approximately 100 are added to food products for nutritional reasons and are called "nutrient supplements." Most of these chemicals, however, are used not to supplement the human diet, but to replace essential nutrients lost in earlier processing. Ascorbic acid or Vitamin C is added to fruit juices and carbonated beverages to replace the Vitamin C lost in the freezing or canning. If milk is bleached, Vitamin A is destroyed in the process and is replaced by Vitamin A palmitate in the curds used for blue or gorgonzola cheese. Since the milling process removes the natural vitamins, minerals, and protein from grain products such as flour, cereal, corn meal, and noodle products, calcium salts and lysine cysteine (essential amino acids), iron, niacin, phosphorus, riboflavin, thiamine, Vitamins D_2 and D_3, and yeast will be introduced. Other "nutrient supplements" are used only in specialty products or in restricted diets requiring particular items, such as the substitution of potassium chloride for sodium chloride in low-sodium diets, and the addition of d-Pantothenamide for special dietary use where pantothenic acid activity is required.

By far the greatest use of chemical additives in food processing is to permit food processors to solve a production

[145]

problem, to allow food products a longer life on the shelf, and to create color and flavor artificially where none existed before or where it has been lost. Hydrogen peroxide is used as a preservative for milk and cheese to inhibit bacterial action, while formaldehyde is used in beer and maple syrup. Butylated hydroxyanisole and butylated hydroxytoluene, alone or in combination, are ingested at almost every meal. These antioxidants, used to prevent breakdown of fatty molecules, appear in ice cream, candy, baked goods, gelatin desserts, potatoes, dry breakfast cereals, dry yeast, dry mixes for beverages and desserts, smoked dry sausage, shortening, enriched rice, and chewing gum.

As one of the pioneers in developing the common use of butylated hydroxyanisole, known in the food trade as BHA, the Universal Oil Products Company recently asked the readers of *Business Week* a rhetorical question when they advertised, "Chefs rely on UOP ideas . . . should munchers?" The company went on to explain that "UOP pioneered the everyday use of BHA as a food additive to inhibit rancidity. Now, the UOP Chemical Division supplies a dozen Sustane BHA formulations for the food industry. Everybody crunches crispier potato chips because BHA is added to the cooking oil, and often the package as well." It would appear that as to the question of reliance, potato chip munchers do not have much choice.

Another antioxidant much in favored use is the sulfites. Sodium and potassium sulfites and sulfur dioxide not only inhibit rancidity in fat, but also inhibit bacterial growth and act as an anti-browning agent for cut, dried, and frozen fruits. However, the sulfites and sulphur dioxide will destroy Vitamin B_1 and will cover up meat spoilage by maintaining a nice red color. They are therefore prohibited by the Food and Drug Administration for use in meat while they are readily used in the preparation of other foods.

"Anyone can make an eye-appealing, taste-appealing pie or pudding with today's instant fillings and toppings. They're foolproof and really instant because Hercules Cellulose Gum is in most of them. This thickener and stabilizer prevents fillings from sagging . . . whipped toppings from running . . . meringues from weeping. Wherever used, Hercules Cellulose Gum is tasteless and gives a pleasant texture unobtainable with substitutes." This advertisement remedy for pie-filling failures by Hercules, Incorporated, graphically demonstrates the use of the multitude of stabilizers, thickeners and emulsifiers now in use in food products. In many instances, such as commercial bread, they enable the substitution of form for substance. Gluing ingredients together, often as a suspension of air bubbles, they can create the appearance of body with a modicum of other components.

Bleaches, starch modifiers, buffers, acids, alkalies, color sweeteners and synthetic flavoring agents are all part of the pantry shelf in the food processing industry. Bee's wax, carnauba wax, paraffin and shellac are used to help put a glaze and polish on candy. Latex rubber and butyl rubber go into chewing gum. Caffeine is introduced as a stimulant in cola beverages. Mineral oil coats fresh fruits and vegetables, urea is used as a yeast food, and talc is added as an anti-caking agent.

Of all the food processing done as food moves from its original natural state to the table, the addition or subtraction of color is most basic. Either food is whitened with bleaching chemicals or given a new and better color with an additive. The second-most-popular alteration in the preparation of food for the table is synthetic flavoring. Chemical additives are also used to increase the acidity or alkalinity of foods. Foods are chemically treated to make them water-repellent or to make them retain water. They are chemically preserved or made to age faster. Thickeners make foods more cohesive, and anticaking agents keep them free flowing.

From the point of view of the food salesman, the chemicals called food additives are functional when they improve the salability of the product by enhancing its appearance, extending its shelf life, making it easier to handle, or intensifying its flavor.

Nutrition plays practically no role in the functional concern of chemical additives, and whatever additional nutrition is provided or remains in the food is either partial replacement in most instances or the result of a secondary sales effort. The fact that a chemical food additive is functional from the seller's standpoint does not necessarily mean that it is either biologically desirable or biologically satisfactory to the consumer.

Some of the chemicals most widely used in the production of food have been found to be harmful to animals in laboratory tests. Nitrogen trichloride, also called agene, was used for decades as a bleaching and maturing agent in flour. It had a great functional use for the milling industry. It was then discovered that this compound produced running fits in dogs. Even though no evidence was ever uncovered that agenized flour caused any disorders in man, the bread industry discontinued its use.

Certain types of polyoxyethylene derivatives were widely used in the United States as emulsifiers before they were banned as potentially hazardous by the Food and Drug Administration. The head of the FDA in the early 1950s, Commissioner Charles W. Crawford, described the agents as "good paint removers." Coumarin, an ingredient of imitation vanilla flavors, was used for seventy-five years in a wide variety of confections before it was found to produce serious liver damage in animals used for experimentation. Dulcin, an artificial sweetening agent, was used for more than a half century as a sugar substitute before it was found to cause cancer in animals. Butter yellow,

[148]

a food coloring, also was used for several years before it was found to cause cancer of the liver. Mineral oil, long used as a salad dressing and a substitute for food oils, was found to interfere with the absorption and utilization of the body of several vitamins, primarily Vitamin A, in foods. It still has a number of uses in the food industry in small quantities.

By the early 1950s the indiscriminate use of additives began to bother a number of scientists, and raised concern over the effect such additives in food might have on human health. It wasn't easy to get Congress interested in probing this potential problem. The food industry was well organized, the consumer was not, and, after all, there were no hordes of people coming down ill from food, at least not from additives. The persistence of a few concerned voices, however, finally brought into being a select committee of the House of Representatives chaired by James J. Delaney of New York. The Delaney Committee set in motion the machinery which led to the passage in 1958 of the Food Additives Amendment to the Federal Food, Drug and Cosmetic Act. It was now believed that the government could control all the chemical additives that went into food and protect the health of people from this environmental insult. Unfortunately, this is not the case.

One part of the definition of the term "food additive" in the 1958 Amendment exempted substances used in food prior to January 1, 1958, which, through scientific procedures or experience, were generally recognized to be safe when used for their intended purpose. This definition and other exempting phraseology produced the famous GRAS list, the published list of substances Generally Recognized As Safe by the FDA. Today a substantial portion of substances added to food and exempted by the 1958 Act have not gone through a thorough scientific examination of their effects. In addition there has been little consideration of the synergistic effects of additives, of the

[149]

problems of dual toxicity, or an evaluation of the effects of various manufacturing processes. As a result, the protection which the public receives is rather meager.

Late in 1969, the federal government ordered the halt in production of cyclamates, the nation's most widely used artificial sweeteners added to soft drinks and foods found in an estimated three-quarters of the country's homes. As a result of laboratory tests which indicated the shattering of genetic material in rat cells and a high incidence of birth defects in chicks, and evidenced the development of cancer of the bladder in rats treated with high doses of cyclamates, the Secretary of Health, Education, and Welfare acted to remove the cyclamates from the market. The Secretary's order, made under a section of the 1958 Delaney amendments that requires that a food additive that causes cancer in either humans or animals must be removed from the market, immediately called into question all food additives that are generally recognized as safe, but which have not been demonstrated to be free of hazards.

Even though FDA has authority for the inspection of foods to eliminate contaminated food from interstate commerce, the appropriations support has hardly kept up with the growth of the population, or the growth and development of the food industry, much less allow for the complete testing of additives.

Food production, manufacturing, distribution, and service account for 80 billion dollars a year. More than 8,000 food items are available in grocery stores and new products are being put on sale at the rate of nearly two dozen a day. No part of man's environment has been so changed by man than the way he feeds himself. Two-thirds of the so-called convenience foods now available did not exist in 1946.

Technological changes are occurring so rapidly in the food field that neither government nor industry is able to perceive the full impact upon public health. Industry is spending $100 million a year to develop new food products, each of which pose potential food safety problems. But the government agencies concerned with food have limited budgets, limited authority and work with limited knowledge. Therefore they are unable to keep pace with the health aspects of industry's new development.

There may be no daily epidemic of illness resulting from what's in our food and how it's prepared; in fact, for those who can afford it, our nutrition may be about the best in the world. But if people aren't sick or dying from additives in food or the processing of food, it isn't because we have solved all our problems. We don't know the residual effect of the additives. The denial of permission to review the manufacturers' records of how chemicals, once they are approved, are being used precludes the Food and Drug Administration's being able really to judge how safe they are.

Meanwhile, the public can only wonder about the long-term health effects of chemical residues, additives, radioactive fallout and nutritive changes in newer types of food products. New ways of processing, packaging, storing and dispensing open many opportunities for adding, removing, modifying and interacting with substances important to environmental health. Preservation of foods may involve use of high temperatures, short-time processing, freezing, vacuum dehydration and radiation with high energy sources. Preparation often requires blending and reprocessing and packaging in assorted metal, glass, paper and plastic containers.

The consumer never really knows what he's getting, and neither industry nor the government really is able to tell him.

6

DRINKING

On May 27, 1965, more than the usual number of children in Riverside, California, suffered from cramps, fever, and headaches, nausea, vomiting, and diarrhea — typical symptoms of food poisoning. The sharp increase in the number of these complaints, officially diagnosed as gastroenteritis, was the first indication that an epidemic was in the making. The natural reaction of the county health department was to focus its suspicion on a new dried milk product that had been distributed widely in the area. But a public health survey which was concluded two days later ruled out the dried milk product as the culprit. In the meantime the number of reported illnesses climbed steadily, and adults as well as children were stricken. By May 29, two days after the outbreak had been recognized, some 2,000 persons in Riverside were ill. As the mysterious bug claimed more victims in Riverside, a second public health survey was started. It indicated that the only common source which could be transmitting this disease was the community water system.

On May 31, technicians sampling the city water supply

found evidence in the water of *Salmonella typhimurium* organisms, the germs that carry food poisoning. Two days later they had five *Salmonella*-tainted water samples from areas in which most of the sick lived. They followed this discovery with an intensive house-to-house survey covering 2,400 homes in the Riverside area. This study added to the evidence of contaminated water and showed that the concentration of cases was higher in the areas served by the city water system. As a result the city water system was identified as the transmitter of intestinal disease.

Water originally had been ruled out as the carrier because tests made the day pediatricians began reporting the spread of illness failed to show the presence of *Salmonella* in the water supply and because salmonellosis normally is considered to be a food-borne disease. Health authorities knew of only one other instance in which water had been the suspected transmitter of *Salmonella*.

Nearly all of Riverside's water supply comes from wells. Twenty-two deep wells in the San Bernardino Basin provide 75 percent of the water and fourteen wells in the Riverside Basin provide another 20 percent of the water. The remaining 5 percent is taken from the Colorado River. The water in the San Bernardino and Riverside basins comes from the run-off from the steep slopes of the Sierra Madre and San Bernardino mountains, which passes through a geological conditioning in the mountains resulting in the creation of underground water basins of excellent quality.

The San Bernardino Basin, being closer to the mountain streams, receives its water directly from the clear brooks, and its water is considered the highest quality available in the area. The Riverside Basin is located downstream from the San Bernardino Basin, and its water is considered of slightly lower quality. This basin receives some penetration from irrigation waters and some of the treated municipal wastes dumped into the surrounding stream system. The water from the Riverside Basin therefore is used primarily to meet peak demands. The 5 percent of the water supply drawn from the Colorado River must be filtered and chlorinated by the municipal district before being introduced into the system.

The water from the three sources is mixed together at various points of the supply system and stored together in reservoirs. Distribution is considered to be good, and bacterial tests of the Riverside water system have been performed regularly by a private laboratory under contract since 1926. The hunt for the cause of the outbreak turned into an engineering investigation of the Riverside water system.

The hunt uncovered an unusual situation that had occurred on May 11 and 12. For the first time in four years, all of the wells and transmission lines bringing water from the high-quality San Bernardino Basin had been shut down; for forty-two hours the fourteen wells in the Riverside Basin and the water from the Colorado River were used to supply the system.

The transmission line had been shut down to permit the construction of new connections for a new booster pump station; and in the course of this construction the transmission line had been entered at three points. But it was quickly established that this tap-in had not been responsible for the contamination of the system and the resultant epidemic outbreak of gastroenteritis in Riverside.

The investigation finally narrowed the geographic area in which the *Salmonella* organisms could have entered the system to the six wells in the northern part of the system and to the San Bernardino Basin transmission line. An intensive survey to determine whether water pipes had been crossed with non-water pipes was made. Food-processing plants, laboratories, animal shelters, and other establishments known or discovered

[154]

to handle biological materials were checked. In particularly suspect areas, door-to-door surveys were made. Several cross-connections were found to exist, but all lacked one or another factor necessary to have precipitated a salmonellosis outbreak.

In addition to the cross-connections, the source wells and the storage reservoirs were closely inspected in the suspect portion of the system. No findings implicated the wells as a source of contamination. Linden reservoir, the terminal of the transmission line, was carefully investigated. The investigators discovered off in one corner some distance from the reservoir a pile of dried sewage sludge, which had been brought to the reservoir three years previously to fertilize the landscaping in the city parks. The only application of this sludge near the reservoir site had been made six months prior to the disease outbreak, and special care had been taken to keep the sludge underground and away from the reservoir. And so the sludge was eliminated as a possible contaminator.

In 1968, three years after 18,000 residents of Riverside had been stricken with gastroenteritis, officials and engineers were still unable to pinpoint the origin of the disease germs and the point of their entry into the water system. According to current ideas about water system design, construction, and operation, no serious defects were located in the Riverside system. Still, an outbreak of waterborne disease had occurred.

Most people drinking a glass of water, when they stop to think about it, consider the water pure if the water is colorless, tasteless and odorless. The only ingredients other than solid, visible matter which might normally come to mind in considering tap water are chlorine and iron. Repeatedly and painfully, however, man is shown by nature that such a view is much too simple; the means by which humans are reminded of the innumerable potential elements of drinking water is usually illness. Too often, as was found to be the case in Riverside, municipal and private drinking water supplies carry germs — bacterial or viral contamination.

There is no such thing as absolutely pure drinking water. In most major urban areas located downstream from other densely populated communities, some portion of the drinking water is sewage — either processed or raw. For other urban areas, where the water supply is from wells, it is possible that new residential areas will have a portion of their drinking water coming from their septic tanks. With sewage comes the continual danger of bacterial contamination.

Some portion of urban water supply is the run-off from agricultural fields which have been doused with organic or inorganic fertilizers and insecticides, fungicides, pesticides, and herbicides. Some portion is rainwater which has washed the particles out of the air and picked up radionuclides. Some portion is the water which has been tampered with by industrial wastes. Some portion is the ground water which has picked up various trace metals, toxic chemicals, and ions.

Americans assume that their community tap water is pure or automatically safe. Their attitude comes as a result of the disappearance of major epidemics of typhoid and other waterborne diseases which before World War I were among the chief causes of death in the United States. The assumption today that the major municipal water supply systems in the United States are relatively safe is generally correct. Not only has the once dreaded typhoid fever been practically eliminated as a serious water-spread disease, but most other illnesses caused by germs carried by drinking water have been sharply curtailed. Much of this is due to the establishment in 1914 by the United States Public Health Service of drinking water standards and to the development of municipal systems which filter and chlorinate water in order to meet the standards.

However, although death and major epidemics are no longer

[156]

a concern, minor epidemics indeed are, and the price of maintaining safe drinking water is a continuous and extensive surveillance of the community water supply as more and more demands are made upon it. Despite the advances in technology and the improvement of the quality of water systems, there is not infrequent occurrence of incidents such as that experienced by Riverside, California. The fact remains that nearly 50 million Americans drink water that does not meet the Public Health Service drinking water standards; another 45 million Americans drink water that has not even been tested by the Public Health Service. Furthermore, the question has been raised as to whether the Public Health Service standards for drinking water adequately reflect present-day health requirements.

There is no question that the most commonly recognized waterborne diseases in the United States are presently under control. But the reporting of information on illness associated with drinking water is grossly inadequate.

During the fifteen-year period from 1946 to 1960 there were 228 known outbreaks of poisoning attributed to drinking water. The reporting of such outbreaks is not complete, and the accuracy of the figures reported is in extreme doubt. More than likely, the number of slight illnesses resulting from infections brought about through drinking water are substantially greater than what is on record. With this incomplete reporting it is difficult to determine trends in the occurrences of epidemics, but it is generally believed there is a consistent downward trend in the number of outbreaks of waterborne disease. The severity of illnesses has declined, certainly.

There is virtually no information available concerning the health implication of trace substances — metals and chemicals — in drinking water which may produce disease only after a very long period of time. Individual outbreaks of disease related

[157]

to drinking water usually affect no more than a handful of people. Of the several hundred such outbreaks reported in the fifteen-year period ending in 1960, the vast majority affected fewer than fifty people, and most of the remainder affected a maximum of several hundred. Yet the massive outbreak still does occur.

Waterborne pathogenic disease outbreaks generally have been traced to eight sources: surface pollution of shallow wells; cross-connection with polluted supply; contamination of springs; contamination of stream by pollution of its watershed; untreated water from river or irrigation ditch; inadequate chlorination as the only treatment; inadequate control of filtration and allied treatment processes; and seepage of surface water into gravity conduits.

In late October and early November 1963, a large number of persons in Island Pond, Vermont, experienced fever, headache, vomiting, abdominal cramps and diarrhea. Their illnesses lasted somewhere between a day and two weeks, with six people requiring hospitalization. Laboratory analysis determined that the disease was caused by *Salmonella*.

A door-to-door survey of Island Pond was conducted in late November. Sixty percent of the people living there were able to be contacted and were included in this survey. The results indicated that approximately 325 of the 1,300 persons living in Island Pond had suffered food poisoning, and that either milk or water was the source of the poisoning.

The people in Island Pond received their milk, pasteurized and distributed in bottles and cartons, from one distributor supplied by four farms. Samples examined during the epidemic established that the milk was not the cause of the outbreak.

The water used in Island Pond was obtained from two untreated sources on opposite sides of the town. The water from each source flows into the town through pipes, which join and mix in the center of the town. Although contamination of the water could have occurred at a number of points, it was never definitely established whether the water transmitted *Salmonella* or not.

Epidemic outbreaks of *Salmonella* are interesting for their mystery. While the person stricken suffers acute physical discomfort, the disease is not usually critical or lethal.

Typhoid, however, has a severe public health implication, much more than any other waterborne disease, and although typhoid has been eliminated as a serious disease in the United States for the most part, it still shows up in the most unusual places. A study made between 1946 and 1960 reported thirty-nine outbreaks of typhoid affecting 507 individuals.

In August 1963, three cases of typhoid fever were reported to the Louisiana State Health Department. Two of the cases were in the same family, and all three individuals affected had been swimming in the Bogue Falaya River at Covington State Park in Louisiana. In September another suspected case of typhoid was reported; that individual reported he had swum in the Bogue Falaya on August 12 and again on August 19. About twenty other persons had gone swimming along with this fourth victim, and it was discovered that eighteen of this group had developed gastroenteritis. Still another case of typhoid was reported in Jefferson Parish, Louisiana, in July 1963. This individual had done his swimming in the Bogue Falaya in June of that year.

Health investigators inspected the swimming area. The inquiry revealed a broken sewer line leaking beneath a small stream that emptied into the river immediately below the swimming area. During high tides the river backflowed, and as a result the leaking sewage contaminated the swimming area.

On November 6, 1959, a six-year-old boy was admitted to the Elliot Community Hospital in Keene, New Hampshire. He was suffering from severe and recurring nosebleeds, high fever, nausea and vomiting. Between November 10 and 14, four more individuals were hospitalized, all running high fevers and with the same general symptoms as the boy. Physicians believed they were dealing with typhoid fever. By November 17, after nine more cases were admitted to the hospital, they knew they had a typhoid epidemic.

The ill were interviewed in an effort to identify a common source of drinking water, milk or food. Their backgrounds were examined to see whether they shared living conditions or work places or had family histories of typhoid illness. The study soon showed that the only known common denominator for all the patients was the city water supply.

About the time the investigation was being conducted reports were received that a water-main break had occurred in the distribution system: one well supplying water to the city had been flooded. At this time too a logging operation was underway near the upper end of a pond which supplied water to the city system. Investigation quickly ruled out the break in the main and the flooded well as sources of the disease, but a check of the logging operation turned up incriminating evidence.

Three people occupied the camp set on a slope about 200 to 300 yards above the pond. There were no toilet facilities in the camp, and all wastes, including that from two horses, were accumulated five to six feet deep beside a barn. From there they drained away from the pond to a small stream about 125 feet away, which flowed to a confluence with Roaring Brook, one-quarter of a mile downstream. From this point the contaminated water fed into the city's water system.

Between 1946 and 1960 infectious hepatitis was confirmed to be a waterborne disease, although the understanding of its transmission is still incomplete. Viral hepatitis is one of the most prevalent virus diseases reported. It is spread for the most part by water. There have been many outbreaks of infectious hepatitis in which drinking water supplies have been directly implicated. Between August and December of 1961 seventy-three persons using a bowling alley in Marion County, Oregon, became ill from infectious hepatitis. A study revealed that only two items were consumed by all who became ill: tap water and an orange drink made from a concentrated fruit syrup and tap water. Water for the bowling establishment was supplied from a well which had been drilled in 1956. This well had a history of repeated problems including excess amounts of air and lowered water pressure in the water lines. Persons interviewed told of dirty and foul-smelling water obtained from all faucets, including the drinking-water faucet. Water samples from all outlets showed this contamination.

The sewage disposal system for the bowling alley consisted of a 1,000-gallon septic tank located on the opposite side of the building from the well and an effluent line of unknown construction leading out behind the building to a tile field located in a former orchard. This tile field reportedly consisted of four tile lines, each 100 feet long. The possible carrier source for the hepatitis outbreak was an individual who had showed symptoms of hepatitis on August 11. During the early infectious period of his illness, he had spent up to eighteen hours a day at the bowling alley.

For a short period in the summer of 1960 an unusual number of cases of infectious hepatitis were reported from the town of Brookfield, Connecticut. Thirty cases occurred in two months. The cases reported during July mostly involved students in grades three through six in a single school, and the August cases were found to be contacts of the July cases. The water from a well supplying the portion of the school used by the upper grades proved to be the vehicle for the infection. The manner in which this infectious hepatitis virus may have been introduced into the consolidated school water was never determined.

Nearly 25 percent of the American population obtains its water from wells and underground springs. These waters cannot be reached except by pumps and circulate very little over a period of time. Many years can pass before pollution is detected, and still longer periods may be required before pollution, once detected, can be removed.

Ground water pollution also has become a problem in some areas as a result of the rapid development of suburbia. In too many subdivisions septic tanks are installed as a substitute for a community waste disposal system. As the population increases and the number of houses multiplies, tanks located close together begin to exceed the carrying capacity of the soil. This results in the seepage of toilet and kitchen wastes into the ground water supply. Often these same newly developed areas lack a treated water supply system, instead using untreated water from local wells.

During the middle of August 1965, some 2,500 persons in Madeira, California and the surrounding San Joaquin Valley contracted acute gastroenteritis. There was a great concentration of the illness reported in the southwestern area of Madeira; on August 13 a physician had reported to the county health authority that on the preceding day an unusually large number of his patients from the city's southwest section had been suffering with diarrhea. The source of the outbreak was traced to sewage contamination of one of the fourteen deep wells of the municipal water system, and water from the two wells serving the southwestern section of town were examined.

The two city wells were closed, and townspeople were advised to boil their water for domestic use until further notice.

Investigations subsequently showed that only one of the wells was contaminated.

A field twenty-two feet from the edge of the contaminated well had been irrigated with sewage effluent on either August 10 or 11. A sounding tube leading into the well water was discovered to be uncapped and to have been that way for some time. It was then experimentally demonstrated that sewage-contaminated water could have seeped from a gopher hole at the edge of the field into a valve pit next to the well and then leaked either through a wooden barrier or through the uncapped sounding tube into the well shaft, thereby contaminating the water.

In the first week in January of 1960 the Ravina-Coeymans area in Albany County, New York, experienced a sudden and extensive outbreak of dysentery: about 1,400 cases occurred within a population of 3,200. Forty-five percent of the population became ill, and 75 percent of the families in the community were involved.

The two villages of Ravina and Coeymans share a common public water supply and sewage system. The water supply for the two communities travels from storage reservoirs to a treatment plant which consists of a mixing basin where alum and some chlorine are added. Then it moves into a settling basin and rapid sand filters, after which chlorine is added and the water passes into the small, clear well under the filter beds.

Public health officials believed that the water had become polluted upon leaving the reservoir on its way to the treatment plant before moving into the community water system. Engineers noted seven or eight houses in the immediate vicinity of the storage reservoir, and they thought it possible that sewage from some of these houses might drain into the impoundment area, where instead of being diluted by the 5 million gallons of water in the impoundment, it could hug the shoreline and go almost directly into the exit pipe. The twelve-inch pipe from the impoundment to Ravina runs almost a mile along a course lined by many homes and business establishments known to have septic tanks and cesspools.

During the day of September 28, 1962, 480 of the 6,000 employees of the New York Shipyard, which is a 400-acre establishment on the New Jersey side of the Delaware River, reported to the infirmary suffering from diarrhea, nausea, vomiting and stomach pains. It soon became apparent that a large percentage of the labor force of the shipyard was ill with gastroenteritis. In addition to those who reported to the infirmary, 200 more called to say that they were sick and would not be coming in.

The water supply for the shipyard comes from two sources: Camden and Gloucester, both in New Jersey. Each city serves water to the part of the yard within its jurisdiction, with the largest amount of water coming from the Camden system. Because of the large number of employees involved, it was suspected initially that the entire water supply was contaminated. A subsequent investigation limited the contaminated water supply to the immediate pier area and its adjacent shops. Finally it was determined that the contamination most likely occurred through a cross-connection between fire-fighting river water and the drinking water line. Some temporary connection, where there was a general intermingling of hoses and confusion of lines, most likely on the pier or dock, had made such an occurrence possible.

In 1951 an outbreak of an estimated thirty-five hundred cases of gastroenteritis occurred in a community which was using untreated water from wells which had been contaminated by flood waters. Other diseases caused by drinking water (besides gastroenteritis, typhoid, and infectious hepatitis) are diarrhea, shigellosis, salmonellosis, and ambiasis. In 1960, over 1,400 persons in one community of 3,200 persons developed an intestinal disorder known as shigellosis from a treated water supply. Authorities believed that chlorination treatment of the raw water had failed for a day and that the system had become heavily pathogenically polluted.

Tap water may be clear, odorless and tasteless, but still it contains a wide variety of organic and inorganic chemicals. Most of these are present in small amounts, but as Oregon State health officer and chairman of the American Medical Association Panel on Household and Economic Chemicals Dr. Edward Press said, "Over the years experience has shown that unless the amounts are continuously and carefully monitored, they often become large enough to cause adverse symptoms and illness."

Most of the drinking water in the United States comes from surface and underground sources through rivers, streams, lakes and wells that are exposed to scores of chemicals, as well as to contamination by human and animal wastes. In addition, more and more water is receiving varying amounts and kinds of purposeful treatment by communities and industry, only to be recycled and used by communities downstream.

As our population increases and the industrial and commercial uses for water multiply, more and more water is required for day-to-day living and working purposes. This increasing need for water is intensified by the ever expanding concentrations of people in metropolitan areas and the growth of contiguous clusters of urban areas along rivers and other water bodies, thereby requiring the recycling and re-use of water in order to avoid shortages.

The development of insecticides and various new detergents,

[165]

as well as the multiplicity of industrial processes that add new synthetic chemicals to the sewage effluent, all introduce a wide variety of chemicals to the water. Many of these present special water-treatment problems, requiring that they be removed to allow the water to be drunk without adverse effects. Some of these chemicals pose so great a problem that their presence in drinking water must be regulated legally.

Detergent-contamination of drinking water supplies results from the buildup of these detergents in household and industrial wastes where the water is continually recycled and re-used. Such contamination is common now and can be seen in supplies from both surface and ground water sources.

The United States Public Health Service drinking water standards set in 1962 limit certain concentrations of chemical substances. These standards apply only to water used in interstate commercial passenger transportation, however, and even then the Public Health Service allows some compromise. The 1962 drinking water standards also set levels for the maximum concentrations of ten trace metals in water. The elements involved are arsenic, barium, cadmium, chromium, copper, iron, lead, manganese, silver and zinc.

A concentration of .05 parts per million of arsenic in water is considered sufficiently harmful to be unsafe, to cause symptoms and illness, and to give the Public Health Service grounds for rejecting the water supply as unfit for human consumption. The general symptoms associated with the ingestion of arsenic in these concentrations include weakness, malaise, headache and weight loss. In certain concentrations and over long periods of time, arsenic may be carcinogenic.

The widespread use of inorganic arsenic in insecticides and its presence in animal foods and tobacco give it a natural means of access to water. In certain parts of the country the geological formation and the soil composition are such that rain or ground water going through certain layers of earth will absorb sufficient arsenic to cause symptoms if ingested regularly.

A wide variety of organic chemical compounds used — such as insecticides, fertilizers, detergents, automotive fuels, lubricants, paints and industrial products — find their way into surface water supplies through natural water run-off or irrigation water run-off or through sewer and municipal and industrial sewage treatment plants. In many instances, pesticides, which are slow to disintegrate into harmless components, go from the surface waters into the ground water, so that significant concentrations of certain chemicals remain in both the surface and subsurface waters. Measurements have shown significant amounts of the following organic chemicals and pesticides present in surface drinking water sources: DDT, aldrin orthonitrochloropenzene, tetralin naphthalene, chloroethyl ether, acetophenome, diphenyl ether, pyridine nitriles, acidic materials, aldehydes, ketones and alcohols. Exactly what are the safe limits of these substances in water, particularly if ingested over a period of years, is not known.

DDT already has been recovered from the largest rivers in the United States in relatively high concentrations. It is now so widely found, primarily in animal sources of food, that most persons have in their fat tissue an average of at least 2 or 3 parts per million of DDE, which is one of the metabolic degradation products of DDT. Although many surface water supplies have low concentrations of DDT and other chlorinated hydrocarbons in them, these chemicals are extracted and concentrated in animal protein and fat at much higher levels.

Chlorides, sulfates and general dissolved solids affect the taste of water and also may give it laxative properties. Cathartic effects are commonly experienced with water containing sulfate

[167]

concentrations of 600 to 1,000 milligrams per liter, particularly if much magnesium or sodium is present. The United States Public Health Service recommends that waters containing more than 250 milligrams per liter of chlorides or sulfates and 500 milligrams per liter of total dissolved solids not be used if other less mineralized supplies are available.

"Phenol" is a chemical compound produced from coal tar, among other things, and it is a strong corrosive poison. It is introduced into water supplies in the effluent from a variety of industrial processes. Even when phenols are in low concentrations, exposure to chlorination so frequently used in water treatment produces an off-taste. Fortunately, the concentration that produces the unpleasant taste is somewhat less than that which causes harm, and this odd taste usually prevents people's ingestion of sufficient quantities to cause physiological impairment.

Silver is often used as a disinfectant for waters. If excesses of it are ingested, a blue-gray discoloration of the skin, eyes and mucous membranes results. Excessive amounts of other substances such as cyanide or barium could be fatal.

Practically all municipally treated water contains certain residuals of the substances used to treat or purify the water. Chemicals such as aluminum, ammonium, iron, copper sulfate, chlorine, ammonia, limes, magnesium oxide, sodium phosphate, alkalies and acids are all introduced into water through treatment facilities.

As with so many other aspects of environmental deterioration, little concern is expressed over what these trace substances might do to humans over a period of time. The absence of any identifiable illness or distress associated with these substances in drinking water results in the acceptance of their use without challenge.

Drinking water quality is particularly susceptible to the

[168]

apathy syndrome. Few people associate any illness with drinking water. It looks clean, has no smell and is generally tasteless. This is a case where such a good job has been done in eliminating the obvious hazards that the subtle danger remains nearly impregnable to attack.

II

THINGS

7

DEATH OF A LAKE

There was a time when Lake Erie was a broad expanse of water; a time when it was a cool and pleasant boat trip down the Detroit River from the city of Detroit, past Wyandotte, Trenton, and Bob-ho, through the mouth and around the bend into the lake and on to the bathing beaches at Cedar Point. Then the fresh bluish-green waters were inviting. The smell was clean and good. The breezes were fresh. People could spend those journeys hanging over the side, entranced by the clear view of the whitefish or the walleyes and bathed by the spray. They stepped ashore from the small lake steamer fully alive and with a feeling that nature was good — man's best sanctuary.

How long ago that was. Although the distance is the same, and the direction is the same, the trip is now far different. This trip is not in a pleasure boat taking picnickers from Detroit to the parks and beaches, for now it is a startling rarity for such a craft to ply the waters still called Lake Erie, and there are no beaches. This trip is in a government survey boat. The only other water-bound craft one can see are commercial vessels — barges, small ocean freighters, and dredges. Late in the afternoon the survey boat moves slowly across the murky ominous fluid. There is no breeze, and the gaseous combination of odors and suspended particles glow red in the setting sun.

Once, when a boat left the mouth of the Detroit River and rounded the bend into the broad Western Basin of Lake Erie, you saw water all the way to the horizon. But things are different now. This is a different lake. In fact, it is really no longer a single lake. Coming out of the Detroit River into the Western Basin the survey boat enters the largest remaining open section of water in that part of Lake Erie. This is the turning basin for the Port of Toledo, Ohio, the constantly dredged harbor of what is now one of the nation's major ports. It is a crowded basin. There are barges and freighters as far as the eye can see. The shoreline is almost totally bulwarked. There are no natural spaces. Everything is man-made, man-built, commercial, covered with warehouses, depots and office buildings.

Near the docking area the water breaks into patches of color, each color matched with a distinct odor. Muddy brown with the stench of sewage. Black with resinous fumes. Gray, rust-red, and chartreuse with laundry water, rotten eggs, and chlorine. The individual shades and smells gradually blend several hundred yards out from the bulwarks into a murky soup of gray giving off a slight odor of household waste.

The Corps of Engineers long ago dredged a single twenty-seven foot main channel that carries the ocean freighters and most of the barge traffic to Cleveland and the East. Some barge traffic moves on one of the two shallower parallel channels, which are maintained to a lesser degree. A few of the survey boats and some of the other shallow drafts also move on them.

The survey boat takes the channel closest to the south shore,

[174]

which passes through tremendous marsh areas before docking at Cleveland. From a distance the marshes look like Midwestern cornfields. In reality, they are vast green crops of aquatic weeds, cancerous growths feeding on the festering plastic ooze that marks the transition from channel fluid to spongy bog. Farther shoreward, the bogs become progressively firmer until finally there is dry land somewhere near where the shoreline had been a long time ago.

Solid land becomes more obvious as the boat comes closer to the centers of population and commercial development. Between Toledo and Cleveland these centers occur about every ten to fifteen miles and jut out twenty-five miles into what through the 1900s was Lake Erie. These centers were created by land fills that provided space for the commercial growth that followed the population explosion of the 1970s and 1980s in Chipitt — the megalopolis of thirty-five million people stretching from Chicago to Pittsburgh.

Once Lake Erie was about two hundred forty miles long and fifty miles across at its widest point. It is still two hundred forty miles long, but there is no measurable width. From bog edge to bog edge it is in some places thirty to forty miles wide, but from marsh edge to marsh edge it varies only from a mile to ten miles wide.

The water depth is deceiving. Slimy mud banks show in many places. At the edge of the floating bogs it may seem only several feet deep whereas underneath the mass the depth may vary from five to fifteen feet. In general, the consistency after the first several feet becomes progressively thicker and more choked, blurring the distinction between fluid and solid.

The lake bed itself is a graveyard for organic matter such as the remains of floating algae, the carcasses of low-level animal life and the fragments of decaying vegetation from the bog,

[175]

all mixed together with the silt and sediments dumped by the lake's tributaries to form a putrid gruel of organic decomposition. This is the last stage in the death of the lake.

Lake Erie was the oldest, southernmost, and warmest of the Great Lakes. The shallowest lake, and the only one with its entire water mass lying above sea level, it contained the smallest volume of water and was the most turbid. It had the widest fluctuations in water level, the flattest bottom, and most violent wave activity. At one time, its water surface area covered 9,940 square miles. The dying agonies of Lake Erie have become increasingly more convulsive in the past few years. The rate of change has accelerated. After the algae growth reached its peak in the Western and Central basins, the water turned a dark viscous brown and the rooted vegetation sprang up from the enriched bottom and quickly advanced ten to twelve miles into the lake from the old shoreline. The offensive attacks of marshland into the lake were secured in turn by the deathly buildup of weeds which became matted bogland. Once the bog became anchored, man arrived with his dirt and his machines.

Earth excavated for highways and buildings multiplied in volume and, along with the trash of man's containerized existence, was dumped on these tangled vegetative masses, extending the firm shoreline faster and faster and farther and farther into the lake. Rapidly behind the dumping of the dirt came the construction equipment and the road-building equipment; up went the buildings, in came the roads.

Cleveland extended its shoreline more than ten miles beyond its shoreline of the 1960s. Three new towns now exist fifteen miles to the north of Lorain, Ohio, which once was situated on Lake Erie's southern shore. Kelley's Island, formerly a state park several miles offshore, is now connected to the mainland and is a city of seventy-five thousand, and Reno-by-the-Lake is

[176]

now known as Reno-by-the-Marsh. An effort has been made to contribute some of the new land to agricultural and recreational use, to create an environmental blend, but every bit of usable land has become very precious and rational planning has succumbed to the market's demand.

The immediate economic benefits from eliminating water have been more obvious than future economic cost. Land has been needed to satisfy population growth. But for new communities this soon comes to mean diminished ability to capture water. The sluggish river-lake that now exists drains away much of the potential water supply. Sealing up large ground areas with concrete and asphalt promotes rapid rain run-off and eliminates the vegetative cover that helps to provide storage. At a time when the demands for water are becoming greater, the supply is becoming smaller. Water shortages are now a serious problem to industry and municipalities. Water is now a luxury.

Recreational use of Lake Erie has long since disappeared. Even before there were the suffocating growths of rooted vegetation along the shorelines, the use of the lake for water sports was dangerously impaired. At first the rapid growth and death of large blooms of blue-green algae combined with the oil, the debris, and the human trash to cover the shoreline beaches and their adjacent waters with a blanket of rotting slime. The gelatinous mixture stuck to the skin, glued the hair, and identified the adventurous bather with its particularly putrid perfume.

Later, even those foolhardy people who just didn't give a damn about algae and the odor stopped bathing in the lake. The bacterial population of the water skyrocketed, exotic forms of biota appeared, the level of toxic chemicals rose, and the water became dangerous to health. Occasional reemergence of typhoid, polio, hepatitis, and skin infections are blamed on the water. In some places certain algal strains are poisonous. There have been several episodes of livestock or pets entering the lake, drinking the water and dying within a few minutes.

The sport fisherman also left Lake Erie long ago. At first he ignored the thick scum that fouled his boat, boots and equipment, and tried to overlook the unpalatable taste of his catch so long as there was the thrill of hooking game fish like the walleye or the blue-pike. Now they are gone. All that is left are a few roughfish and the scavenger — the giant carp. They are all that can survive in the kind of environment the water of Lake Erie supplies.

As the conditions of the environment have become more fouled, the oxygen has dwindled, and the dead algae and sediment have suffocated the food supply for the gamefish: the minnows and mayflies, the hellgrammites and dragonflies, the stoneflies and caddis worms. In their place on the bottom sludge the leeches, bloodworms, and sludgeworms multiply, feeding on the wastes and excrement that filter down, while in protected areas, above, the rat-tailed maggot is able to send its snorkle air tube to the surface and breed along with the sewage mosquito. This is the menu for the tremendous number of giant carp that live in the muck and root through the bottom sludge, keeping the waters turbid.

For most people who still live in the vicinity of what is still called Lake Erie the water is repugnant, the view repulsive, and the stench overpowering. They remain because they have to earn a living. Summer homes and lakeside homes do not exist any more, and property values are determined by commercial and industrial usage of the great new landfill areas. Those with the economic means now commute several hours a day to reach their business establishments rather than live in the bog or marsh area.

The rivers and streams that feed into the remaining channels

[178]

of Lake Erie are like an open sewer. The degradation of Lake Erie and its tributaries has reached such a magnitude that all attempts at control are gone. Lake Erie is dead, and the virulent condition is spreading downstream to Lake Ontario.

Niagara Falls is no longer a romantic vista for honeymooners and tourists. It is now restricted to industrial power usage. As the waters of Lake Erie flow down the Niagara River and over the falls, the agitation of the fluid releases gaseous fumes which burn the eyes and choke the lungs.

At the base of the falls, the old dock of the *Maid-of-the-Mist*, which used to take tourists for a closer look at Niagara, is lost in a mountain of brown foam. The detergent content of the water has mixed with the dead algae and air creating a suspended factory of decomposition, which spews its fumeous product into the gorge.

The gangrenous death of Lake Erie is spreading upstream as well. Now the lake is so polluted and choked that there is a back-up effect into Lake St. Clair, between Huron and Erie. The situation was like squeezing a bottle. As the shorelines are extended, the water levels begin to rise, and the back-up causes flooding along the Detroit River and the Lake St. Clair shoreline, destroying property, creating stagnant areas, and accelerating the putrefaction in the Upper Great Lakes.

It is difficult to remember how this all happened. Years ago the width of open water in Lake Erie was 20 to 30 miles; before that it was 30 to 40 miles; hardly anyone is aware that it should be 40 to 50 miles. The populations have increased, and there has been need for more and more space to build houses and buildings and roads. Marshland was of little value to anyone, and it was both cheap and an easy place to bring dirt and refuse and dump it. And the more dirt that was brought and dumped, the more solid that land became. The more solid it became,

[179]

the greater its value. Few people bothered to notice the changing characteristics of the lake.

So the steel and concrete blossomed, the roads went out, and the shoreline was extended further and further. There always used to be an effort to control the effluents into the water, but it never quite seemed to stay apace of the growing amounts of waste that had to be discharged into the water.

Soon the burgeoning algae gave way to the thickening marshes and the bogs, and there was no recreational land left along the southern shoreline. Navigation and commerce were so endangered that the Corps of Engineers was authorized to create and maintain a certain amount of reservoir space and channel access in the Lake Erie area.

Each community along the shoreline has wanted to expand and invariably has shifted the burden of responsibility for the deterioration of the lake to their neighbors, not realizing that the rate of change has been quickening.

In 1910 three million people lived in what was called the Lake Erie Basin. By 1960 ten million inhabited that same area. In 1910 no one conceived the possibility of Lake Erie dying. By the 1960s many realized that its death was imminent. How did it all happen?

———

Every body of standing water on this planet began to age the very moment it came into existence. Any lake, at the beginning, is clean, clear and pure and has little chemical content. But as local drainage runs into it, the fertility increases and the body of water has a greater capability to grow living material. The living materials that have the greatest aging effect on the body of water are the algae and, later, the rooted vegetation along the margins.

[180]

The elements brought into the lake that usually influence the size of the algal crop are nitrogen and phosphorous. Algae are plants, like corn, beans and potatoes. All have the same basic nutritional requirements. To produce large crops of these plants in soil, it is oftentimes necessary to add nitrogen, phosphorus and potassium to the soil. Except for potassium, the effect is the same in water: to obtain larger yields of algae you would add these same elements to the water. Potassium is rarely if ever an element deficient in water, but nitrogen and phosphorus are, and they must be added in order to increase algal crops. What is ordinarily a clear, pristine lake slowly becomes a slightly green lake, colored by the living algae.

As the production of algae in the aging process continues, the algae die, as do other living things in the lake, and settle down to the bottom where they decompose. Gradually the oxygen content in deep water begins to diminish, as it is being consumed faster than it can be replaced. This is one of the symptoms that the aging process is taking place. As a result of the loss of oxygen, there is a loss of the desirable kinds of fish that depend on oxygen in the deep, cold water. At the surface, the water has now taken on a deeper greenish shade, which is a reflection of the increased presence of algae.

At some point the human being comes along and further alters the pace at which all of these things are happening. Principally, human beings have done this through the development of a water-carriage system that permits the discharge of sewage and other kinds of waste into the water. He has done it also by introducing fertilizers that run off with the rain. One of the characteristics of sewage is that it contains both nitrogen and phosphorus, the nitrogen content averaging from eight to twelve pounds per person per year, the phosphorus averaging from one-and-one-half to four pounds per person per year.

[181]

Even after conventional sewage treatment there is still enough nitrogen and phosphorus left in discharged sewage to cause trouble in the lakes. Thus we have a situation called accelerated eutrophication — which means simply the speeding up of the process of aging — because the nutrients in the lake have been increased by people. Were it not for man, there wouldn't have to be much immediate concern about eutrophication in most lakes. That's because the natural process would take thousands of years. But the introduction of human beings alters the effect. It has been estimated that in the fifty-year period from 1915 to 1965 man has speeded up the natural aging process of inhabited lakes by hundreds or thousands of years.

One of the primary means of phosphorus entering sewage is from detergents. It has been estimated that in some communities, as much as 50 to 70 percent of the phosphorus reaches sewage in this way. We concentrate our thinking about control procedures on phosphorus, not because nitrogen isn't important, but because nitrogen can get into lakes in ways over which we have no control. For example, in Lake Michigan, the estimated annual nitrogen input into the lake as a result of rainfall and dust-fall is as much as five and a half pounds per acre per year. There are also fourteen species of blue-green algae that have been identified so far as having the capability to convert atmospheric nitrogen compounds used by plantlife. (By the same process certain bacteria in the nodules of leguminous plants add fixed nitrogen to the soil.)

The ability to convert atmospheric nitrogen into soluble compounds means that if the point is reached that nitrogen-fixing algae are numerous, control through the limitation of nitrogen in sewage is extremely difficult. Therefore, control efforts so far have centered on phosphorus because the amount of phosphorus that comes in from the atmosphere with precipitation amounts to less than a half-pound per acre per year. It is a "conservative" element, and none of the algae known can fix it. Yet it is essential for the maintenance of algae. Without phosphorus, algae will not grow, despite an abundant supply of nitrogen. If municipal disposal plants treat sewage to remove 90 percent of the phosphorus, which is possible with today's technology, we would be on the way to controlling the production of algae in many lakes.

The Lake Erie area is among the most highly urbanized and industrialized in the nation. Population projections indicate that the population will more than double in the next fifty years. Water-oriented recreational resources are already inadequate, particularly in the large metropolitan areas. It is clear that recreational waters will continue to be in short supply unless developed artificially at great expense.

Most of the ten million inhabitants of the area are now within close reach of Lake Erie. But there is little to entice them there. The beach at Sterling Park near Monroe, Michigan, has been posted as unsafe for swimming since 1961. Annual attendance dropped from over a million before 1961 to less than 300,000 by 1964.

Lake Erie never did have big, wide sand beaches. But at Cedar Point, at Sandusky and at Erie, Pennsylvania, there were good beaches. These were highly developed recreational areas which attracted thousands of people each year. The beaches in most other areas were relatively narrow. Some cities such as Cleveland had provided some man-made beaches to serve the people in the area, but these beaches have been hard hit by pollution. Out of a total of sixty large public beaches stretching along the Lake Erie shoreline from Detroit to Buffalo, in 1968 only three were considered unquestionably acceptable for swimming. Thirty-seven of the beaches had bacterial pollution problems of the type that make bathing a probably dangerous activity; eleven had been judged completely unsafe due to excessively high coliform bacterial pollution. Almost all the areas, including those with good-to-excellent water quality, were found to have aesthetic problems from rotting algae, dead fish, oil, garbage, trash, or other debris. Not one beach out of the sixty was untouched by bacterial pollution or aesthetic impairment.

Lake Erie was also used extensively for fishing and boating. In 1964 it was estimated that nearly 192,000 pleasure boats used the lake. But this form of recreation is also on the decline now because of pollution and the disappearance of game fish. Oil slicks and floating debris are damaging the boats. The foul odors and lack of fish are discouraging the boaters. Thus pollution is preventing use of an important recreational asset in a region where recreational development is needed badly because of population concentration. In many areas commercial fishing has all but disappeared as well. The loss of Lake Erie's fish production capacity comes at a time when there is a rapidly increasing need for protein in this country and throughout the world. Compared with the thousands of commercial fishermen who were able to make their livelihood fishing Lake Erie only a few years ago, now only a small percentage are still in business. Many of these men fish on a part-time basis. The fishing industry of Lake Erie has lost most of the production of the more desirable species such as the pike and whitefish. What industry does remain must subsist largely on the medium-priced varieties like yellow perch and white bass, and on low-priced, often unmarketable roughfish such as sheepshead and carp, which are useful only as fertilizer. Other fish are present, like the gizzard shad, for which markets do not exist. These fish are not harvested at all. Even the yellow perch and the white bass that are now netted can sometimes quickly be identified as to origin when served on a restaurant table.

[184]

Dr. Alfred F. Bartsch, one of the nation's leading eutrophication experts, tells the story of going into a restaurant near Hatley, Wisconsin, where he was doing algae control work on a nearby lake some years ago. "I ordered, and was served, some yellow perch," he recalled. "After I had tasted it, I called the waitress and said to her, 'I see these perch came from Mayflower Lake.' The waitress was startled by that and said, 'Yes, how did you know?' I said, 'Well, I know there is a bloom of *Gleotrichia echinulata* in Mayflower Lake, and that's exactly what these fish taste like.' And I was right!"

There are many factors that have caused the decline in the variety and quantity of desirable fish in Lake Erie. Prime among them is the depletion of oxygen in the cool bottom waters of the lake. It is known that as many as 2,600 square miles of bottom water in Lake Erie are utterly devoid of oxygen during the summer or have reached levels below which even roughfish cannot live. Thus gamefish that require a relatively high oxygen content are rapidly being eliminated from the waters.

A second factor affecting gamefish survival is the toxicity of the water. As man dumps his industrial and municipal wastes into the lake, concentrations of calcium, sodium, potassium, sulfates, and chlorides build up. Other substances in sewage and drainage from chemically treated croplands — pesticides, weedkillers, complex and exotic chemicals — can also create a poisonous environment for the fish and other animal life.

The increased growth and death of algae and the introduction of sediments into the lake further inhibit the maintenance of abundant fishlife by fouling the spawning grounds and altering the food supply. The eggs of the fish and insects are buried under the rain of sediment or are suffocated by oxygen depletion. Rising toxicity of the water, a dwindling of the normal food supply, and oxygen depletion all contribute to the demise of commercial and gamefish.

[185]

Gone the fish, gone the boat rides, gone the sport fishing, gone the pleasant aspects of Lake Erie. Going as well is the water supply necessary to sustain the kind of population growth projected for the future.

The present adverse state of affairs in Lake Erie represents a stage in a process that has been under way for thousands of years. But at the present population level, the speed of the natural geological clock has been advanced to run over three hundred times faster than normal. Every day Lake Erie ages another geological year. Every day man adds more nutrients to the lake.

This human pollution is basically from three sources: sediment resulting from agricultural or construction activities, municipal sewage, and industrial wastes. Over 152,000 pounds of phosphorus and 820,000 pounds of nitrogen are added to Lake Erie each day. In one year man adds sixty-six billion pounds of sediment to the lake. In addition, human activity contributes acid and alkalies, oil and tar substances, iron, copper, zinc, ammonia, cyanides, phenols, chlorides, complex organic chemicals, pesticides, herbicides, old automobiles, tin cans, bottles, and the kitchen sink. Two-thirds of the phosphorus added each day is retained by the lake, locked by the sediments, recycled and re-used by the algae and other aquatic life. Thus, as a result of human activity, phosphorus is in evergrowing supply in Lake Erie, used, re-used, and increased.

At present, approximately ten million people inhabit communities which discharge their sewage effluent directly into the lake or into rivers tributary to it. In addition almost three hundred industrial sources discharge to the lake or rivers. Now, almost all municipal and industrial wastes receive some form of treatment before being discharged toward the lake. This treatment usually includes chlorination to suppress or eliminate

[186]

bacterial health hazards, although some viruses are known to be resistant to chlorine. Primary treatment includes screening and settling of solid material, but it generally removes only 50 percent of the suspended solids and one-third of the oxygen-consuming materials. Secondary treatment removes more of the solids and about three-fourths of the oxygen-consuming materials. Neither type of treatment, however, removes all the dissolved nitrogen or phosphorus, the synthetic chemicals such as household detergents, or those industrial wastes which may be resistant to screening, settling and oxidation. These elements continue to be added to the lake despite treatment. At present the waste of over half the population does not receive secondary treatment, the less effective primary treatment still being typical in major metropolitan areas such as Detroit, Cleveland, and Buffalo.

Even in areas where there is treatment, some raw domestic sewage flows into the receiving waters. This occurs where there are combined sewer systems or treatment plants with overflow bypasses. Combined sewer systems collect both domestic wastes and storm water runoff. After periods of heavy rain or overload conditions, the flow in these lines is too great to be handled by the treatment plants and the raw domestic sewage and storm water is either bypassed directly into the lake or tributary rivers or is inadequately run through the treatment plant. Detroit, Toledo, Cleveland, Erie, and Buffalo have combined sewer systems serving one-third of Lake Erie's ten million residents.

The recommended permissible phosphorus input to Lake Erie from municipal and industrial sources to meet a proposed minimum federal standard is 9,000 pounds per day. To meet this standard, a 90 percent reduction in phosphorus discharge is required. If the phosphorus in detergents could be eliminated, and if municipal wastes could be treated to remove 85 percent of the remaining phosphorus, this level of daily input could be reached. At present, however, the wastes of less than half the population receive secondary treatment, a level of treatment which removes much less than 85 percent of the phosphorus. At present there are periods of quick storms and rapid drainoff when municipal wastes are treated not at all or only superficially. At present the use of phosphorus-containing detergents has not been eliminated. At present the population, the industry, and the agriculture surrounding Lake Erie are growing.

In 1965 a United States government report identified the magnitude and the sources of municipal and industrial waste discharge into Lake Erie and its tributary rivers. This report showed that 271 industries discharged wastes into the lake or its tributaries. Two-thirds of these industries were found to have inadequate treatment facilities.

Three years later the identified sources of industrial wastes discharged into Lake Erie and its tributaries had grown to 360. Over 50 percent of these industries were classified as having inadequate treatment facilities. The Federal Water Pollution Control Administration's 1968 Lake Erie Report also identified the twenty largest United States producers of industrial waste water in the Erie Basin, responsible for 86 percent of the non-power industrial waste water discharge.

Dominated by the steel, chemical, oil and paper industries, the twenty top industrial waste water dischargers identified in the 1968 FWPCA Report are: Ford plants in Dearborn and Monroe, Michigan; Republic Steel in the Cleveland and Buffalo area; Bethlehem Steel at Lackawanna, New York; Great Lakes Steel in Michigan; and Jones & Laughlin Steel in Cleveland. The next five industrial waste water dischargers are Wyandotte Chemical and Pennsalt Chemical in Michigan; Gulf Oil at Toledo; Mclouth Steel in Michigan; and Allied Chemical at Detroit and Buffalo. Interlake Steel at Toledo;

Scott Paper at Detroit; Standard Oil at Toledo; Midland Ross in Painesville, Ohio; and United States Steel plants in the Cleveland area continue the FWPCA listing. The final group of the twenty largest American producers of industrial waste water draining into Lake Erie are Mobil Oil in Michigan and Buffalo; Hammermill Paper Company at Erie, Pennsylvania; Monsanto Chemical in Michigan; Diamond Shamrock at Painesville, Ohio; and Consolidated Paper in Michigan.

In 1965 federal installations were found to be substantial contributors of untreated or inadequately treated wastes. One was the Erie Army Depot at Port Clinton, Ohio. Approximately 200,000 gallons of waste water per day from boiler blow-down, air conditioning, compressor cooling, plating-rinse solutions and laundry facilities were discharged into a storm sewer system without treatment. No attempts had been made to handle these wastes adequately, and the facility was eventually to be phased out.

Until the 1965 report, Niagara Municipal Airport Air Base Group discharged 80,000 gallons per day of sewage and airplane wastes into Cayuga Creek with inadequate treatment and no chlorination. Subsequently this was remedied.

Post offices in Silver Creek and Springville, New York, were found to be discharging their septic tank wastes directly to small streams, and several Coast Guard light and life boat stations on the lake were identified as sending either raw untreated sewage or the discharge from rudimentary septic tanks directly into the lake.

Subsequent to these findings the President issued an executive order to prevent, control, and abate water pollution by federal activities.

Presently, the Lewis Research Center of NASA and the Cleveland Army Tank Automotive Plant, both located near Cleveland Airport, employ about five thousand workers and

[189]

share a common sanitary sewer which discharges into the Cleveland city sewer system, a combined storm and sanitary system. When storm water is added to the human sewage, the system is inadequate to transport the wastes from the two installations; the wastes bypass the sewer system and feed directly into the Rocky River without any treatment.

The U.S. Army Corps of Engineers presently is dumping the solids from its dredging operations either in the open water, or along shoreline areas. This material contains large amounts of chemical wastes and trapped nutrients.

The Detroit, Cuyahoga and Maumee rivers — flowing through Detroit, Windsor, Cleveland and Toledo — are the major carriers of municipal and industrial wastes into Lake Erie. The basins of these three rivers contain two-thirds of the total population of Lake Erie and most of its industrial activity.

Ninety percent of the water entering Lake Erie is carried by the Detroit River, the drainage outlet for Lake Huron. When the water leaves Lake Huron, flows into Lake St. Clair, traverses the approximately twenty-five-mile length of the Detroit River and enters Lake Erie, it is bacteriologically, chemically, physically, biologically, and aesthetically polluted. It contains excessive densities of coliform bacteria, phenols, iron, oil, ammonia, suspended solids, dissolved solids, chlorides, nitrogen compounds and phosphates. During this twenty-five-mile trip the water receives the sewage effluent of 3.8 million people and the industrial waste from the automotive, steel, chemical, pulp and paper, petroleum refining, and rubber industries along the way. At the end of the trip, the Detroit River fills Lake Erie with about 80 percent of its total polluted material.

In the lower Detroit River all forms of water sports are hazardous because of bacteria; navigation is fouled by oil and debris; fish, migratory birds, and other wildlife are threatened; and municipal water supplies are endangered.

The materials introduced into the Detroit River are carried by the almost two billion gallons of processing and cooling water flowing daily from industry and municipal sewage plants. While almost the entire area is served by a combined sewer system, only a little more than a tenth of the total population receives secondary treatment. The city of Detroit's sewage treatment plant itself contributes almost all the municipal wastes to the river. During and after heavy rainfalls, completely untreated sewage is bypassed directly to the river and the lake. This will occur somewhere between 33 to 45 days a year.

Each day the Detroit-Windsor area adds over five times the 9,000 pounds of phosphorus felt to be the daily maximum the lake can receive without skyrocketing eutrophication.

The Cuyahoga River flows through one of the greatest industrial complexes in the world. Akron, Ohio, supplies three-quarters of the rubber tires used in the world, and Cleveland is a tremendous steel and fabricating area and includes automotive manufacturing and chemicals among the sixty-five or more industries operating along the Cuyahoga Basin and the adjacent lakefront. Because of this industrial concentration, the Cuyahoga River is also one of the filthiest, most polluted streams in the nation and the second-largest contributor of industrial and municipal wastes to Lake Erie.

The lower reaches of the Cuyahoga are continually clogged with debris, trash, oil, trees, paper, dead fish, and tin cans. In the navigation channel through the downtown Cleveland industrial complex, a major concern is fire. Oil accumulating on the surface presents a continual threat to tugboats and downtown buildings. In some areas fire breaks have been constructed to concentrate and separate the oil scum.

At the point where the Cuyahoga enters Lake Erie, a short

distance from Cleveland's Municipal Stadium, a breakwater has been built to act as a holding basin for Cuyahoga River water. This breakwater spreads the waste materials floating down the river for several miles in a narrow band along Cleveland's lakefront. As a result, every beach in the Cleveland area is unsafe for swimming.

One thousand organisms per hundred milliliters is the recommended limit for swimming, and here counts more than one hundred times that high are quite frequent. This additional aesthetic impairment due to foul odors and debris has removed this shoreline area from any recreational use.

The major industrial polluters of the Cuyahoga are Republic Steel, United States Steel and Jones & Laughlin Steel Corporation. These industrial giants add 137.5 tons of suspended solids a day, 182,200 pounds of sulfate, chloride, phenol, cyanide, ammonia, magnesium iron, and oil. Their contribution is joined by the industrial wastes from Harshaw Chemical, Ford Motor Company Zirconium Corporation, Sunoco Products, and the Akron rubber industry — B. F. Goodrich, Firestone Tire and Rubber Company, and Goodyear.

The effect of Detroit and Cleveland on the Detroit and Cuyahoga rivers and Lake Erie is repeated item for item at Toledo and the mouth of the Maumee River. Oils and solids are discharged by Standard, Gulf, and Sun Oil companies as well as Interlake Iron and Libby-Owens-Ford. The Toledo Sewage Treatment Plant, a secondary facility, each day still discharges waste materials which will consume 27,000 pounds of oxygen. It is also a combined storm–sanitary system unable to handle large overflows. Large concentrations of dangerous bacteria such as *Salmonella* are detected, frequently making the water dangerous to health for water sports. The waters in the lower Maumee look bad, smell bad, taste bad, are bad.

The small communities that border the streams feeding the

three rivers differ from their big brother cities only in size of population, variety of industry, and amount of wastes that are introduced into the watershed eventually feeding Lake Erie. Everywhere along Lake Erie and its tributary streams that man gathers to work and live, he speeds its death.

Napoleon, Ohio, a community of about seven thousand residents on the Maumee River, discharges phosphorus and material using up an estimated 184 pounds of oxygen every day from its sewage treatment plant. The Campbell Soup Company, also in Napoleon, each day discharges wastes consuming about 1200 pounds of oxygen plus 268 pounds of oil into the Maumee en route to Lake Erie. At the same time the Campbell Soup Company has difficulty obtaining odorless and tasteless water from the Maumee River for its processing operations each summer. At Napoleon the Maumee is six to ten feet deep because of a downstream dam. During the summer months the oxygen content of the river here sometimes drops to zero.

Perrysburg and Waterville, Ohio, have a combined population of 8,700, and combined sanitary and storm sewer systems, and together they add to the Maumee wastes consuming 575 pounds of oxygen daily.

At Defiance, Ohio, the combined sewer system often backs up and the raw sewage is dumped directly into the Maumee River. The Defiance system cannot handle the large amounts of phenol which come from the Johns-Manville Fiberglas Company and adds these compounds to the river along with cinder and ash material from the Central Foundry Division of General Motors deposited several miles below the treatment plant. During periods of low temperature and ice cover, this city of 16,000 experiences water taste and odor problems associated with high phenolic concentration when the water imparts a medicinal taste and odor enhanced by chlorination.

[193]

During the spring, the water has an intense earthier taste; at these times the water has been described by area residents as musty, moldy, earthy, fishy, and rotten. All during the summer the oxygen content of the Maumee at Defiance drops. During the summer of 1964 the fecal streptococcus level in the upper Maumee in this area rose enough to present a danger to health.

Presently Lake Erie is used as a source of municipal water supply by twenty-seven waterworks serving many municipalities. These municipal systems supply 3.2 million people and a number of industrial firms with over 600 million gallons per day. In addition, industry uses an estimated 4.7 billion gallons of water daily. These requirements and demands for water are going to increase greatly in the future.

Accelerated eutrophication and the defiling of our nation's waters have not been restricted to Lake Erie. Each of the Great Lakes has been gravely impaired by man's careless activities, and all the country's water bodies have felt his degrading touch. In the spring of 1969, the Food and Drug Administration seized almost 30,000 pounds of coho salmon taken from Lake Michigan because of heavy residues of the pesticide DDT. At about the same time, the Federal Water Pollution Control Administration reported that Lake Superior, the largest, deepest, and cleanest of the Great Lakes, was being seriously contaminated.

Water for consumption must be free of harmful organisms, relatively clear, and without unpleasant odor or taste, and water for most industrial purposes such as food processing must be free of odor and taste. It is estimated that the largest fresh water supply this entire nation can expect to have under ideal conditions is about 650 billion gallons per day.

Presently, the nation uses 400 billion gallons per day. It is

[194]

estimated that by the year 2000 one trillion gallons per day will be required by Americans and American industry.

In order to preserve the quality of water, the rate of eutrophication must be drastically reduced. To make the Lake Erie's water fit for recreation, for swimming, and boating, and a healthful environment for the return of gamefish, the geologic clock must be turned back many years.

8

IN THE BEGINNING

Every year thousands of Americans visit Colonial Williamsburg in Virginia. There they are treated to a view of the past that is clean and pleasant. The main thoroughfare of the restored village is closed to automobiles during the day; its streets are clean and its homes are well kept. Still thousands of other Americans travel to Greenfield Village in Dearborn, Michigan, to gaze upon the restored mementos of the last century. There they see a picture of stately homes, wide streets, much green open space punctuated by pleasantly flowing brooks and a cool, clean lake. The only crowds at either place are those intruding upon the past. The air is clear, the trash is hidden.

Wells Street, Chicago, and Gaslight Square, St. Louis, have borrowed the architecture and the gas lamps of the 1890s. More than a few suburban developments have masked the electric streetlight in a gas-lamp dressing. Restoration of the past is a growing activity. More and more Americans look back with nostalgia and attempt to re-create what once existed. So it is with the environment. Bring back the pristine quality of seventeenth and eighteenth-century America. Do away with the twentieth-century phenomena of dirty air and water and refuse in the street.

But if we were to restore the quality of our environment to a naturally pure state, we'd have to go back even further than the development of the North American continent. We'd have to go back to a time without cities and to a time when the countryside contained too few people to despoil what nature had made.

If we look back to a time when the brooks and streams and rivers ran cool and clear; when the waters were full of fish; when the air was clear, and when there was no trash because no one had ever heard of tin cans; when boxes were few and garbage miraculously disappeared; when streets were clean, and no foul odors were emitted from the vehicles using them; when the homey handling of produce and food made every meal seem as if it was served at mother's table — if we look back to such a period we will find a time without people, or at least not very many of them.

Such a time was early rural America. Far away from population centers, the running waters in those early days were affected only by natural eutrophication and silt runoff that occurred after heavy rains. What farmers there were used no pesticides, for no pesticides existed. Even manure fertilization was limited. Air contamination was almost entirely dust and dirt whipped up by heavy winds. And what noise there was on the frontier generally was welcome.

But the story is not the same for population centers, not even in the seventeenth and eighteenth centuries. Epidemics and disease, nonexistent today, were not uncommon then. And the quality of air, water and land was far below what most seek today. Cleanliness was wanting. The waters lacked the industrial effluent of today, but they didn't lack raw sewage of human life dumped unceremoniously into the open waters.

[197]

There were other environmental problems then that now intrude on our romantic notion of the past. Drinking water generally was dangerous. There was no such thing as a purification plant; people generally didn't know that water transmitted disease, and certainly didn't understand how it happened. Air pollution as we think of it today didn't exist, but dirty air was still a concern for the early colonist. Soot and ash were whipped about by the wind, along with an assortment of debris. Many people believed that the epidemics of the day were spread by a corruption of the air. While some blamed this air pollution on extraterrestial influence, there were those who laid it to decaying matter, dead bodies, filth and stagnant waters.

Odor was an established environmental hazard, even if it wasn't called that. Evil smells were believed to be a cause of disease. To control the odor nuisance some trades, such as "lime burners" and "blubber boilers," were ordered to restricted areas.

In the early colonial period and through the eighteenth century, public health agencies were occupied mainly with attempts to control smallpox and yellow fever. The control method then was through quarantine, and laws to quarantine infected individuals were adopted by most of the colonial governments from the 1660s through the mid 1700s. But other legal efforts to protect the public health were made as well, and these were in what then were considered nuisance areas. Sewers and drains at that time were privately owned, and thus Massachusetts in 1692 provided for commissioners of sewers and for regulation of drains. South Carolina passed an act dealing with swine and weeds, more for comfort than for health. Soon the colonies began to control slaughterhouses because of their noise and filth.

Controls and regulations eventually were extended in an

effort to protect water quality and end the practice of indiscriminate disposal of garbage and refuse, and as the colonies emerged into a nation, public health became more involved in community sanitation. Information and programs were developed to protect the physical environment or at best to limit people's assaults against it.

By the late 1700s accumulations of filth had begun to offend human senses in the cities. A survey in New York by a citizens' association in the mid 1800s reported that "domestic garbage and filth of every kind is thrown into the streets, covering their surface, filling the gutters, obstructing the sewer culverts and sending forth perennial emanations which must generate pestiferous disease. In winter the filth and garbage, etc., accumulate in the streets to the depth sometimes of two or three feet." But not until the late 1700s or early 1800s did keeping the growing cities clean begin to be related more specifically to the causes of disease and epidemics.

The idea that cleaning the cities would substantially reduce communicable disease was developed largely in Great Britain by Edwin Chadwick in the early 1800s. As Secretary of the Poor Law Commission he studied the social conditions associated with ill health and developed a report called *Sanitary Condition of the Laboring Population of Great Britain*. With that report he became the father of modern sanitation. The result of the report was the creation of a General Board of Health which inaugurated what C. E. A. Winslow in his book, *Man and Epidemics*, said has come to be known as the "Great Sanitary Awakening."

The idea of the Awakening spread to the United States in the mid 1800s through Lemuel Shattuck of Massachusetts, who took Chadwick's approach of statistically studying the incidence of disease in the unsanitary areas to prove the need for cleaning up. As chairman of a commission to make a sanitary survey

[199]

of Massachusetts, Shattuck issued a landmark report, which has gotten an excellent press today but which made no impact when it appeared. The 1850 report is considered to be for the United States what the Chadwick report was in England, yet it took Massachusetts nineteen years to establish a state board of health, one of the major recommendations of the report.

The Shattuck report recommended a system of sanitary police within state and local health departments, a method of analysis and collection of vital statistics, a health program including provision for the sanitation of towns, studies on health of schoolchildren, special investigation of tuberculosis, control of alcoholism, supervision of mental disease by boards of health, and the building of model housing and public bathhouses. It also recommended control of smoke and regulation of food and drugs, better education of nurses, teaching of preventive medicine as a part of the medical curriculum, preaching of health from the pulpit, and routine physical examination.

Shattuck contributed to the growing view that the environment was being unnecessarily abused. People were beginning to see that mis-use was producing an ill effect upon the health of those living in the area where the abuse was greatest. But the concept of the relationship between the population, the environment, and health was in its infancy, and environment meant many things to many different people. Aesthetic concern about the environment was limited to the few well-to-do. Any student of the environment typically concentrated on just one phase. The complexity of environmental problems was only beginning to be appreciated.

Edgar Sydenstricker noted in his 1933 book, *Health and Environment*, "there is a physical environment in which innumerable conditions and relations may affect, directly or indirectly, health." He wrote that the more advanced the progress of civilization, the more man alters the physical environment

[200]

or alters himself to fit in it. Climate, for example, has not been changed much by man, but its effects are modified by clothing and buildings, by supplying heat or overcoming heat. Sydenstricker continued: "Soil is changed by cultivation, by use of chemical fertilizers and by irrigation. Topography is changed by constructing roads. The obstacles it presents may be so readily overcome by further development of aviation as to constitute no barrier to communication. Animals and plants are altered by breeding. Distance is overcome by telegraph, telephone, radio and speed of travel. Physical materials are rearranged and changed in form so that an almost infinite variety of mechanical tools and instruments exists."

But environment is not merely physical; it is social as well. Man's relationship to man determines the environment, and the number of men becomes the central issue in the quality of environment. Population growth, population location and population density are the most significant aspects of environment, for it is the human being individually *and* collectively that makes the greatest impact on the physical world in which he lives and, therefore, upon the quality of health.

A man as a social being is driven closer and closer together with other men. So as the total population of the United States has increased more people have congregated in communities and a smaller percentage have remained on the farms and in the small communities. And as communities have grown man has used his space in a most inefficient manner, without considering how it would damage his natural environment.

Less than two hundred years ago the population of the original thirteen colonies was less than 3 million. Now we are growing at an annual rate of 3 million. Between 1790 and 1950 the population of the United States doubled five times. The first three times occurred in the 75 years between 1790 and 1865. The fourth doubling took 35 years to the date 1900, and the fifth took the next 50 years. During that last period of doubling population the United States also changed from an agricultural land to an urbanized and industrial one. This population change poses our most basic environmental threat.

Frank Fraser Darling, writing in *The Crowded Planet* on "The Population Explosion and the Natural Environment," notes that erupting hordes of human beings and folk wanderings have been a phenomenon of world history and prehistory. But, he wrote, "We are now up against something new in the eruption of population and behavior of people." Commenting on the situations in the most highly materially civilized country, he says: "None of us knows very well how to investigate effectively the new phenomena of human wear and tear over more or less natural countryside of all kinds, shores, mountains, forests and even deserts which are so rarely absolute deserts."

One of the things that becomes clear in looking back is that the first pollution is people pollution. As the number of human beings indiscriminately increases and as the number congregate in illogical patterns, the effect on the physical environment is terrifying.

Yet it is in the city that creativity booms. It is in the city that commerce and culture blossom. Throughout history man has been irresistibly drawn to the city. He has come because that's where opportunity is, where freedom is, where choices of action and activity are innumerable. The city is the challenge. It is the challenge for the individual and it is the challenge for society.

Yet the very attractions bringing men to the city help create conditions that make cities less livable. As the city increases the number and variety of its activities, more people are attracted to it. And the more people are attracted to it, the more its activities must increase. As this cycle continues and the population grows, the physical environment is taxed more and more.

The breaking point occurs when the numbers congregating in a locale exceed the level at which the natural terrain can absorb them without changing the ecology of life. When the number of people is so great that the waste they throw into a river is more than the river can naturally assimilate without lowering its quality, environmental damage has occurred. It's called water pollution. The same process occurs with the air, land, and space that people have about them. By the time what we call a city has been created, the population is generally above a level at which the environment can maintain a natural balance.

In the United States, the problems of the urban areas have become acute. The old classic pollutions have intensified and new pollutions have appeared. At the heart of the problem is population growth, but it is not growth itself that causes the problem but the failure to plan for the growth and to take the steps necessary to adjust to the growth. While the total population has multiplied 50 times since the nation was founded, the urban population has multiplied 700 times. The country has gone from a rural nation with 200,000 city dwellers to an urban nation with 140 million city dwellers.

Cities have played an important part in the development of the United States. In the seventeenth century, urban centers were developing for the exchange of goods. Yet by 1800 only three percent of the population of the nation lived in the cities. Even then, urban life formed the substance of American civilization, for it was in the cities that the greatest change in the nation's life occurred. Urban ideas, tastes, and ambitions dominated the nation.

The early communities produced a varied and colorful environment. Work generally was done to fit man's physiological needs, and life was leisurely and relaxed. In this early stage of urban development, farms lay directly outside the cities and it was a short stroll from the marketplace, where the main cultural activities occurred, to the fields and woods. Many city dwellers continued to farm on a small scale after becoming urban craftsmen. In a number of cities, most notably Boston, a common was set aside for those residents who wished to maintain their own cows. And it was well into the twentieth century before most cities outlawed the keeping of pigs within the city limits.

The modern metropolitan area differs from the classical city in several basic aspects. Not only is its population up to ten times larger than the biggest pre-industrial cities, but with modern transportation increasing the commuting radius is more than one hundred times larger than the biggest cities of the earlier era. In the modern urban area political and community leadership no longer relates to a single entity. Even the function of providing production and services is widely spread.

In fact, the modern metropolis is not really a city but a number of urban districts separated occasionally by open space. The fringes are not really country but rather open space with fingers of settlement jutting forth. There is no pattern for the location of work and residential areas; where once these were combined within the city boundaries, now they are often in widely separated parts of the urban area. Similarly, industry and business activities, once grouped in a fairly confined area within the city, now are widely dispersed. For example, in New York City most of the textile industry used to be located, based on the traditional pattern, within a limited number of blocks, and not too many years ago a man could canvass all the job opportunities or do all his business with the existing textile industry without leaving lower Manhattan. Today, however, transportation and communication and population growth have combined to extend the textile business area as far as a hundred miles out from the center of the city.

The transformation of the city into an urban area began late in the nineteenth century with the invention of the telephone, streetcar, subway and the railroad, and it was accelerated by the invention of the automobile and truck. The consequent increased communication and mobility changed the nature of the city. Distance became less important, and man-made political boundaries began to lose their meaning.

The move to the city from rural areas began in earnest in the last two decades of the nineteenth century and occurred in the Middle West as well as on the East Coast. It coincided with an increasing influx of immigrants. These two trends combined to create living conditions and social needs that compelled inventors to devise mechanical solutions. Man began to modify his physical environment in ways he had never dreamed of before. If the cities were dangerous after dark, he found new ways to provide better lighting so as to increase the safety and tempo of activity. This allowed for factories and businesses to operate after dark, and it stimulated the theater and amusements. In turn this brought more people to the city.

If the cities were running out of space, man devised an elevator to allow buildings to rise higher and modes of transportation to carry people farther from the center. This too brought more people to the city.

If the distances man had to travel as his city expanded made it more difficult to communicate with other men, he invented the telegraph and telephone to close that gap. And again this brought more people to the city.

But if man was ingenious in finding ways to facilitate the

development of the city for economic exploitation, he was somewhat less successful in maintaining a quality environment. This was particularly true when it came to wastes. Wastes are things no one wants. Things that have no utility. Their cost is a burden. So while New York, Boston, and Chicago developed public underground sewers for discharging sewage into nearby bodies of water, these facilities lagged behind the growing need spurred on by the growth of population. Most other cities simply allowed surface drainage to clear the streets while citizens handled home wastes in private vaults and cesspools.

Garbage disposal was hardly better handled. In New York, Boston and other ports refuse and garbage were carried to sea in scows and barges and dumped. Inland, the garbage was delivered to farmers who fed it to swine — incidentally increasing the danger of transferring trichinosis to human beings. By the mid 1880's the volume of garbage and refuse had reached such levels that some other means had to be found to dispose of it. Again necessity was the mother of invention, and the first crude incinerators were developed for burning garbage.

While need had compelled man to look at his drinking water supply, the growing volume of urban waste interfered with his development of a usable drinking water system. Water was constantly being contaminated by both raw sewage disposal and the cesspool system. In 1878 only 600 cities had public water supply systems; during the next two decades this number was to rise to nearly 3,000. As the germ theory of disease grew in acceptance more and more attention was paid to the purity of the water. However, there was no profit in water, and the interest in developing a good water supply system varied from community to community.

As the city grew, the challenge was to accommodate as many people as possible within a given area without creating claustrophobia or pollution. The challenge was to develop a community free of congestion, ugliness and despair.

But man hasn't risen to the challenge. He has made cities incomplete. He made them to produce goods efficiently. He made them to provide for new technology. He made them for trade and the extension of knowledge. He made them in order to exploit the Industrial Revolution. He has yet to eliminate the disorder, squalor, ugliness, noise and pollution.

9

INDUSTRIALIZATION

Modern environmental problems in America had their beginning with the Industrial Revolution. This revolution, which began to make itself known in England around 1750, took nearly a hundred years to change that country's economic structure from that of a stable agricultural and commercial society to that of a modern industrial society. The Industrial Revolution had a later start in the United States, but it benefited from the experience of England in that machinery made of wood and driven by water and wind power in England was made of steel and driven by steam power in America. Power, steel and the railroads provided sustenance for the revolution; they led to more efficient and faster ways of producing and distributing greater volumes of goods. The spinning frame and the power loom changed the nature of textile production as machine manufacturing increased the volume of output. Coal mines became important to produce not only fuel for steam power, but for steel furnaces as well.

The Industrial Revolution brought the machine and the factory into being. It also brought into being the requirement constantly to improve technology to bring about increasingly more efficient use of capital, energy, raw materials, and specialized labor. Out of this grew railroads and communications that linked sources of manufacturing to sources of raw materials and created a means for the finished product to be distributed nationwide. All this combined to change the United States with startling speed from a nation of farmers and small town merchants to an industrial society.

While the beginnings of the Industrial Revolution in the United States can be traced to the early 1800s, the full impact of the economic change wasn't felt until the decades immediately after the Civil War, when America's Industrial Revolution was spurred by the development of transportation and communication. After being slowed by the Civil War, railroad construction spurted forward, and in the period from 1870 to 1893 railroad mileage multiplied more than five times, providing transportation and communication linkage to more than 30,000 American communities by 1890. Another burst of railroad construction added 23,000 miles of rail lines in only seven years, and the United States entered the twentieth century with a railroad network of 193,000 miles of track.

Railroad construction itself affected industrial production. It created a market for the products of stone quarries, lumber mills, and iron factories. It had its greatest effect, however, upon the basic iron and steel industry. The railroad not only created the demand for rails, locomotives, rolling stock, and bridges, but it provided the conditions for satisfying the demands. By providing a fast, cheap, dependable method of bringing iron ore and coal together, the railroads helped increase steel production.

The railroads stimulated the economy in yet other ways. National markets encouraged businessmen to produce in large

[209]

quantities at lower costs and to experiment with the development of low cost mass production methods.

The development of electricity during the first half of the twentieth century provided industry with a new source of energy. In addition to creating power, electricity ushered in a new era of rapid communication and improved methods of production design and control, thereby increasing efficiency and lowering unit costs. Whereas total industrial use of electric energy in 1912 amounted to but 11,250 million kilowatt hours, it had grown to 194,835 million kilowatt hours by 1950, an increase of over 1700 percent.

The development of the internal combustion engine provided industry with yet another power source in the twentieth century. This engine also revolutionized American transportation when it was installed in the motor vehicle and the airplane, spurred the development of the oil and chemical industries because of its fuel requirements, and propelled the automotive industry into a major place in the nation's economy. As a vehicle of social and environmental change, the internal combustion engine helped establish the urban-suburban complex and a network of concrete and macadam pathways connecting metropolitan areas.

Where has the Industrial Revolution led us? In 1968 the thirty-eight companies listed by *Fortune* Magazine as being at the top of big business were dominated by twenty-three financial institutions — fourteen banks and nine insurance companies. Included also, however, were twelve giants of industry, six of them oil companies — Standard Oil of New Jersey, Texaco, Gulf Oil, Mobil, Standard Oil of California, and Standard Oil of Indiana. The combined assets of these oil companies were more than $44 billion (reflecting oil's tremendous investment in plants and equipment — refineries, drilling equipment, and pipelines — since the oil reserves are not counted as assets when they are under the ground).

Other industrials in the "Top of the Top" — as *Fortune* called its list — were two of the "Big Three" automobile manufacturers (General Motors and Ford), a rail and transportation giant (Penn Central), a representative of the steel industry (U.S. Steel), IBM and GE. Although financial institutions are the biggest of big business, *Fortune's 1968 Directory of the 500 largest U. S. Industrial Corporations* reports that eighty-three industrial companies had sales of over $1 billion in 1968, almost 60 percent of the top 500's total sales. These eighty-three companies indicate the tremendous growth of industry in the country in this century and are, as might be expected, dominated by the primary metals industries, oil, chemicals, rubber, and automotive or heavy machinery manufacturers.

But, along with growth in industrial assets and sales there has come a corresponding deterioration in the quality of our environment. As industrialization proliferates, so do the waste effluents spewed into the air, discharged into the waters, and dumped upon the ground by expanding and varied industries.

The appetite of American Industry for water is voracious.

In 1965 the Environmental Pollution Panel of the President's Science Advisory Committee reported to the White House that 84 percent of all the water used by United States industry in 1958 was used and discharged back into the environment by only four major industrial groups — paper, chemicals, primary metals, and petroleum — and that only 25 percent of this discharged water received any sort of treatment at all. Total industrial withdrawals for 1965 — estimated at over 46 billion gallons each day — plus that withdrawn for use and discharge by the steam-electric power industry — 84 billion gallons a day — amounted to approximately one-half of all the water withdrawn in the country in 1965.

Harrison Brown of the California Institute of Technology in his book, *The Challenge of Man's Future*, indicates that the per capita industrial consumption of water was over ten times greater than per capita home consumption of water and goes on to say, "Five gallons of water are required to process one gallon milk, 10 gallons to produce one gallon of gasoline, 100 gallons to make one gallon of alcohol, 10 to 75 gallons for every pound of finished fabric, 80 gallons for each kilowatt-hour of electricity generated, 300 gallons in the manufacture of one ton of steel. The list could be many pages long."

Brown's list extended certainly would include paper and pulp. In 1899, domestic production of paper and paperboard amounted to more than two million tons. By the middle of this century, the domestic pulp and paperboard producers were turning out more than twenty-four million tons and had increased the capital invested in the manufacture of paper, pulp, and their products to over $3.6 billion. This increase in investment and production included a corresponding increase in the wastes associated with the pulp and paperboard processes.

In the Second Report of the Task Force on Economic Growth and Opportunity of the United States Chamber of Commerce, entitled *The Metropolitan Enigma*, Roger Revelle of Harvard's School of Public Health described one of the waste products which the pulp and paper industry introduce into the water:

Both the sulphite and kraft processes of the paper industry produce large residues of organic material — in the case of the sulphite process, about 500 pounds of oxygen demand per ton of pulp. . . . This industry alone probably puts more organic material into United States water bodies, in terms of biological oxygen demand, than is contained in all the municipal sewage in the United States.

[212]

The basic process in the production of pulp and paper products is the conversion of logs into bleached and dried pulp or wood fibers. In the process, logs are de-barked and reduced to chips and then introduced to a digester where they are cooked in chemical liquors — most commonly acid sulfite or alkaline sulfate (kraft process) — to free the wood fibers by dissolving the lignin and non-fiber materials binding the fibers together. After being cooked in the liquor the unpure pulp is screened and washed to remove the liquor chemicals, the dissolved lignins, and other impurities. The pulp is then bleached and washed again to remove the remaining chemicals, and, after being dried and baled, is converted into a variety of paper products.

In the de-barking and chipping process, and also in the drying and paper conversion phases, large amounts of suspended solids are created which are discharged into surface waters, where the solids block out light penetration and create turbidity and large amounts of sludge to cover the bottom. In the sulfite process, in which there is less effort to recover cooking liquors, the digester chemicals are likely to be dumped directly into surface waters where the chemicals and dissolved portions of the wood create color problems, make a very high biochemical oxygen demand on the water, and are toxic to plant life. Evaporation and burning of the cooking liquors in the sulfite process (as is normally done in the sulfite or kraft process) will reduce the pollution impact of the wastes upon the water through recovery of some of the chemical content. In some instances waste waters contain spent cooking liquors, the non-cellulose parts of raw wood, and the bleaching chemicals, all in addition to the suspended solid matter. These wastes discharged into surface waters are themselves acutely toxic to marine life, and the sludge deposited upon the bottom will decompose to produce toxic and odorous gases. The color

[213]

changes and turbidity of the waters produced by the wastes also inhibit the growth of microscopic animal and plant life.

In addition to fouling the waters, the pulp and paper industry fouls the air. From sulfate or kraft mills come lime kiln dust and particulate matter produced in recovery furnaces, and from pulp mills come sulfur dioxide, and organic sulfur gases, which are contained in digester, furnace and evaporator gases. In addition to spreading foul odors, these sulfurous gases will destroy vegetation around the area of the mill and attack homes and personal property.

The International Paper Company operates a kraft pulping and papermaking operation at Ticonderoga, New York, near the shores of Lake Champlain. In addition to being a significant contributor to the economy of this upstate New York region, International Paper's Ticonderoga plant also was found in 1968 to be the largest industrial polluter of Lake Champlain. The plant was reported to be discharging 28,400 pounds of suspended solids plus organic matter equivalent to that for a population of 315,000, into Ticonderoga Creek every day, about two miles above the point where it flows into Lake Champlain. These wastes from International's operation have built up a delta area of sludge and fibrous mat near the mouth of the creek. At places the sludge measured over twelve feet deep, and its decomposition was releasing foul gases and floated solid clumps onto the surface. Farther out into the lake the sludge turned to a dark, slimy ooze.

Providing the backbone and sinews of industrial growth in the United States has been the job of the steel industry. Rails, cars, and engines for the railroads; engine blocks and sheet steel for automobiles; structural shapes and beams for industrial plants and urban construction have all emerged from the smoldering maw of the blast furnace and the rolling mills. In 1899, the book value of capital invested in the manufacture of iron and steel products was 870 million dollars. Almost fifty years later this investment had grown to over 13.7 billion dollars. In the first fifty years of the twentieth century, production of steel ingots and castings increased from just over 10 million long tons a year to nearly 86.5 million long tons in 1950, while rolled iron and steel production had grown from 9.5 million long tons to 67 million.

In 1960 eight steel companies — United States Steel, Bethlehem, Republic, Jones & Laughlin, National, Armco, Youngstown Sheet and Tube, and Inland — provided over three-quarters of the steel-producing capacity of the United States. Seven years later these eight steel companies were among the top 125 big industrials according to sales, and five of this group each had sales over $1 billion.

The production of steel is a big, dirty business, and unfortunately much of the dirt and wastes are spewed into air and dumped into water. In the preparation of coke for the blast furnaces, soft coal is carbonized to remove the coal tars and gases. The flaming coke is then drenched with water from a stream or river to put out the combustion, and the tars and gases not recovered escape into the atmosphere. And the cooling water is later discharged, at a high temperature, back into the stream, introducing large amounts of organic materials into the water which are both toxic to stream life and create odor and taste problems.

In the blast furnace itself, the smelting of iron ore involves the addition of coke for fuel and for reduction of the iron, and of limestone for picking up the impurities in the ore. To keep the process going, large volumes of hot air are forced into the base of the furnace. As the air is piped away from the furnace it carries with it great quantities of particulate matter — particles of iron ore dust, limestone and coke. In addition, the blast furnace drives off a variety of gases including metal fumes, fluorides, and sulfur oxides. Much of this particulate matter and gas escapes into the air, with the heavier dust settling on the surrounding area to produce its familiar red coating. In steel plants, where a scrubbing process is used to remove some of the particulate matter from stack gases, much of this matter is discharged with the scrub waters to the nearby streams, thus substituting water pollution for air pollution.

From the blast furnace the iron moves to other furnaces such as the hearth furnace, where further impurities are removed and elements are added to give the steel its desired properties. Now the steel is poured into molds to form ingots and is sent to the rolling mills.

In a hot-strip rolling mill, the steel, when heated prior to shaping or rolling, rapidly oxidizes and forms large amounts of scale. This is removed by high-pressure spraying with water which, after a short stay in a settling tank, is flushed into a handy nearby stream. In addition to the mill scale, oil and grease leaking from bearings and coatings enter the waters in the rolling mills, especially in the cold-rolling mills where, as the steel is not reheated before stretching or rolling, large amounts of soluble or emulsified oil are used for lubrication. After rolling, the steel must be cleaned prior to plating. This involves pickling, or passage through an acid bath. When the acid has become too weak to clean efficiently it is discharged, and the spent pickle liquor ends up in the surrounding waters.

In the latter half of 1963 the U.S. Public Health Service conducted a survey of industrial wastes in the Indiana Harbor Canal in the area where it empties into Lake Michigan. They found that the canal was grossly polluted and contained no dissolved oxygen, that its banks and waters were covered with oil, and that the waters extending from it into Lake Michigan were rust-colored and carried the pollutants from the harbor into the lake.

[216]

Flanking the canal at this point, in East Chicago, Indiana, are the steel plants of the Youngstown Sheet and Tube Company and the Inland Steel Company. These two companies were found to be the largest contributors of industrial waste to the canal at this point. The two steel plants discharged organic wastes each day equivalent to the sewage from 300,000 people, plus significant quantities of ammonia, phenol, cyanide, and oil. Five years later, in 1968, the quality of the water entering Lake Michigan from the mouth of the Indiana Harbor Canal was still grossly polluted.

The American chemical industry today produces nearly half the non-Communist world's supply of chemicals. The diversity of chemical production is staggering. An estimated 10,000 individual chemicals or chemical compounds were produced in some 13,500 chemical plants in each of the fifty states in 1965. Expanded research and development expenditures by the industry as well as additional capital investment from outside promise more chemical products and greater volumes of production. In addition to providing industrial solvents, catalysts and coatings, the chemical industry provides base ingredients for food, drugs, dyes, fibers, plastics, paints, fertilizers, pesticides and cleaners.

The diversification of chemical products and chemical processes are reflected in the variety of waste materials introduced into the water and the atmosphere. Incomplete reactions, unrecovered by-products, contaminated batches, and operational spills may introduce many complex chemicals into the environment. The rapidity with which new chemicals are developed and produced and then reach the market is often too great in relation to knowledge of their stability and long-range effects.

In the *1968 Deskbook Issue on Environmental Engineering* published by *Chemical Engineering* magazine, chemical plants

[217]

are indicated to be a major source of several common water pollutants such as chromates, and biological oxygen-demanding wastes, phenols, phosphates, and acidity/akalinity. Chemical plants also introduce into the air hydrogen sulfide, oxides of sulfur, fluorides, organic vapors, acids, particulate matter and odors.

A couple of examples illustrate the problem:

On March 20, 1968, a two hundred thousand dollar lawsuit was filed against the Hooker Chemical Company on charges that its fertilizer plant in Houston, Texas, was violating Texas Air Control Board regulations and spewing into the air excessive amounts of gases and vapors, including acid mists and fumes. Before the lawsuit reached trial, Hooker settled the case, and under court order to cease polluting the air paid a penalty of ten thousand dollars to Harris County, Texas.

On June 26, 1968 through an operating error at the Geigy Chemical Company, a slug of their pesticide diazinon was dumped into Alabama's Tombigbee River, poisoning its waters and killing an estimated 51,000 fish.

Many of the new products of the growing chemical industry not only are extremely toxic in small amounts, thereby complicating operational and handling problems, but also are very persistent and do not readily decompose or break down. The introduction of non-decomposing detergents in ordinary sewage disposal systems and through bacterial action rapidly has contaminated our lakes, streams, and water supplies and threatened to cover us with a mountain of foam. Again, chemical pesticides and artificial nitrogen fertilizers used in agriculture, because of their long-term life, are increasing the level of poisons and nitrates in water, on the land, and in our food.

Between 1918 and 1956, the total input of crude petroleum and natural gas liquids into refineries increased from

328,476,000 barrels to 3,040,168,000 barrels. By 1967 there were sixteen oil companies each with sales of over $1 million.

The production of crude oil and natural gas, their transport by pipeline or tanker, and their eventual refining into a wide variety of products create a large number of wastes introduced into the water and the air or dumped upon the land. High-grade oil and gas fields in West Virginia, Texas, Oklahoma, and Kansas are associated with large amounts of salt brine. The production of petroleum and natural gas from these fields have introduced large amounts of man-made brine or salt pollution into area waters, contributing toward making these waters unsuitable for industrial, agricultural, or municipal use.

On January 28, 1969, thousands of gallons of crude oil began to gush uncontrolled out of a Union Oil Company well five miles offshore from Santa Barbara, California, and put a slick, iridescent coat upon the Pacific Ocean. Eleven days and a quarter-million gallons of oil later, the company managed to seal off their "blown out" well, but still was not able to end the leakage as the oil poured out of nearby fissures or fault lines in the floor of the Santa Barbara Channel. This massive oil leak fouled miles of Southern California coastline, threatened species of animal and marine life, brought about damage suits in excess of $1 billion, and engendered a national discussion about offshore oil drilling. As the oil continued to bubble to the surface of the Santa Barbara Channel in the beginning of June 1969, a special White House study panel recommended that the best solution to ending the oil leak would be to develop fully and drain the undersea oil field. This study panel, with a heavy representation of the oil industry, also admitted that such a procedure might require many additional wells and years of pumping.

The possibility of such breakages or spills has been introduced by the transportation of crude oil, natural gas, and petroleum products by pipeline or tanker. Ships cleaning out their leaking tanks or breaking up in heavy seas have caused several major incidents of oil spillage, such as the break-up of the tanker *Torrey Canyon*, which released 30 million gallons of oil off the coast of England in March of 1967, and one year later the splitting in half of the *Ocean Eagle* at the mouth of the harbor of San Juan, Puerto Rico.

The dike of the waste lagoon of the American International Refining Company at Bruin, Pennsylvania, broke at the end of October 1968 and sent a twelve-mile slug of water-soluble petroleum sulfonate into Bear Creek and then down the Allegheny River. As the sludge passed over dams and through locks on the Allegheny it was aerated into a foam ranging from six inches to six feet in thickness. Before the petroleum wastes had reached the Ohio River, an estimated half-million dollars' in damage had been done: over a million fish had been killed when the sludge had coated their gills; four water companies had been forced to close their river pumps and turn to emergency supplies; one industry had canceled two shifts of work because operations would have drained emergency municipal supplies; and a power plant, which also had turned to emergency supplies, had reopened its river intakes before the slug had completely moved by, promptly gumming up their innards.

As other industrial groups have grown they too have increased their contribution to environmental deterioration. Power plants burning fossil fuels send particulate matter and sulfurous compounds into the air at the same time that they add vast quantities of heat into the waters. Food-processing plants send the offal and grease from meat-packing plants, the whey from dairies, the washings with pesticide residues and fruit and vegetable discards from canneries into the waters,

[220]

while they send the stench of decomposing organic matter spreading across the sky.

The textile industry adds to the waters oily residues and chemicals from the bleaching of cotton, as well as dirt, soap, and germs from wool washing. A 1965 U.S. Public Health Service Industrial Waste Guide for the synthetic textile industry — makers of rayon, acetate, polyamides, acrylic, polyolefin, and polyester fibers — indicated that any synthetic-producing plant, consuming from a few thousand to several million gallons of water each day, might discharge with its waste waters any one or a combination of nearly ninety chemical compounds used in the particular processing. Typical synthetic textile wastes are detergents, soda ash, common salt, Gauber's salt, dyes, dye carriers, fixing agents, starch, synthetic resins, gelatins and acids. Coal mines add acid to the water and sulfur fumes to the air. Automobile manufacturers discharge oil solids, phenols, iron, ammonia, acid, cyanide, chrome, cadmium, copper, and other heavy metals in their liquid wastes, and can foul the air with a combination of chemical fumes.

For many years industry tried to ignore the corrosive elements of industrialization — the waste of industry, capable of poisoning the society which it helped to build — and to minimize its role in this degradation. As late as June 1963 Jack T. Garrett, Chairman of the Water Resources Committee of the Manufacturing Chemists' Association, Incorporated (MCA), a nonprofit trade association of 199 companies representing over 90 percent of the productive capacity of the chemical industry in the United States, testified before the Special Subcommittee on Air and Water Pollution of the United States Senate Public Works Committee as follows "I would like to make the point that we of the chemical industry do not feel that there is any impending crisis of nationwide significance in the area of water supply, and we do feel that the nation's water pollution problem is being brought under control."

In stating the point of view of the chemical industry on water pollution legislation Mr. Garrett also presented MCA's concept of their responsibility for industrial water pollution:

> I think the preceding testimony indicates that the chemical industry is quite impressed and has indicated its willingness to spend its dollars for this problem. It has been accepted the same as any other production problem. It is one of the problems of making chemicals for money. This is what we are in the business for, to make money for our stockholders. This is just one of the problems that cost us money that we don't get anything back for except good public relations and possibly good community relations and also to keep people off our back.

Fortunately, this opinion and philosophy were not held by all industries, and in those in which it was it has been gradually enlightened since then through factual demonstration and argument as well as increased public and private concern over the effects of mass pollution.

10

BIG POWER

The square building with a large dome behind it looks like any other windowless plant. You could drive right by the installation and not know what it was were it not for the word "nuclear" on the sign, and the tell-tale "transmission farm" in the rear, with its array of transformers and switching gears. But nearly everyone now knows of the locations of electricity-producing nuclear power plants because of the controversies which had accompanied their construction in the last few decades. This particular plant caused the first of the intensive debates that have occurred.

Back in the 1960s, in the first rush of construction, about twenty-five such plants were built; decades later more than one thousand had spread around the country. And as the plants themselves had increased, so had the disputes over the locations.

At the time when this plant was built, the question of future growth of an urban area was still barely being considered by public bodies. There were those who said, "There will never be an accident of consequences to be concerned about." And there were those who said, "How can you be sure?" Aesthetic problems had diminished by then, for, unlike with coal-fueled plants, there was no longer a need for the enormous complexes of railroad car yards or the huge piles of coal. If some new means of conducting power from the plant could be found, even the transmission farms could be eliminated, further improving the appearance.

The most recent development then was the cryogenic system, using underground transmission of power by means of a low temperature cooling conductor. But plants using this system were still few, and most were wired just as they had been in the 1960s. Wires still criss-crossed the landscape as they had since the time of Edison, despite increasing pressure for underground wires and transmission by microwave.

When the debate over this particular plant began, there were only a handful who seriously concerned themselves with the fact that ultimately the urban area would build up to and around the nuclear power plant.

After all, hadn't our plant designers been ultra-cautious, and hadn't they investigated in advance every conceivable aspect of the plant's erection? Since the 1940s we had known every single fission product produced, and knew their characteristics far better than the characteristics of burning gasoline in a combustion plant. In fact, it had been said for decades that we knew far more about the dynamics and intimate nature of nuclear fission than we knew about combustion.

It was certainly agreed that environmental dangers did exist, but most authorities insisted their hazards had been adequately estimated and steps had been taken to keep them within bounds. Presumably, reasonable levels of safety standards had been arrived at. Few people expressed concern over the seepage of gases from nuclear plants. Monitoring certainly was done at the Hanford plant, the Savannah plant, and other privately owned installations. However, one of these functioned for two or three decades before it began to be recognized that inadequate consideration had been given to the problem of radioactive gaseous emissions. As a result, this early plant was now in a sealed-off area, unused and surrounded by open land. High wire fences sealed it off and it was visible only from a distance.

Now there is no argument about locating plants inside metropolitan areas. Population densities have increased to such a degree that there are not even any arguments about where growth patterns are likely to push urban areas. Now the concern is over the dangers that emerge from the many plants that have been built. It finally came to be recognized, a decade or so ago, that even though the experts said that the chances of something happening at a nuclear power plant were so small, the risk involved so many people that even the small probability required the location of the facilities as far away from the population as possible.

In the first decades of nuclear power, it was the possibility of human error that most concerned people. The question was whether construction had been done under the closest inspection and the highest of quality controls. There was worry over the possibility that foreign objects would be lodged in the containment vessel, or that somebody would fail to make an X-ray inspection of the joints and the welding gear. All you needed was one weak point. The concern was driven home when, in the mid 1980s, in Europe, a newly designed power plant had what was called a "nuclear excursion," a runaway chain reaction. The resulting contamination of the population in the general area of the plant, and the tremendous biological-physical damage that resulted from the release of fission products in the atmosphere caused many million dollars' worth of damage and an enormous amount of human misery and injury.

Even though there had been progress by that time in recognizing radiation hazards, still no one was prepared for a disaster on this scale. It was clear that in the United States private industry itself was not going to undertake the responsibility for such accidents; as a result, a law was passed for the government to assume greater liability in case of injury or damage.

Technology does not stand still. And so an intense competition grew up between nuclear fuel and fossil fuel. To meet the challenge, nuclear engineers designed new and advanced ways to increase efficiency. While the new designs were more efficient, they also involved a higher specific power — more power per unit volume. This meant pushing the thermodynamic limits of the reactor closer to the edge. Since no accidents had occurred of any serious nature in several decades, there was a greater disposition to take a little more risk to get a little better efficiency. Reactor design constantly escalated the nuclear technology, and constantly pushed the standards of safety.

It wasn't long ago that nuclear power's promise for the future was hailed for bringing new hope to mankind. Some worried about what adverse effects there might be: might waste products be a problem? would new developments in reactors and fuel-handling create unforeseen difficulties? A few talked about escaped gases; but effluents were carefully considered, and the AEC assured the public that it was well in control of all dangers. Even though the public had stopped worrying about human error, most nuclear problems that arose were still due to human error. With the present number of plants three or four times those of decades before, the possibility of human error increased substantially. When voices were raised, however, urging further safeguards and procedures for control and safety, they were always answered with the argument that nuclear power would make possible significant technological advances very much in the cause of all mankind. Those who raised questions about environmental problems growing out of increased use of nuclear fuel were brushed aside as uninformed harbingers of disaster.

So the use of nuclear energy has spread not only for the generation of electricity, but for the conversion of sea water into fresh water, for the production of chemical fertilizer, for the development of food factories, and for scientific farming. Yet with all this "peaceful use of the atom," people still seem to be concerned about the number and location of nuclear power plants. Not that anyone can point to a stream of major accidents, but there is nervousness. And new nuclear fuel reprocessing plants lately have contributed more than the power plants to this nervousness. Once there were but three, now there are ten, and the volume of processed material has soared a hundred fold.

The number of reprocessing plants built outside the Western United States has not substantially increased, but there have been major additions to existing facilities as well as new plants in the West, so that concern over the disposal and storage of immense quantities of waste material is growing. Many people have been equally worried over the transportation by special railroad car of the expended cells from the power plants of the processing plant. These used fuel rods are carried in railroad coffins and there is always the specter of a derailment, throwing the cars on their sides, breaking open the coffins, exposing the radioactive material to the atmosphere.

The total physical environment is not large enough to dilute the enormous quantities of highly toxic radioactive waste to levels that are safe. The only alternative has been storage for hundreds of years, and such storage has to be carefully controlled. Years ago, more than enough space existed for such storage, but as the manufacture of energy with nuclear fuel increased, storage has become more and more of a problem, a problem which is complicated by the fact that radioactive fission products produce heat which must be removed. Most of the high-level waste has been stored in tank farms costing hundreds of millions of dollars. Some of the tanks in which the storage has occurred are now generations old, and great concern exists over the condition of the steel and concrete holding this waste.

There are other radioactive hazards. The coolant used in the immediate vicinity of the reactor core becomes radioactive when it is bombarded with neutrons and, though it is much less radioactive than the fission produced in the spent fuel, there still are disposal problems.

Still another potential environmental effect is the accompanying increase in thermal pollution. "Hot waters" they are called, and dozens of rivers are without fish because of the high temperature of water. There is nothing exotic about this kind of pollution; it is as old-fashioned as hydrocarbons and carbon monoxide and comes from coal and oil plants as well as nuclear power plants.

Not much of this glimpse into a future of massive nuclear power unveils any new worries. The difference between today and tomorrow is more one of degree and population growth. Of course it is more difficult to read the future of nuclear energy than it is to predict tomorrow's patterns of crowding and water pollution. There may very well be technological developments or other discoveries which will raise new health safety questions; but the questions that have already been raised can produce public tension in the future without requiring any new discoveries.

A conventional power plant and a nuclear power plant produce electricity the same way. Both use steam to drive a turbine generator. The difference is in the fuel used to turn water into steam. In a conventional thermal power plant, coal, oil or gas is burned, and the heat from this combustion boils water into steam. In nuclear plants there is no "burning," although the word is often used; there is heat but no flame. Instead, fission takes place. The fission reaction generates heat, and this heat is used to create steam. A heavy element such as uranium is required for the fission process to take place.

Uranium, the heaviest atom in nature is found extensively in ore deposits, and in its natural state it is essentially a mixture of two isotopes, which are atomic forms chemically alike but varying in mass. One of the atoms of these isotopes is uranium 235, which has a nucleus of 92 protons and nearly twice as many neutrons. When a neutron strikes a nucleus it can produce nuclear fission — an instantaneous splitting of the nucleus into high-speeding fragments. The energy of the flying fission fragments as they collide with surrounding atoms is converted to heat. The neutrons released in the first fission strike other uranium nuclei, and a chain reaction ensues.

The energy from such a chain reaction using 100 pounds of atomic fuel will produce enough electricity to supply 9,000 households for one year. The 100 pounds of atomic fuel, if fully fissioned, produce the same heat as 230 million pounds of coal.

When it comes out of the ground, the hundred pounds of fuel is contained in ore weighing 40,000 pounds. It is mostly rock. In the United States nearly all known deposits of commercial grade uranium rock are in northwestern New Mexico,

[229]

central Wyoming, or near the Colorado-Utah border, and come from the thousand or so mines that honeycomb the Golden Circle where Utah, Colorado, New Mexico and Arizona come together. The rock can come from shallow open pit mines, but most likely it is out of an underground mine. Generally these are just small tunnels dug into hills where the miner has cut the rock with a jackhammer, drill or pick. The larger mines, which may be cut with a jumbo drill, use diesel-powered loading and hauling equipment.

Blasting or drilling the rock releases liquid, solid and gaseous wastes. The solid waste of one percent uranium oxide is piled near the mine opening. The dust or gaseous wastes usually contain radon 222 and are discharged through the mine ventilation system into the atmosphere. The liquid wastes are considered to have minimal radioactivity. Drilled and blasted loose and machine-loaded into cars, the rock is carried to storage bins and then finally is dumped into trucks that must climb the sides of steep cliffs on roads often no wider than old wagon trails. The trucks sometimes travel several hundred miles over rugged terrain before reaching regular roads.

The 40,000 pounds of uranium ore will go to one of several dozen processing mills in the Colorado Plateau. Since so high a percentage of uranium ore is rock, the mills are located relatively close to the mines to cut down the costs of transportation. At the mill the uranium will be extracted from the ore. First the ore will be weighed and dumped into receiving bins, then it will be crushed and screened to produce small particles. Salt and acid compounds will be added to the ore to dissolve the uranium and separate it from the rock in a process known as leaching, and the solids will be combed for any metal remaining after the leaching.

The uranium, now in liquid form, will start through long

[230]

filter presses which squeeze the liquid out, leaving behind a bright clay-like material called "yellow cake." Now it is uranium concentrate, and it is packed into steel drums and shipped to the country's principal refining plant at St. Louis. In refining, which eliminates the impurities that reduce the efficiency of reaction in nuclear fuel, the uranium goes through a chemical process and then is roasted. At this stage uranium is a fine, brilliant orange powder, but it is turned into a "green salt" before being shipped to a plant in Paducah, Kentucky, for enrichment.

At the enrichment plant the green salt is reacted with fluorine gas so that it becomes a substance that is a solid at room temperature which sublimes to a gas when heated slightly. The enrichment of uranium is a process that partially separates the uranium isotopes so that there is a higher than normal concentration of uranium 235 and a waste called depleted uranium, which is drawn off and stored. The enriched uranium is converted by chemical process from its gaseous state to a powder called uranium dioxide.

The uranium is now shipped as uranium dioxide to a fabrication plant, the last stage before it becomes a reactor fuel available for use at one of the twenty-five or so nuclear power plants, where it is fashioned into plates. Other batches may be in the form of pellets or pins, but whatever the precise shape, the pieces are loaded into thin-walled tubes made of either stainless steel or an alloy of zirconium. Then helium is injected into the tube and the ends are capped. A number of such tubes are then clustered into a bundle enclosed in a long, rectangular steel or zirceloy sheath that allows a coolant to enter and leave the assembly. Each bundle is a fuel element, and hundreds of such fuel elements will be arranged in a carefully designed pattern and held in position by grid plates in a reactor vessel, to become a reactor core. The fuel elements are now loaded into trucks and delivered to a nuclear power plant.

Here, the core will be carefully placed and fitted within the reactor vessel, and — heavily shielded to protect against radiation — the chain reaction will begin which will produce the heat necessary to build steam for activating generators. Engineering perfection at this stage is vital so that all moving parts and central rods function perfectly.

The nuclear fuel's efficiency will fall below a critical point before it is entirely consumed and it will have to be replaced. When the partially consumed fuel elements are removed from the vessel they are intensely radioactive, and as soon as they are pulled from the vessel they have to be stored for several months under water within the plant to allow for what is called "decay cooling."

After removal from the water bins, the spent fuel begins the last journey in the cycle of use. It is loaded into heavily shielded transfer casks and taken to a fuel reprocessing plant such as the one near Buffalo, New York.

Reprocessing is done to reclaim unused uranium and the plutonium by-product created in the fission process. The reprocessing is conducted mostly by remote-control equipment behind massive concrete shielding walls. Much of this process is a series of chemical separations of the used fuel. One cycle removes the fission products; others remove residual fission products from the isolated uranium. Finally the salvaged uranium leaves the plant as a concentrated solution ready to be converted into forms that make it usable once again for reactor fuel.

Wastes occur in all the steps from mining to reprocessing. The million wastes include solid refuse called tailings, which contain most of the radium from the ore. Mills attempt to hold tailings inside controlled areas, but a satisfactory means of disposal is yet to be found, since there is substantial evidence that they get into streams and rivers. In the refining, enrichment and fabrication steps, solid wastes contain small amounts of natural radioactive material which are disposed of by burial in supervised reservations. Acid wastes are diluted, neutralized, and stored to permit decay and then are discharged to waterways. Radioactive gases escape into the atmosphere. Control methods and low volume of use have brought little public attention to these wastes.

Mills in the western United States mine and process the uranium by hydrometallurgical processes in which either an acid or an alkali leach is employed. These plants are a potential source of environmental contamination because the process separates uranium from its daughter products which may then be discharged to the environment. The plants must dispose of about ten curies of radium a day, which usually is pumped to settling ponds near the mill site. Waste generally is permitted to flow or seep into nearby streams or is impounded at some distance from streams and either evaporates into the air or seeps into the ground. These operations also involve mechanical processing of dry powders made of uranium compounds, and here there is an opportunity to discharge uranium dust into the environment.

Of greater concern and volume are the wastes produced during reprocessing. During a reprocessing cycle, highly radioactive waste will be generated from the remains of the uranium fuel. These waste solutions from the extraction process are boiled down to reduce their volume, and the concentrate is stored underground in large steel tanks routinely monitored to check for leakage. Leakage from the reactor system may cause external items to become radioactive and add to the waste.

Of all the aspects of nuclear fuel, the one that requires the greatest vigilance and the most careful planning is the building and operation of a fuel reprocessing plant. It is here that the most highly radioactive material is received and that the biggest waste problem occurs. Today, few people outside the nuclear fuel industry and allied government agencies concern themselves with the existence of such plants. There are three, and they are fairly well obscured from public view — both physically and mentally.

Yet public hackles were raised over the erection of the third plant, and an incident over a purported liquid waste emission once the plant was in operation demonstrated the ease with which public and official tempers could flare.

About thirty miles southeast of Buffalo, near the small village of Springville, a railroad spur of the Baltimore and Ohio Railroad runs into the 3,331-acre Western New York Nuclear Service Center. In the roughly 2-square-mile heart of this reservation owned by New York State is the reprocessing plant of Nuclear Fuels Service, Incorporated. Railroad cars bring to the plant 75-ton casks containing irradiate nuclear reactor fuel. Through the site flows Buttermilk Creek to its junction with Cattaraugus Creek, which continues within the site grounds for 800 feet and then flows another thirty-nine miles to Lake Erie.

The plant processes spent fuel elements in order to separate uranium and plutonium from their associated fission products and from each other, using what is known as the Purex Process. When the casks of spent fuel arrive at the plant they are submerged in a pool of water. Underwater remote-control handling tools remove the fuel elements from the casks and place them in a storage basket, and an underwater transfer conveyor moves the fuel from this storage point to the "process mechanical cell."

In the "process mechanical cell" the fuel elements are cut into 1½-inch pieces in order to facilitate dissolution. These pieces are then collected in a basket and transferred to the chemical process cell, where the basket is submerged in nitric acid. The fuel is dissolved and its hull is discarded as solid waste. The uranium, plutonium and fission products in the solvent go through a series of chemical solvent processes until they are separated.

Liquid, solid and gaseous radioactive wastes are produced as by-products of this processing of irradiated fuels. According to plant officials, the gases and "low-level radioactive liquid wastes" are released to the environment "in a controlled manner." The other wastes are stored. Liquid wastes with high-level radioactivity are stored in underground tanks and funded for perpetual care. Radioactive noble gases, tritium, radioiodine and radioactive particulates are emitted from a stack into the atmosphere. The low-level liquid wastes are released to a small run called Frank's Creek, which flows into Buttermilk Creek.

In 1960, the population of the five counties surrounding the plant area was 1,369,000, and by 1980 this is expected to reach 1.7 million. There are currently no public water supplies drawn from the Cattaraugus Creek in the section between Buttermilk Creek and the point where it empties into Lake Erie, but the stream is a popular recreation spot. Its waters attract swimmers, picnickers and boating enthusiasts as well as fishermen in pursuit of rainbow trout. The creek also runs through one of two Indian reservations within twenty-five miles of the nuclear fuel site.

At one time the water of the Cattaraugus was used for irrigation. Now cattle and some sheep use the creek, and there is the possibility that the surrounding farming area may once again use the water for irrigation purposes. In this section snap beans are the major crop and support local canning plants in the area. Other truck crops such as strawberries and vegetables are grown here, as well as corn, oats, and wheat. In addition, there is a substantial dairy industry producing approximately 500,000 quarts of fluid milk each day from herds grazing in fields within a twenty-five-mile radius of the nuclear fuel site. In April 1966 the AEC granted Nuclear Fuel Services a provisional operating license which required that radioactive material discharged to Cattaraugus Creek from any source on the site not exceed a certain amount — an amount twice specified in the Code of Federal Regulations. The radioactivity released to Cattaraugus Creek is monitored at a station located a short distance downstream from where it meets Buttermilk Creek.

Some time after the start of the plant's operation, the Rochester Committee for Scientific Information charged that excessive strontium 90 concentrations were being released in the liquid effluence from the plant. A sample of this effluence was obtained directly from a plant drainpipe emptying from the last lagoon within the site. Another sample was obtained from Buttermilk Creek. These samples were sent to the director of the Health and Safety Laboratory of the AEC's New York Operations Office with a request for an analysis of the strontium 90. The identity of the source was not revealed to the laboratory.

After analyzing the samples the laboratory informed the committee that the sample from the plant's drainpipe contained substantially more strontium 90 than allowable by the federal regulation. The committee released this finding, and following newspaper publicity the laboratory reviewed its analysis and found that it had been in error in making its calculations, and revised the figures downward. These revised calculations were then sent to the Rochester Committee. Shortly thereafter, the Rochester Committee issued a second bulletin clarifying and correcting its report in the earlier bulletin but still questioning the legality and safety of the plant's effluent.

R. F. Lumb, Director of the Western New York Nuclear Research Center Incorporated, wrote the Atomic Energy Commission Chairman a letter in which he said,

On February 25th the newspapers published an account of a report released by the Rochester Committee for Scientific Information. Subsequent coverage by the newspapers has indicated a serious concern on the part of the public generated by the report. I have recently studied the report and find that the information contained in the report in no way supports the conclusions reached, and in my opinion, the conclusions are wholly unjustified. . . I believe it quite important that this report be discredited. In my opinion, it is quite unprofessional in its treatment of data, and the "experiment" conducted by the committee is not only invalid but totally impertinent. Unless the general public recognizes that these charges are groundless, this report could have a serious adverse effect on the nuclear program in the New York State area, if not the nation.

Lumb also wrote to the chairman of the commitee which released the report. In his lengthy letter, setting out point by point the purported inaccuracies of the report, he ended by saying that he regretted that he had to send copies of the letter to various newspapers. He wrote, "This action pains me since I do not believe that the newspapers are an appropriate media for professional criticism." Nowhere in Lumb's letters or in the material issued by both sides does there appear any explanation of how the laboratory made its error or of what prompted them to review their earlier test data and determine that they did make an error.

Criticism and public concern over the radioactive emissions from the Nuclear Fuel Services plant were not ended by Dr. Lumb's letters to Dr. Berg of the Rochester Committee and the AEC. Rochester attorney Wayne M. Harris, an officer of the Monroe County (N.Y.) Conservation Council, continues to ask questions. More than one year after the initial Rochester Committee for Scientific Information report, Harris asks why milk from farms surrounding Buttermilk and Cattaraugus creeks apparently has higher strontium 90 content than milk from other farms in New York. He also asks why the AEC and the New York State Health Department issued directives to the plant in the early summer of 1968 to limit plant emissions, and why the plant was shut down for a short period in the fall of 1968. Despite the difficulties and the misunderstandings which may be created through the public discussion and questioning of highly technical matters, it may be better than assuming that mistakes are never made.

The reactors themselves discharge only moderate amounts of radioactivity into the environment. This is because in most cases they are closed systems in which the cooling fluid does not normally leave the loop in which it is contained. However, there are exceptions, at Brookhaven and Oak Ridge and at Hanford. At the first two, materials are given off into the atmosphere, and in the third they go into the Columbia River. And in addition to using rivers as a means of disposal, there is the dumping of concrete-lined drums containing low-level radioactive garbage into the Atlantic and Pacific oceans. Because of the corrosive action of sea water and the porosity of the concrete liners in the high-water pressures at the ocean floor, drums may last as few as ten years.

These radioactive wastes, if they should escape from their containers, would have a definite ecological effect. Professor Ron R. Donaldson of the University of Washington reports that, "Available substances are rapidly taken up by the plankton and algae, never remaining long in the water to be diluted and washed away." "This," he said, "is dramatically demonstrated following an atomic test in which radioactive materials are deposited in the water. Within hours the great bulk of these materials can be found in living organisms."

Plankton and some of the algae that are the key organisms in the chain may concentrate within themselves more than a thousand times the amount of radioactive substances found in the sea water. Cases have been identified also in which the concentration of radioactive elements was higher in fish and mollusks than in plants. Eventually the radioactive garbage can find its way back to man because of the uncertainty of the life expectancy of the steel and concrete used to contain the radioactive waste dumped into the ocean.

No one knows the present condition of the steel and concrete radioactive waste containers now being used. Have they been dropped in the proper disposal areas by the barge operators? And if they have been deposited in the designated portion of the ocean, are they still there? Did the tremendous pressures of the depths crush the containers before they reached the bottom? Or did they burst open when they hit the floor? Have the uncharted ocean currents carried the containers away from the original site to some unknown point? These are questions about which there should be no uncertainty.

A more prosaic effect on water from the development of nuclear fuel is that caused by discharge of heat from the plant. In the cooling process water is used to draw off heat from the condenser where spent steam is reduced to water so that it can be used again in the boiler. The amount of heat drawn off by the cooling water and then discharged into the nearby stream or river equals the amount of heat extracted in the condenser.

Thermal pollution of inland waters is not peculiar to nuclear fuel-generating plants. Any manufacturing plant using water for cooling purposes is likely to discharge water of highly elevated temperature into rivers or streams. The vast majority of

[239]

waste-heat discharges come from fossil-fuel-fired plants, since nuclear power plants operating or under construction today still provide only a small proportion of the nation's electricity.

According to Atomic Energy Commission projects, however, there will be an equivalent of seven hundred 1-million-kilowatt nuclear power plants operating in the United States by the year 2000. Even by 1980, nuclear fuel-generating plants may account for 30 percent of the nation's electric production, compared with 5 percent in the late 1960s.

This increase in the number of nuclear power plants will substantially increase the problems of thermal pollution. The electric-power industry uses large quantities of water in power-generating plants, most of it for cooling in the condenser and heat exchangers. Plants that produce equal amounts of electricity may still vary in the degree of heated water discharged, and some nuclear plants will discharge water that is on the average 50 percent hotter than fossil plants of similar electrical capability. With the rise of nuclear projects (even those whose thermal discharges are similar to fossil-fired centers), there will be by the year 2000 a nine-fold increase in the heat discharged from power plants.

Within ten years nearly one-sixth of the total fresh water runoff in the United States will be required for cooling and condensing purposes. Production of electricity will require the greatest proportion of this water. The direct effects of such heated waste discharge are varied. Water temperatures in some extreme instances are elevated to 115 degrees Fahrenheit. Under these high water temperature conditions, algae bloom prodigiously. As a result of the algae, too much dissolved oxygen may be liberated into the water during full sunlight and fish may be killed by a condition called supersaturation. There is also the reverse effect. During darkness or on cloudy or foggy

[240]

days, the dissolved oxygen is removed from the water and carbon dioxide is given off by the algae. The fish then die from lack of oxygen.

In other hot or abnormally warm conditions, unhealthy fish may develop. Disease organisms and parasites thrive more rapidly in hot water, and some game fish require low water temperature in order to complete their life cycles.

Thermal pollution is a common occurrence today. It can be expected to increase in intensity in the years ahead. It is easily understood and easily controlled. Yet little is being done to control it. The effects of thermal pollution can be devastating, and while there is little direct health effects on humans, there is substantial economic effect, not to mention aesthetic damage.

If little public indignation can be roused over such an obvious danger as thermal pollution, how much more difficult it will be to maintain maximum vigilance over other aspects of nuclear power development. Nuclear reactor accidents are an example.

The Windscale works of the United Kingdom Atom Energy Authority is located on a low-lying coastal strip in northwest England. At this site are two air-cooled graphite-moderated natural reactors employed in the production of plutonium. The core of one of these reactors was partially melted down the morning of October 8, 1957, resulting in the release of fission products to the surrounding countryside.

The accident occurred during the regular annealing procedure — which is for releasing, at a carefully controlled rate, energy stored as a result of neutron irradiation in graphite. It happened because energy was released at an excessive rate. The temperature of the core was raised for annealing purposes by using nuclear heat. The release of stored energy was excessive only in certain points of the core, but the local increases in

[241]

temperature that were occurring went undetected because of poor core instrumentation. Failure of a fuel cartridge evidently developed as a result. The metallic uranium and graphite began to react with air and, from the time combustion began on the morning of October 8th until the fire was out the afternoon of October 12th, much of the core was burned.

The first evidence that a mishap had occurred was the observation of elevated beta activity in atmospheric dust collected by an air sampler located in the open a half-mile from the reactor stack. Extensive sampling of the air in the vicinity of the plant indicated a wide variety of concentrations of radioactive isotopes. The highest concentrations were well below the allowable limits for human exposure, and external radiation from the accident was considered negligible. However, the concentration of Iodine 131 released by the accident did reach levels that caused worry. On the afternoon of the accident authorities found cows in the vicinity of the plant contaminated with Iodine 131 and immediately had to establish emergency levels for short-term exposure. Milk from cows found to have a level of Iodine 131 in excess of the limit imposed was confiscated.

In November 1959 a chemical explosion occurred in one of the shielded cells of the radio-chemical processing pilot plant at Oak Ridge Laboratory during a period when decontamination of the process equipment was in progress. No one was injured, and damage was relatively minor. The explosion, however, resulted in extensive plutonium contamination of the pilot plant building and of nearby streets and building surfaces.

The U.S. Atomic Energy Commission Proving Ground for experimental versions of atomic power plants is located in a wasteland west of Idaho Falls, Idaho, three-quarters of a mile away from U.S. Route 20. This installation is known as NRTS, the National Reactor Testing Station. The desolate site was chosen deliberately because it is far from farm lands, towns and villages that might be imperiled by an accident.

In 1960 administrative responsibility for the station was shared by the Army and the AEC, and the site was operated by two companies, Phillips Petroleum and Combustion Engineering, Incorporated. In a building enclosed by barbed wire the stationary low-power nuclear reactor SL-1 had been designed to put the atom to work at remote Arctic bases. It first had gone into operation in August 1958; within a few months, it was running at full power, on uranium fuel, generating three thousand kilowatts of heat.

Two days before Christmas of 1960, SL-1 was shut down temporarily. On the night of January 3, 1961, a crew of three technicians was at work making necessary repairs on the reactor, which was scheduled to start up again the next day.

At 9:01 P.M. an automatic alarm from the SL-1 building sounded at AEC fire stations and security headquarters. The alarm was immediately relayed over the NRTS radio network, and a firetruck started at once on the eight-mile run to SL-1. An assistant fire chief and a security officer jumped into their cars to investigate, and a health physicist, specially trained to deal with the problem of radioactivity, was summoned to the scene. When the vehicles reached the SL-1 area, there was no sign of fire and smoke. In fact, there was nothing to indicate trouble. As the firemen and others advanced, however, they knew there had been an accident, because the meters they carried showed that the area was contaminated with radioactive debris.

They searched the long, low administration and technical support building but found no trace of the men known to be on duty. They proceeded to the entrance of the 48-foot-high

[243]

silo. Equipped with masks known as Scott Air Packs, the searchers entered the silo, but found radiation levels so high that they withdrew to await the arrival of the physicist. The health physicist and one companion headed for the silo, where they were certain the three men on duty had to be.

As the rescue team started up the outside stairs of the silo leading to the operations floor, their meters registered full scale. The two men retreated quickly to get meters that could register higher radiation ranges. With these, a second crew started to climb, and as they moved up they reached a level of contamination of 200 r per hour. A single, massive dose of 500 r is fatal, usually within a month; and knowing this the second crew turned back without reaching the top of the stairs. A third crew then made a quick dash up the stairs and peered inside. The lights were still on, but there was no sign of fire; no one was visible on the floor of the operations area. The radiation meter which they held outside the silo door read 500 r per hour, full scale on the instrument. The two men turned around and hurried back to the emergency headquarters.

At 10:25 P.M. the AEC Idaho Operations Office broadcast a Class I disaster. More personnel and experts were summoned to the site. They had to conduct all operations with utmost speed, since each second of exposure meant more danger for the rescuers. Yet the lives of three men were at stake, so they had to take the risk.

A rescue party of four combustion engineering employees was organized, and two of the group entered the silo, carrying meters with a scale of 500 r. The meters read off the scale, but the two men achieved their initial objective: they saw two of the operators. One was still alive and moving about. The rescuers raced down the stairs and quickly returned with the rest of their party, along with the AEC health physicist. They split into two teams. One team scooped up the living survivor, carried him to the top of the stairs, and whisked him to a waiting truck. The other reached the side of the second victim, verified that he was dead, and then withdrew hastily. This operation had taken less than three minutes. The living survivor was taken in an ambulance to a hospital, but was pronounced dead on arrival.

Meanwhile, a new search party looked for the third man. They found his body pinned to a beam in the ceiling structure directly over the top of the atomic reactor. He is believed to have been killed outright by the force of an explosion. Radiation was so intense near the reactor that there was no immediate possibility of recovering the body; it was not removed until six days later, and then only with great difficulty.

Had this tragedy been caused by an ordinary steam-boiler explosion, it would have become but another statistic in man's contest with the machine. However, because the accident was caused by a nuclear reactor it became an ominous signpost in man's struggle to tame the atom. An elaborate investigation was set in motion, resembling in many ways a probe of an airplane crash. An obstacle to determining the probable cause even more formidable than the lack of survivors and eyewitnesses was the fact that even some seven years later radioactivity still prevented anyone from getting close enough to the reactor to examine it in detail.

Radiochemical examination of the contaminated debris has provided some clues, as did the radioactivity of a gold ring worn by one of the victims. Investigators pieced together other fragments by studying the reactor's three-year performance history. A board of inquiry found that the most likely immediate cause of the explosion appears to have been a nuclear excursion — a runaway chain reaction — resulting from the motion of the central control rod.

What caused an idle machine suddenly to awaken? A nuclear

reactor is a machine with few moving parts. The core of SL–1 contained forty fuel rods holding a total of 30 pounds of special uranium fuel, enough to fuel several A-bombs. However, SL–1 could not detonate like a bomb. Its chain reaction was constantly regulated by control rods which performed the same function as an accelerator and brake in an automobile. When the control rod is inserted all the way into the reactor core the nuclear machine shuts down and its pulses stop. Conversely, as the rod is withdrawn the machine begins to throb. If the rod is withdrawn beyond the safety limit, the chain reaction races out of control or runs away. This is the nightmare which haunts reactor experts.

To prevent or minimize the danger of an uncontrolled chain reaction, manufacturers of nuclear reactors build in elaborate safeguards. In the case of SL–1, there were nine control rods. Only one of the control rods, number nine, could start up a chain reaction by itself. The others served to increase or decrease its tempo, but could not start the pulse. Number nine was located at the very center of the reactor core and, like the others, was connected to a drive mechanism above the reactor.

When SL–1 was shut down, all the control rods were driven into the core and later the drive mechanism was disconnected. On the night of the accident, the three men were making the final reassembly of the control mechanism in preparation for the start-up the next morning. They had removed shieldings from the top of the reactor to permit access to fittings on it. In order to connect the control rods to the overhead drive apparatus, the rods, each about seven feet long, had to be lifted by hand. The rod had to be lifted a distance of four inches to engage the overhead drive. One man could do the job by exerting an eighty-pound pull. The men had been trained to do this job, and they had been instructed that under no circumstances should the rod be moved more than the four inches.

Normally, moving the rod four inches would not start the chain reaction. In fact, the margin of safety built into the machine theoretically would allow a much greater movement — as much as nineteen inches — without awakening the nuclear pulse. It is certain that when the accident occurred the men were lifting number nine. But why did it blow its stack? These questions cannot yet be answered. All that is known is that at 9:01 P.M. on January 3, 1961, there was an accidental start-up of SL–1 and that a blast vented itself through openings in the top of the reactor vessel.

At Los Alamos, New Mexico, December 30, 1958, three batches of plutonium were put in a tank together. Usually the recovery of plutonium produced in a reactor involves handling only small quantities. In this instance, however, an error had been made, and when an electric stirring device was turned on the plutonium worked into a critical configuration. There was a sudden blue flash and an explosion. The workman who had switched on the electricity was looking into the tank when the explosion occurred, and he was thrown from the ladder on which he was standing. After recovering from the fall he ran outside. His skin was reddening quickly, and soon he began to vomit and discharge watery diarrhea. Thirty-six hours after the exposure he was dead.

In October of 1966, the Enrico Fermi Atomic Power Plant at Lagoona Beach, Michigan, was about to start up again. Located thirty miles from Detroit and twenty-five miles from Toledo, Ohio, the Fermi reactor, a plutonium-producing and burning reactor with a molten sodium coolant system, had been plagued by troubles since it was first proposed in 1956. At first, the problem had been legal opposition to its construction; a Supreme Court decision had been required to remove that obstacle. Then a long series of technical difficulties had ensued which had kept Fermi shut down much of the time. On October 4, 1966, the latest difficulty, a malfunction in the steam generator, seemed to have been corrected, and the technicians made the first small withdrawal of the control rods to start up the reactor.

The following day operations to increase power were begun, and by 3:00 P.M., after several hesitations, the reactor was at about one-tenth of its maximum licensed capacity of 200,000 kilowatts. Several minutes later, it was noticed that one of the instruments was sending out an erratic signal, that one of the control rods appeared to be withdrawn too far, and that the temperature at two points in the reactor seemed abnormal. At that moment the high-radiation alarms sounded, and by 3:20 the reactor was completely shut down.

No one was injured immediately, but small amounts of radioactive gases had been released to the atmosphere, and the discovery of radioactive fission products in the liquid sodium coolant indicated that a portion of the reactor fuel had melted. This brought up the danger of a secondary accident. It appeared that the disruption in the reactor core might have released enough uranium so that if it were to be collected together, a spontaneous chain reaction too great to be controlled by the control rods might occur. If this were to result, an explosion could occur, great enough to rupture the concrete-and-steel containment structure and to release larger portions of radioactive gases to the winds. Concern for the possible secondary, but larger, accident prevented investigation of the Fermi core for more than a month for fear that a jar would assemble the melted fuel into a critical mass. Fortunately, the fears generated by the initial accident of October 5, 1966, did not become a reality, and no further damage occurred.

The nuclear accidents which have occurred so far have been due to some sort of human failure or unexpected occurrence. They have occurred despite a high degree of precautionary measures. Nuclear experts maintain that the likelihood is nil of a future accident that can cause ill-effects on the general population. They may be right.

Historically, however, our nation has subordinated concern for public safety to economic enhancement. We have launched into new areas of development with little regard for the effect of that development on other aspects of our living conditions. We could spoil our water and overcrowd our streets without suffering an immediate negative effect. We have learned that the visible results of pollution and crowding will warn us against further folly. But the effects from a nuclear mistake may be more long-term and less visible. What is certain is that the mistake will be more lethal than other environmental damage caused by humans. With nuclear development it isn't enough to be vigilant. The vigilance must be exercised by those who are not sure that the machinery is safe, not by those who are sure.

11

THE NEW TECHNOLOGY

It has been some time since the days when the nation's industrial vocabulary centered on such words as drill, press, steel and copper. Now, with ever-growing frequency, conversation about consumer products is filled with words such as cadmium, ultrasonic, cellulous fibers, lasers, tellurium, indium, and — most of all — radiation. For this is a time of "science industry," when X-ray machines have become common and nearly every housewife has a laser knife.

The X-ray machine has burst the bounds of medicine and now is found not only in every hospital and doctor's and dentist's office, but in most industrial plants and many commercial establishments as well. In this super-industrial age almost no one in the United States can go a day without coming into contact with X rays and radiation. Radiation sources increasingly are being used in appliances and other household items. In offices a growing number of machines expose workers to ultraviolet radiation and to vapors and fumes from exotic chemicals.

The new chemicals, the ultrasonic waves, the exotic metals, the laser beams, and the microwave ovens have brought the most prosaic producer or consumer into intimate contact with the world of science and technology. Dry cleaners, welders, printers, photographic chemical makers, all find themselves using materials with strange names and stranger properties. Aircraft workers, glass makers, machinists, nurses, laboratory technicians, more and more are involved with devices employing radiation sources.

Chemistry has become so sophisticated that chemists are molecular architects. Molecules can be designed and constructed to produce a material with a needed property. Once there used to be an estimated half million chemical compounds used by man; now there are several million. These chemicals are used in the manufacture of clothes, manufacturing materials, furniture, paints for automobiles and containers, and for cleaning and preserving. With few exceptions they are all artificial additions to man's natural environment.

Microwaves, long used in communication, have now become central to many industrial and domestic activities; they are used as a heat source in factories, restaurants, service centers and homes. Science has discovered how microwaves can be used to carry energy from point to point, and tremendous energy levels were now being found in the use of microwave equipment and accelerators probing high energy physics.

Lasers, which commonly generate beams in the ultraviolet and infrared region of the light spectrum, invisible to the human eye, are used to measure and cut, to drill and align. They are a medical tool and an engineering tool; they can be made from kits and are often found in home workshops. They are becoming common in automobiles, used to measure the distance to the preceding car and working the brakes when vehicles come too close. They are competing with nuclear energy as a method of fracturing rocks and tunneling.

Nuclear energy has moved on to new jobs. It is the basic ingredient for the agro-industrial centers developing the world over. These centers are food factories, energy producers and the source of raw materials and finished products. In the agro-industrial centers nuclear energy is used to desalt water and concentrate elements from the sea such as aluminum, copper, and bromine to make ammonium fertilizer, operate irrigation systems and thus produce food with little left to chance or the whims of nature. Crops are bred especially for each region and the conditions that prevail there. The scientific farming at these centers shortens the growing seasons so that several crops can be harvested each year. Vast numbers of people are sustained by the food, power, goods and services each center is capable of producing.

At the heart of these centers is a cluster of huge reactors surrounded by a variety of industrial plants interchanging goods and services through a maze of underground arteries, conveyor belts and pipelines. Out of these centers come solvents, insecticides and plastics produced from hydrocarbons such as coal. Steel is produced by hydrogen reduction, and great electric furnaces turn out phosphates, silica, lime and salts in the form of glass ceramics and ceramic fiber reinforced alloys. The industrial centers produce great amounts of rarer metals such as palladium and rhodium.

On the roads and the streets in the centers are electric automobiles and buses powered by batteries recharged by nuclear-generated electricity. Serving the centers are trains driven by nuclear energy. Automobiles powered by nuclear systems are beginning to appear. On the ocean, nuclear ships have almost completely replaced diesel powered vessels, and in the air, the jets are giving way to atomic planes.

Wherever the old fossil fuels — petroleum, natural gas, and coal — served in the past, man's ingenuity replaced them with nuclear power packages. At first, because of the stubborn engineering and economic problems, the replacement came in the field of big power packages such as ships and trains. Gradually, as new energy conversion devices were developed, the nuclear power packages invaded smaller power markets until about the only thing left undisplaced is the gas-driven lawn mower. (However, this isn't very important because the chemists and bioscientists have perfected obedient grass which grows on schedule and is chemically trimmed.)

In the late 1960s the world of technology began to expand at a phenomenal rate, and in the decades that followed the search for more efficient and cheaper ways to turn out goods and services pushed technological development to higher and higher levels of achievement. The pressures for labor-saving devices and the desire for an easier life brought scientific solutions to everyday activities and into the home at a rate never anticipated. The industrial economy expanded. Work opportunities increased and improvements began to grow and grow.

Air pollution from automobiles by now has declined, yet the quality of air does not seem to improve as the population increases and new pollutants continue to foul the air. People pay less and less attention to water pollution as increasing amounts of fresh water become available through desalting. Artificial recreation areas aid in diverting attention from the need for improvement of water quality standards. Recycling systems substantially reduce waste disposal requirements, but again population increase and consumer appetite offset the advantage. There is an uneasy feeling that as a result of the use of all of the new chemicals, materials and processes of production things that man doesn't recognize or understand are happening to him. The government studies the toxic effects of chemicals and

[253]

trace metals on industrial workers. However, the numbers and complexity of new chemicals far exceed our ability to investigate their effect. Furthermore, the introduction of multitudes of synthetic chemicals and chemical combinations has added a new level of toxic hazard. Whereas two chemicals may have a relatively small biological or physiological effect individually, the hazardous effects of these two chemicals when combined together, sometimes can be vastly multiplied. Chemical combinations can occur intentionally, in the manufacture of a product, in which case the restriction against revealing trade secrets prevents outside investigation until the product is on the market.

Combinations can also occur when separate chemicals added to individual food products come together in the preparation and ingestion of meals, tremendously increasing combination possibilities. Sometimes there are minor outbreaks of allergy problems. Suspected causes of cancer have been uncovered, but mostly the concern has been over long-term disease-producing or genetic effects. The problem is not new. In 1967 more than five hundred thousand chemical substances or combinations of chemical substances were in use. Only a small portion of these had been examined for their toxic effects. Research into the effects of a variety of exotic metals was quite limited and evaluation of production processes and machinery was nil.

In addition to the increased investigative responsibilities thrust upon the industrial, governmental, and private researchers by the proliferation of chemicals and their combinations, the individual worker and consumer is faced with new questions. What effect does exposure to a solvent with narcotic fumes have upon a workman's ability to operate an automobile or machinery after work? What is the likelihood that the new chemical finishes on fabrics will irritate his daughter's skin? Do his son's science teachers have the training to be able to supervise the use of lasers, plasmas, and other high energy sources without affecting his child's sight? What are the possible dangers to his wife in using ultrasonics to clean, microwaves to cook, and laser beams to cut? Will the fiber glass drapes in his living room have sufficient trace metals to set off an adverse reaction if the family comes in contact with them or when his wife takes them down to be laundered? Complex processes and complicated products have brought complex living and complicated questions into the average home.

Accelerated change and rapid technological development have made many of tomorrow's questions relevant today. More than 220,000 X-ray units currently are in use in hospitals, doctors' and dentists' offices, and industrial plants. In addition there are 14,000 active licenses for using artificial radioactive materials with about 60 percent issued by the Atomic Energy Commission and 40 percent by state agencies. Each active license may reflect numerous uses. For example, the U.S. Air Force is represented by a single license. The same is true for many hospitals and labs, where many doctors or laboratory personnel are represented by one license. Between 75 and 90 percent of all X-ray exposures in the United States today occur in the practice of medicine and dentistry, and the number of medical and dental exposures is expected to double every thirteen years. This exposure in the physicians' and dentists' offices or in the hospitals has been going on since the early 1900s.

Jack Schubert and Ralph E. Lapp, in their book *Radiation: What It Is and How It Affects You*, directed attention in the 1950s to the fact that thousands of infants and children in the United States were needlessly being exposed to more radiation in one year than would be allowed atomic energy workers in a lifetime. Schubert claimed that excessive radiation doses to children actually had increased rather than decreased since the 1940s when information on radiation hazards had become universal.

Seven years later, in 1964, a Public Health Service survey on medical and dental X-ray exposure indicated that 58 percent of the nation's noninstitutional population, then estimated at 187 million, had undergone one or more X rays. Involved were some 173 million X-ray examinations or procedures. Of these, 105 million were radiographic examinations, 54 million were dentists', 10 million were fluoroscope examinations, and 3.5 million were X-ray treatment. Nearly a million of the treatments were for non-malignant disorders such as warts, skin conditions, infections, and enlargement of the tonsils. A substantial percentage of this exposure was to children. The percentage did not include exposure to radioisotopes and other radiations.

The connection between X rays used to irradiate the thymus and the increase of leukemia has been pointed out clearly in the reports of the National Research Council. Several cases of cancer of the thyroid have been reported among children after they have been given X-ray treatment around the neck for non-malignant conditions such as enlarged tonsils, suspected enlargement of the thymus gland, adenoids, bronchitis, enlarged glands in the neck, deafness and many other disorders.

In 1956, the National Committee on Radiation Protection stated: "One of the important sources of radiation exposure is that applied by general practitioners. Here we cannot expect for many, many years at best to have any really good idea of what exposures these people are using. They do not know themselves. They have no techniques by which you can really estimate the exposure given in a gastro-intestinal examination. The exposure might be 10 r for a good operator; it might be 200 r for a careless operator." Dr. K. Z. Morgan, Director of

[256]

Health Physics Division, Oak Ridge National Laboratory, testifying in 1967 hearings before the Senate Commerce Committee on Radiation Dangers, estimated that the range of skin exposure in common X-ray examinations varies from 10 mr to 1,000 mr for a chest X ray and from 20 mr to 350,000 mr for a dental X ray. Thus one examination may expose a patient to a skin dose 100 times or even 17,500 times greater than the same exam given in another office with different equipment.

The Public Health Service's 1964 report notes that almost 92 percent of X-ray examinations given annually are performed in accredited facilities, but only 60 percent of these are performed under supervision of a radiologist, a medical specialist in radiation. As for the equipment used, at least 30 percent is more than ten years old. About one-half of all radiographic examinations exposed more of a patient's body to radiation than was necessary for the size of the X-ray picture taken. And more than 25 percent of these exposures used X-ray beam sizes that were two or more times larger than the areas of the X-ray film plus an allowance for 25 percent. Most X-ray machines are equipped with a manual collimator to limit the size of the X-ray beam to the area of the body under study. In many cases, the Public Health Service found that the manual collimator was not used at all.

The Public Health Service found that the most accurate and reliable method of limiting X-ray beam size to film size is through a system of automatic collimation. This method could reduce the genetically significant dose distributed among the population from 55 millirads to 19 millirads, a reduction in dosage of about two-thirds. Although the U.S. Public Health Service has developed, built, tested, and clinically used an automatic collimation system for X-ray machines, there was not one automatic collimator commercially available in 1968 for use on the more than 100,000 medical X-ray machines.

In addition to limiting the X-ray beam to the film size, it is possible to reduce needless X-ray exposure to the genetically significant areas of the body, the male gonads and female ovaries, through the use of relatively simple aprons or shields. A study of over 5,000 medical X-ray facilities conducted by the Public Health Service from 1962 to 1967, however, found that less than 40 percent of the facilities had gonadal shields present for potential use.

In his testimony before the Senate Commerce Committee in 1967, Dr. Morgan indicated that many medical diagnoses are carried out by doctors who have little or no training in the use of X-ray equipment. Often their techniques are poor while the equipment they are using is substandard. He went on to say that the X-ray machines that doctors, dentists, or X-ray technicians operate may be obsolete, may fail to meet many of the minimum standards of such equipment and that the operator may have little or no training knowledge about the best use of this equipment from the standpoint of obtaining the best possible radiographic information with the minimum amount of patient exposure.

One of the tragedies of radiation injury is that although the adverse effects of penetrating radiation were recognized very early by the pioneer scientists, Roentgen and the Curies, society was slow to react and set up standards to protect itself. While one reason for this preventive inaction was the strange nature of the rays themselves, another was the refusal of the medical profession to allow the establishment of outside regulation and control.

Schubert notes the possibility that repeated dental X rays to children may so damage the tissues of the gums that serious after-effects may be expected to develop in their adult teeth. The younger the child the greater the sensitivity to radiation, and it may be that the greatest amount of damage is to the unborn child resulting from irradiation of pregnant women.

The medical profession has long recognized the possible X-ray dangers for pregnant women. Still, the U.S. Public Health Service reports that in 1963 there were 4.1 million women who had live births, and almost one-quarter of these women received one or more X-ray examinations — 915,000 who had one or more medical X rays during pregnancy, and 420,000 who had one or more dental visits. In addition, an unknown number of women are subjected to irradiation in the pelvic region during the period when they are unaware of being pregnant.

As early as 1929, Schubert and Lapp point out, a study of 75 children born to healthy but irradiated mothers showed 38 with some obvious degree of malformation. Studies of children who had been irradiated in the uterus during the atomic bombings in Japan also showed an increased incidence of abnormalities. The National Research Council's report of 1956 said

A study of 4,400 individuals who have been exposed to the bomb in utero, or as children up to the age 10, revealed 33 cases of microcephally, with associated mental retardation in 15 cases, and 19 cases of leukemia. There were also cases of marred visual disability among those now 16 to 19 years old who were exposed within 1,800 meters of hypocenter. Observations on 205 children, 4½ years old, who had been exposed at Hiroshima within approximately 1,200 meters of hypocenter, during the first half of uterine life, indicate that central nervous system defects were produced.

British medical investigators in the 1950s discovered a correlation between the diagnostic X-raying of pregnant women and the later incidence of malignant disease in their children. These studies showed that a statistically significant number

[259]

of children whose mothers had been given diagnostic X rays prior to the children's birth were genetically damaged or developed leukemia or cancer. Schubert and Lapp cite other effects that have been observed in children irradiated before birth, including coordination defects, mongolism, skull malformations, cleft palate, club feet, genital deformities and general mental and physical subnormalities.

While the potential damage to children irradiated before birth is recognized and under investigation, the effects of irradiation upon the genetic materials of potential parents are relatively unknown. It is known, however, that radiation can alter the makeup of genetic cells and chromosomes, those hereditary patterns that pass on the determining characteristics of physique, health, and intelligence from generation to generation. It is known also that irradiation of sex cells of fruit flies and mice will produce mutations in succeeding generations. In the case of man, the need to study several generations and the complexity of human characteristics make definitive conclusions difficult.

Because man behaves genetically like the mouse, there is reason for concern and investigation. This is especially appropriate in a period of increased X-ray examination of potential parents, particularly so for males, as the male reproductive organs are more exposed to radiation, lacking the natural shielding afforded the female ovaries. In 1964 an estimated 60 percent of the total genetically significant dosage from medical examination was concentrated in males between the ages of fifteen and twenty-nine.

In the early years of this century, thousands of people in the United States actually ate or drank radium. Physicians prescribed and provided radium treatments for a host of problems. About 1903, small amounts of radioactivity were discovered in French and English waters. The radioactivity was found to be due to radon, a gaseous daughter of radium, and it was believed that the healing power ascribed to the drinking and bathing in the water of natural springs and spas was actually produced by radon. Radon drinking water became very popular.

Two doctors, writing in the *Journal of the American Medical Association* in 1913, summed up the results of radon use as unquestionably valuable in treating chronic and subacute arthritis of all kinds. Some physicians then began to inject radium itself into patients, and radium treatments were given for hypertension, acne, heart trouble, ulcers, gout, diabetes, mental disease, infected wounds and skin disorders.

The early 1920s brought the first reports of radium poisoning. Yet in the mid twenties a number of beauty shops in the United States began installing X-ray machines for the removal of superfluous hair. Some ambitious operators extended the treatment to acne and other skin ailments. The victims and the operators of the machines thought that the treatment was safe and successful, since there were no obvious harmful effects from the radiation. This use of X ray opened up a lucrative business opportunity, and firms sprang up all over the country catering to women who wanted hair removed permanently and painlessly from the face, legs, thighs and breasts.

Some of the operators knew the dangers of X rays but were unconcerned with the long-range effects. Still, a growing awareness among the public resulted in masking the X-ray treatment by calling it "short-wave treatment," "epilex ray," or "light treatment." Not until 1929 did publicity and action by the medical profession bring an end to the widespread use of the X ray for cosmetic purposes.

Although unprofessional use of radium and other cosmetic irradiation is on the wane, there are still cases of "quack" practices. In the early 1960s a supply of radium pills, powders and tablets was discovered in a Pennsylvania homeopathic laboratory, and in 1964 "Texas Cones," porous, cone-shaped casing containing a radioactive ore used in jugs of drinking water, were being used in the southwestern United States.

The medical caution *"Primum non nocere,"* or be sure that the cure is not worse than the disease, has also restricted the use of radium salt applicators in non-malignant cases and the use of therapeutic X rays by dermatologists, especially on children. In a 1967 professional textbook on dermatology, however, the potential dangers of radiation are cavalierly ignored in instructions to dermatologists on how to calibrate their X-ray machine. This involves creating an erythema, an abnormal redness of the skin. In the fifth edition of *X rays and Radium in the Treatment of Diseases of the Skin,* the dermatologist were advised:

In order to determine the erythema dose, the flexor surface of the dermatologist's forearm can be used as a test site. An opening 1 inch square is cut in a lead shield. The radiation used for this purpose should have a half-value layer between 0.5 and 1.0 mm Al. Three hundred roentgens are applied to one area, and 350 r to another on the same forearm. Three, five, seven, ten, fourteen and twenty days after irradiation the test areas are observed in daylight. Notes should be made regarding the time of the erythema's appearance, evolution and involution. Should no erythema be discernible in either exposed area, the test can be repeated using 375 and 400 r on two areas on the flexor surface of the other arm. Should the test site which received 300 r show severe erythema, 250 and 275 can be given to two areas on the flexor of the other arm. . . . While the erythema dose is far from precise, it is the best and most easily performed biological test that the dermatologist can make.

There are also scores of examples of the use of X rays as a novelty. The television program *Omnibus* once displayed a fluoroscopic study of a girl as she dabbed her lips with lipstick. Hildegard once bared her heart to the fluoroscope for the benefit of the Chicago Heart Fund while standing in the window of a Chicago Savings and Loan Association.

In some prisons and industrial plants fluoroscopes have been used to detect concealed items, weapons or pilfered items. Fluoroscopes and X-ray machines have also been used in post offices to examine packages and in conservation departments to identify banded animals. At one time, an estimated 10,000 fluoroscopes were used in shoe stores for fitting until gradually they were regulated or banned by state laws. The industrial use of X rays, or other radiation sources, to detect structural or product flaws is growing.

Sources of radiation in everyday life are on the increase and are not advertised or indicated as such to the general public. Each example may seem minor, but together they increase total exposure. One brand of everyday dishware used a uranium ore emitting a small amount of radiation to produce its distinctive orange glaze. A new kind of false dentures that is said to produce more natural-appearing teeth contains irradiated material. Smoke detectors used in public buildings and museums depend upon a radiation-emitting source for their detection function. The exit signs common in airplanes depend upon artificial radioactive isotopes to achieve their uninterrupted luminescence.

While the use of radium in luminous compounds for instrument dials has been replaced by less hazardous artificial radioactive isotopes such as tritium, the use of these isotopes is increasing, both in number and variety of products. None of the luminous uses of the radionuclides represents a significant radiation hazard under normal use. If too many of these devices — watch dials, instrument faces, house numbers, light switches, and so forth — are warehoused in one location, however, a hazard may develop. Further, final disposal of increasing sources of radiation-emitting materials presents another problem.

The increased use of high-voltage electron tubes in electronic equipment also presents a growing source of possible irradiation in educational institutions and in the home. Electron microscopes and their power supplies, as well as transmitting tubes such as those used in commercial and some amateur radio transmitters, can emit X rays. The most common source of possible irradiation in the home from a high voltage electron source is color television. In 1967, over 150,000 color television sets were checked in private homes or recalled because of excessive irradiation.

Experts estimate that the dose from man-produced ionizing radiation in populations of technologically developed countries has, in recent years, approximately equaled the doses received from natural sources at sea level. Most of this has resulted from the use of X rays in medical and dental practice with a somewhat smaller component due to fallout from nuclear weapons and a growing component due to occupational exposure.

Automatic collimation, fast film, gonadal shieldings and better trained technicians could be large factors in the limiting of patient exposure in medical and dental practice. These are physical improvements in the amount of each exposure. The greatest problem, however, is judging the proper number of exposures per patient. Today the demands of lawsuits, workmen's compensation requirements, industrial personnel policies, a transient population, inadequate records, and difficulties in transferring previous X-ray films have all caused unnecessary X-ray examinations. Today's patients are receiving more exposure to radiation and X-ray exposures than they need for their immediate health and future welfare. The X-ray examination is not a panacea. It must be used with a regard to the consequences of misuse.

Although 90 percent of the exposure to man-made X rays now occurs in medical and dental practice, the remaining 10 percent cannot be ignored. Non-medical applications of radiation are growing in industry, commerce and research. Industrial X-ray machines, particle accelerators, Van de Graaff generators, flash X-ray units, well-logging devices, and neutron generators all are finding greater use in industry. Experiments are underway to use ionizing radiation from machines or radioisotopes to preserve fresh foods for the commercial market, which, if successful, can multiply the number of industrial radiation sources and the size of individual X-ray machines.

The National Center for Radiological Health estimates that there are some 150 particle accelerators, 150 neutron generators, 400 Van de Graaff accelerators and 10,000 industrial X-ray machines in use in industry training and research. In the past five years about 8,000 X-ray tubes have been sold for non-medical equipment. Other data indicate that sales of industrial X-ray equipment is increasing at about 10 percent annually. About 20,000 people use this equipment and may be exposed in their occupations.

Man's genius for technological innovation makes it difficult to predict all the sources from which radiation may come in the years ahead. But there is enough experimentation today to indicate uses that can be expected to proliferate in the future. Propulsion is a case in point. Already there exist practical demonstrations of the use of nuclear power to propel ships — both surface and subsurface. There is extensive experimentation underway on the development of atomic-powered airplanes, locomotives and automobiles. These possibilities raise serious questions of public safety.

Land propulsion by nuclear power is the area of greatest concern. Vehicles so powered would operate in metropolitan areas. How will the reactors be encased? What will be the effect of jostling, jars, shocks, vibrations, and the stop and go of motion? What will happen should a collision occur? If the

[265]

fuel box were torn open, radioactive debris could be spread into the atmosphere. The entire vehicle, the ground and things in the surrounding area could be seriously contaminated. A single accident in a metropolitan area could have severe consequences.

There would also be a public danger from nuclear-powered aircraft. The power plant would be located near the tail of the craft to conserve space. The reactor would have to be as compact as possible. Yet a reactor for an atomic airplane would generate as much radioactivity as a nuclear power plant for a good-sized city. This means that in a period of time, the aircraft reactor would build up fission products with the radioactive equivalent of many tons of radium. Should such a plane crash, the radioactive contamination of the local atmosphere would be devastating.

Since nuclear energy already is used for propelling ships, it is reasonable to expect the development of medium-sized vessels powered by nuclear reactors delivering about 20,000 shaft horsepower to the ships' screws. The development of supertankers will require a much more powerful plant, possibly equal to that required to supply a fair-sized city with electrical power. The radioactive danger to metropolitan areas from ships is small compared to land and air transport, since most of the operation of the ship's reactor would be at sea. Still, there could be an accident in port, since it is unlikely that auxiliary power would be used at dockside, and so the reactor would be far from shut down.

The term "radioactive" creates substantially greater fear among the public than the term "chemical contaminant." The specter of nuclear accident, injury, or disease from irradiation is frightening, but there are a Federal Radiation Council, a Center for Radiological Health in the Public Health Service, and the Atomic Energy Commission all working extensively to guard against accident or injury from atomic causes. However, the average person today comes into far more contact with chemical contaminants than he does with irradiation, despite the multiplication of X-ray equipment and other radiation sources.

The problem of chemical contaminants in the environment is quite different from the problem of radioactive material. The toxicity of a chemical or compound exists only under certain conditions. Thus in one circumstance a chemical substance may be more toxic if inhaled than if touched. A radioactive element, on the other hand, is toxic under all conditions.

Man can be exposed to chemical agents which may prove harmful through dusts, fumes, mists, vapors and gases, where he works or where he lives. The exposure may be through inhalation, ingestion, or absorption. These toxic chemicals may produce a variety of diseases. Toxic dusts are known to have produced pneumoconiosis, systemic poisoning, dermatosis of an allergic nature, and cancer.

The lack of knowledge of effects of toxic dusts and fumes is an even greater worry. During the past few years, intermetallic compounds have become important because of their unusual thermo-electric properties. One of these, bismuth telluride, is a material used in the manufacture of refrigeration equipment. The manufacture and production of components made from bismuth telluride expose workers to the dust and fumes of these substances. Exposure may occur as a result of machining, etching, polishing or heating to high temperatures. However, the knowledge of the manner in which bismuth telluride affects workers exposed to this compound is limited.

Recently, electronic devices such as photocells, thermistors, transistors, solar cells and radiation detectors have become important in industry. Another intermetallic compound, indium antimonide, is used in the production of these components.

Knowledge of how indium antimonide affects workers handling the compound is almost nonexistent. Exposure to the compound comes from handling it and from dust and fumes given off in its processing.

Recent studies of atmospheric lead have raised a controversy over its effect on health. Some studies have indicated a rising level of lead accumulated in the body of workers but still below the blood levels associated with clinical lead poisoning. However, there is extensive difference among experts as to the margin between average levels of lead in the population and levels known to be harmful.

The 1965 report of the President's Science Advisory Committee, "Restoring the Quality of our Environment," notes that no baseline data on body burdens of lead were obtained before leaded gasoline came into general use in the 1920s. A growing body of experts, however, believes that discharges of lead into the atmosphere from the combustion of leaded gasoline in autos is an unnecessary threat to human health. One thing is certain: no one knows the long-term effects such atmospheric contaminants have on human beings.

No one knows for certain the health problems caused by used asbestos or asbestos-like materials, but a growing body of experts indicates that it is substantial. Since the turn of the century the inhaling by asbestos workers of asbestos fibers or bodies has been linked with a variety of disabling or fatal lung diseases, of which pneumoconiosis and lung cancer are the most serious. The association between the inhalation of asbestos dust and disease — in this case, asbestosis — was first made in England in 1907. It was not until the late 1930s that mention was made of lung cancer in connection with asbestos dust, and the first reports of tumors were published in 1955.

The common assumption concerning asbestos inhalation and disease was that it was, first of all, an industrial or occupational problem associated with asbestos textile manufacturing, or asbestos mining, milling, and processing operations. Secondly, it was generally assumed that the asbestos fiber was causing lung disease. Recent studies, however, indicate that the problem may be much more extensive. These investigations indicate that hazards to health may occur to large segments of the population who experience low-level exposure to asbestos dust. Also, experimental exposures of asbestos workers revealed other materials in addition to the asbestos fiber which might act as a cause of disease.

In the early 1900s it was known that asbestos minerals contained other materials, particularly small amounts of metal. The health significance of these metals, however, was not recognized at that time. Subsequently, studies were made to determine the role of these metals when inhaled along with asbestos fibers. The metals can be present as independent minerals in asbestos ore or as alloy metals associated with the ore. They can form a part of the crystalline structure of asbestos textile fibers, or they may be released as particulate matter into the air through the abrasions in the processing of asbestos.

A 1967 study by scientists at the U.S. Public Health Service's National Center for Urban and Industrial Health, entitled "Exposure to Metals in the Manufacture of Asbestos Textile Products," found that asbestos-textile workers processing chrysotile ore were exposed to significant airborne levels of nickel, chromium, and manganese as well as other metals. This study indicated that exposure to metals in airborne dusts was likely in the other phases of asbestos operations from mining the ore to milling and processing, and concluded that scientists looking at the relationship between asbestos fibers or bodies in human tissues and disease must also consider the role of metals as a causative agent.

Hospital autopsies in a number of cities have found that the occurrence of fibrous bodies in lungs is increasing. These fibers were routinely considered to be asbestos bodies because of their structure. Now they are referred to as "ferruginous" bodies, and in addition to being present in increasing numbers are also being found in the lungs of urban residents who are not generally associated with the asbestos industry and who come from general urban areas rather than certain isolated localities. It is also known that there are low levels of asbestos dust and other types of dust in the urban communities of the industrialized societies of the Western world. The wearing away of asbestos brake linings, clutch facings, and building materials has contributed to these levels.

Studies in the 1960s have reported the presence of asbestos bodies or asbestos-like bodies in 28 percent of persons autopsied in Miami, Florida, and 41 percent in Pittsburgh, Pennsylvania. While the dangers of dusts to industrial workers are known, so far it is not certain that such low-level urban exposures constitute a health hazard to the general public. Dr. Harriet L. Hardy, Assistant Medical Director of Occupational Medical Services of the Massachusetts Institute of Technology, speaking to an environmental study committee in 1967, said that studies of asbestos, beryllium, and manganese exposure in areas around great smelters appear to indicate a higher than normal incidence of lung malignancy in the residents living in these areas. She went on to say that this has been kept under wraps partly because of the tremendous litigation that might arise.

Problems of toxicity or allergin reaction in the skin, involving use of chemicals or exotic metals, can jump up almost any place. Waterless cleaners are made for rapidly removing greasy dirt from the skin without using water. These cleaners are particularly of value in many industrial operations where water is difficult to obtain. There is nothing new about the waterless cleaner. Auto mechanics and painters used crude paste-like or liquid products, containing petroleum solvents, twenty-five years ago.

In the early 1950s an outbreak of dermatitis affecting 55 workers in one plant was found to be caused by a waterless cleaner. As a result, many companies were reluctant to continue using the cleaners. The obvious convenience of these cleaners, however, made them increasingly popular in industry, offices, and at home, despite the reported dermatological effects. A 1957 study of waterless cleaners by the Occupational Health Program of the U.S. Public Health Service indicated that 11 of 15 cleaners tested were satisfactory while the other 4 were considered inferior, and that cleaners classed as wetting agents were found to be preferable to those classed as solvent types.

In 1883 it was discovered that a heavy stream of water directed at the cutting edge of a tool would permit an increase in cutting speed. Subsequently, carbonate of soda was added to the cutting fluids to prevent rust. Later, cutting oils were made by mixing soap with mineral or coal tar oils. Today, cutting oils are perfumed and pastel-tinted emulsifiable oils with a water-base synthetic or chemical coolant. Even with this sophisticated formulation, dermatitis from these cutting and grinding fluids continues to be a problem.

Skin problems occur also from the manufacture of plastics. This was observed almost as soon as the industry began. Phenol, urea, formaldehyde, and hexamethylenetetramine were the chemicals first used in making synthetic resins, and these were shown to be dermatitis producers. Later, almost every new plastic such as styrene, alkyd, melamine, acrylic, and poly-vinyl became associated with outbreaks of dermatitis in their respective industries.

With the introduction of epoxy or epoxide resins in American industry, an opportunity has been afforded to observe many cases of dermatitis due to handling of these resins and their amine hardeners. The epoxies have become commonplace in many United States manufacturing plants and in many homes. They are used widely in electrical equipment manufacturing, in automobile appliances, in surface coatings, and as adhesives in aircraft plants. Some epoxy resins are irritants and sensitizers, or both, but the major problem in handling these materials occurs from the dye or amine curing agents, which are, for the most part, also irritants and sensitizers.

In industrial chemical usage, difficulties can sometimes emerge in a most unusual way. In 1963, a leaking drum of a highly toxic phosphate pesticide, phosdin, contaminated a shipment of boys' blue jeans during transit. When the unwashed jeans were worn, the pesticide in the fabric was readily absorbed through the skin and six boys were poisoned, two of them seriously.

Occupational disease is an ever-present adversary on the farm as well as in industry. For the most part, the tools, the chemicals and the metals are the same as in industry. In industry, petroleum products, cement, solvents, fiber glass, plastic and infectious agents are the most frequently reported causes of skin diseases. Most of these agents are common to the farm as well.

On the farm, however, the problem can sometimes go a step further. Recent studies indicate that harvesting celery has been associated with the development of skin eruptions. It was found that diseased celery contained a phototoxic material which is highly reactive on human skin.

U.S. Public Health Service researchers found that among fibrous bodies in the lungs of persons recently autopsied in hospitals in a number of cities, there was a significant percentage identified as coming from talcum powder. The Service then undertook a 1968 study with twenty-two cosmetic talcum products, including body powders, bath powders and all-purpose

[272]

powders, to analyze their fibrous content. They found that all the twenty-two products analyzed had an appreciable fiber content ranging from 8 to 30 percent of the total talcum particulates. The average was 19 percent. The fibrous material was predominantly talc, but contained minor amounts of tremolite, anthophyllite, and chrysotile as well. Four of the twenty-two products analyzed showed sufficiently high levels of silica, chromium, and nickel to raise a concern about their potential contribution to disease.

Castor oil is used in the manufacture of paints, enamels, plastics, and plasticizers and specialized lubricants. It is extracted from the castor bean. After the oil is taken from the castor bean, there remains what is called a castor bean pomace. This is used as a component of fertilizers, since it is an excellent source of nitrogen, phosphorus, and potassium. It is also an excellent source of toxic and allergenic substances not present in the oil. In workers or those coming in contact with the pomace, it sometimes results in symptoms including irritation of the nose, eyes, and throat, asthma, chills, fever, nausea, vomiting, muscular aching, weakness and headaches. While outbreaks can be controlled through proper usage, in 1958 and 1959 several occurred in Eastern seaports. In one instance at least one hundred twelve men were affected.

The isocyanates are one of the two principal ingredients used in the manufacture of polyurethane plastics. This industry has been rapidly expanding during the past ten years and produces lacquers, fibers, and foam plastics. When the isocyanates are mixed with resins to make polyurethane foams, carbon dioxide is liberated. The gas is trapped within the plastic, producing the foam. The physical properties of the foam are determined by the specific chemicals used and the proportions in which they are mixed. The most commonly used isocyanate is toluenediisocyanate, commonly referred to as TDI. At the same time that TDI has wide use in the manufacture of polyurethane foams, it is reported to cause asthmatic symptoms in man, and ulcerated bronchitis and pneumonia in experimental animals.

Problems from toxic chemicals have been with us for some time. Even the difficulties arising from the use of various kinds of common metals in various forms have been known for many years. Now intermetallic products and some more exotic trace metals used in advanced technology have opened up new possibilities of danger. However, the newest and probably the most extensive products of technology to be affecting man in the future are the microwave and the laser.

For some time microwaves have been used in communication. Now they are increasingly being used as a prime source of heat. Since 1945, when it was discovered that microwaves from a laboratory radar device could pop corn in a paper bag, the idea of using this form of electromagnetic energy to cook or heat food has received growing interest. Commercial models of microwave ovens are now in use in many industrial and institutional areas to heat sandwiches, sweet rolls, soup or similar items, or to thaw and heat precooked frozen meals. Already, microwave ovens are being manufactured, advertised and sold for home kitchen or patio use.

The properties of microwaves which make them useful to cook or heat food, however, can also create a health hazard. Microwave energy, similar to the energy propagated by radar installations, has been found to be capable of producing several types of reactions when absorbed by the human tissue. Basically, the microwave energy is converted to heat, and if the organ or tissue absorbing this energy cannot dissipate the heat generated, a biological reaction will take place. Unlike the normal gas or electric range there is no warning surface burn — deeper tissue damage already has occurred.

[274]

An example of this is the development of cataracts in eyes exposed to microwave beams. The source of a microwave in an oven is the magnetron located within the casing of the oven. The microwaves are produced and directed toward the cooking area where the food is to be heated. The entire unit is enclosed in a metal cabinet, and safety devices are generally put on the doors to prevent them from being operated unless the door or outer casing is closed.

Problems have been noted from two sources. One is the leakage of microwaves through worn-out or missing door seals. Surveys have indicated that many units in use today have faulty door seals. The other danger is that the safety interlocks can be jumped and the ovens operated with the outer casing of the oven removed. A 1968 Public Health Service survey shows that in order for repairmen to test microwave ovens, they have to place their faces and bodies close to the energized magnetron. Eight repairmen were examined and found to have side-effects of radiation from microwave ovens, including cataracts and thermal damage to the skin and even deeper.

A recent survey on lasers, only partially completed, showed that some 9,400 units had been manufactured and distributed in this country. Lasers in industry are used for measuring or alignment, and for drilling or cutting. The low-level lasers, generally used for alignment, are green to red in color. High-intensity lasers, invisible to the eye, can be detected only through the patterns they cut.

Lasers are easy to make and have already shown up in some home workshops. The future is expected to see substantially more lasers used in home workshops for cutting and drilling. They are also being used to take three-dimensional pictures, and their use is expected to increase for that purpose. An automatic laser can-opener is also predicted for home kitchen

[275]

use. Much of the anticipated health hazards due to lasers will come from inexpert knowledge and inappropriate use of the laser.

Lasers promise to be of meaningful medical value. At the same time, what can be of great value if properly used can be quite hazardous if used indiscriminately. While medicine has used the laser to fuse a detached retina into place, improper use can cause extensive eye damage. On record already is the case of an optometrist in Illinois who routinely uses lasers to examine people's eyes. Another example is a San Francisco salesman who demonstrated lasers by indiscriminately bouncing the beams off store walls in the presence of customers.

One of the newest devices for advanced technological production is the plasma torch, a device that has the ability to develop extremely high temperatures and is expected to be used increasingly in industry. Plasma is defined as the state of matter in which the individual atoms are separated into free electrons and positive ions. The glowing area of an electric arc is a man-made plasma. True plasmas, those in which complete ionization occurs, exist only at extreme temperatures. Since they will vaporize any known material, the plasmas cannot be contained within any device for unlimited periods of time.

Increased use of the plasma torch will mean that a large number of workers and individuals will be exposed to potential health hazards. Noise exposures encountered in cutting operations will increase. Investigations of other potential hazards associated with the plasma torch operation should include the exposure to ozone, to oxides of nitrogen, to particulates and radiant energy. The atmospheric contaminants, generated by plasma torch operation, do not differ greatly from those generated from more common metal-cutting or metalizing operations, and can be controlled by proper ventilation and masking. However, new types of contaminants with unknown toxicities may be generated. The possibility of X-radiation must also be considered with the plasma torch. There have been incidents of sunburn or severe reaction to exposure on covered parts of the body. Exposures to unprotected parts for only a few seconds have resulted in severe effects under certain conditions of operation.

Carbides, oxides, and borides; new intermetallic compounds and ceramics; titanium and magnesium nitrates; new compounds of gases; radiation, microwaves, plasma torches, and lasers; this is the stuff that tomorrow is made of. These and other things currently known and unknown will be the tools and props for the future. If the past is any measure, the speed with which these exotic devices and materials will come into common usage will accelerate at an ever-increasing rate. New discoveries will compound the influx of items to live with, work with — do almost everything with.

The question will be: what do these new "things" do to human health, either individually or in combination? The problems of crowding, of pollution of lakes, of the manufacture of electricity with nuclear fuel all become complicated by man's constant seeking to improve the ease with which he conducts his life. Unfortunately, what may seem to be the easiest way today may turn out tomorrow to be the most injurious — to living men and to their children.

12

DISPOSING OF LIQUIDS

Late in November 1963, from the northern border of Louisiana to the tidal waters at the mouth of the Mississippi River, great numbers of many varieties of fish were discovered to be dead or dying. Catfish, drum, buffalo and shad were turning belly-up in the fresh water portions of the river while whole schools of menaden, mullet, sea trout and marine catfish died in the brackish waters near the Gulf of Mexico. At that time the number of fish estimated by the state of Louisiana to have been killed was over 5 million — the most since 1960, when an estimated 3.6 million fish had been killed. Massive fish kills on the Lower Mississippi River had been observed annually in Louisiana from 1960 to 1963 and recorded by the State Wildlife and Fisheries Commission, but the November 1963 kill report was unusually severe.

In one 8-mile stretch of the Mississippi near Baton Rouge, thousands of fish were seen at the surface of the river, unable to maintain an upright position and often convulsing frantically. The abdomens of nearly all the fish were distended, and examination showed that the stomachs and intestines of the

[278]

fish were devoid of food material and filled with gas and frothy liquid. Many of the fish that were observed displayed areas of hemorrhaging on the skin and internal organs.

In the investigation following this massive fish kill, the state of Louisiana and the United States Public Health Service reviewed the kinds and quantities of pollutants being dumped into the Mississippi. It was known that no major city on the river below Minneapolis and St. Paul had proper sewage treatment plants. Baton Rouge had primary treatment, but such major cities as St. Louis, Memphis, Vicksburg, Natchez and New Orleans allowed raw sewage to be dumped directly into the Mississippi without any treatment at all. In the four lowest states on the river — Tennessee, Arkansas, Mississippi and Louisiana — almost 90 percent of the wastes collected by sewer systems were dumped into the river without any treatment.

In 1963, New Orleans, dependent solely upon the Mississippi River for its supply of drinking water, was the third largest city in the country that did not provide even elementary treatment for its sewage. Every day, the raw wastes collected from the 840,000 people served by sewers in New Orleans were returned to the river. In the four states of the Lower Mississippi Basin almost one and one half million people were being served by sewers leading directly to the Mississippi. One hundred percent of the population served by sewers along the river in Tennessee and Mississippi dumped their sewage in the river without any treatment. In the states of the Lower Mississippi River Basin, 1,135,000 persons drew their municipal water supplies from the Mississippi. One million of this number were in Louisiana.

A 1963 report to the New Orleans Sewerage and Water Board analyzed the results of tests for bacterial pollution and the amount of oxygen dissolved in the water at various water supply intakes above and below New Orleans, including the intakes for the city itself. The report stated, "Tests show that the degree of pollution is increasing to the extent that it is endangering the water supply of the communities below the city and at times of the city itself." The tests indicated that "the dissolved oxygen content of the river's water at the Carrollton intake . . . at times barely meets the Southwest Mississippi Basin standard." As for the coliform bacteria content, the report added "much of the time this water does not meet the Southwest Mississippi standard."

Downstream from New Orleans the situation was far worse. At the St. Bernard water intake several miles downstream from the major New Orleans raw sewage outfall, tests showed very large concentrations of coliform bacteria. Large floating solids occasionally observed in the sedimentation basins of the St. Bernard water purification works were believed to be from sewers.

In spite of the indications of large bacterial contaminations in the water, sewage pollution of the Mississippi was not held responsible for the massive fish kills in the fall of 1963, and the search turned elsewhere. The investigation next focused upon industrial pollutants.

In the four states of the lower Mississippi there were sixty-two industrial plants discharging wastes to the Mississippi, all involved with a variety of products and processes: chemicals, metals, fertilizers, wood products, paper, vegetable oils, tires, textiles, petroleum, pesticides, cane sugar, petroleum, meat, cement, and, in Louisiana particularly, petrochemicals and synthetic chemicals. There are two heavily industrialized areas on the Lower Mississippi River; one is the stretch between Baton Rouge and New Orleans, and the other centers about Memphis, Tennessee.

At the time of the kills the Velsicol Corporation was a major producer of the powerful agricultural pesticide Endrin. Investigation of the Velsicol plant and the surrounding area indicated that Endrin was being discharged into the Mississippi River through solid and liquid waste disposal from the plant, and further investigation revealed Endrin in concentration in the Mississippi River below Memphis and in the water supplies of Vicksburg, Mississippi and New Orleans.

Laboratory studies of the dead fish revealed that Endrin was present in the blood of dying Mississippi catfish in concentrations equal to or higher than in fish of the same species that were killed in controlled laboratory exposures. The symptoms were identical in the dying fish in both the river and the laboratory, and the kidney damage found in the river fish was similar to kidney damage recognized to be caused by chlorinated hydrocarbons like the pesticide Endrin.

It was believed that the extensive use of Endrin in the sugar-cane regions of the delta could have contributed to the concentration of Endrin found in the river and in the bodies of the dead fish, and that surface run-off and sedimentation could have carried residues of Endrin into the surrounding waters and contributed to the acute toxicity.

Endrin is a particularly powerful chlorinated hydrocarbon created by the chemical industry as an agricultural pesticide. It is very toxic in relatively small concentrations and difficult to detect through normal analytical methods. But since no acute reactions occurred in humans because of the presence of the small quantities of Endrin in the water of the Mississippi used for municipal water supplies, its tolerance levels and the long-range effects of human ingestion or continuing contact with small dosages of the pesticide were not precisely established.

Sophisticated analytical methods are required for the detection of the presence of the wide variety of organic chemicals such as Endrin which are produced by the petrochemical and synthetic chemical industries. More importantly, and in addition to the difficulties in monitoring the presence of these chemicals in municipal water supplies, present methods of water treatment cannot remove them from water intended for human consumption. Such being the case, chemical pollutants, known to be dangerous to aquatic life, present a threat of unknown potential to human health.

Future projections for the Lower Mississippi Valley predict great expansion of the chemical industries and an increase in agricultural intensity with chemical usage. At the same time greater demands for human consumption will be made upon the waters of the Mississippi. Under these conditions the likelihood of exposure to chemical pollution will be increased.

Further development of the Lower Mississippi is recognized to be dependent upon the continued supply of water in a quantity and quality which would support multiple uses. The quantity of river flow is relatively finite and fixed. The quality of the Mississippi River will vary according to the type and quantity of waste placed on it. In a period of population growth and industrial expansion the waste load will increase, and the capacity of the river to dilute the effluents will diminish if the traditional methods of waste disposal are continued.

More than just the states bordering the Mississippi River are affected. The river is the nation's largest drainage ditch. A drop of rain falls in western New York. Several thousand miles away snowflakes settle on the mountains of Montana. In thirty-one states and two provinces of Canada such raindrops and melting snow soon become a trickle of running water beginning the long, slow return journey to the sea. Growing into rivers, the water courses toward the main stem of the world's fourth largest water basin — the Mississippi River. Running for 2,350 miles through the mid-section of America, all the way from northern Minnesota to the Gulf of Mexico, the Mississippi receives the run-off water and the wastes from an area covering over 1,245,000 square miles and collects the flows from several major tributaries — the Missouri, Ohio, Arkansas, and Red rivers — mixing waters which can have originated as far apart as four thousand miles.

By the time the Mississippi River reaches Louisiana and the last several hundred miles before the delta and the Gulf of Mexico, it is flowing at a rate which normally ranges between 300,000 and 1 million cubic feet per second. Even when the flow is lowest, the Mississippi delivers approximately 100,000 cubic feet of water per second in its final stages, and at maximum flood level the volume may be twenty times as great. The volume of water which the Mississippi carries through the state of Louisiana is so large that a system of protective levees and dikes make the river a walled corridor. In addition to leveed containment, portions of the Mississippi are diverted to the Atchafalaya River and the Bayou Lafourche to help control and disperse the tremendous flow of collected water.

Blessed with an abundance of local rainfall and a relatively high water table, the state of Louisiana is classified as water-rich. It is the continuing use of the Mississippi River, however, that has been the greatest single factor influencing the growth, development, and expansion of Louisiana and the Lower Mississippi Valley. In 1803 the Louisiana Purchase removed international legal obstacles blocking commerce on the river, and the development of the steamboat in the 1830s opened up the length of the Mississippi Valley and the middle third of the United States to navigation, exploration, development, and commercial expansion. This also turned New Orleans into one of this country's major seaports.

Louisiana has experienced a second period of rapid growth and development since World War II. Between 1940 and 1960 the population of the state increased by some 38 percent. The major portion of this expansion occurred in the parishes through which the Mississippi flows in the final segment of its trip from Baton Rouge to the gulf, and the growth was facilitated by the capacity of the Mississippi to provide municipal water supplies and to flush away municipal wastes.

During the same period, and in the same river area, Louisiana also experienced accelerated industrial growth, which was led by the development of new petrochemical plants along the 140-mile stretch of the Mississippi between Baton Rouge and New Orleans. Since the end of World War II, over three and one-half billion dollars in new industry has been built along the river to capitalize upon Louisiana's rich resources of salt, sulfur, gas, and Mississippi River water — needed by the chemical industry for cooling, for use in processing, for steam generation, and for waste disposal.

In addition to the newer, burgeoning chemical industries, the Mississippi River supports more traditional agricultural, processing and manufacturing industries in Louisiana — sugar cane growing and processing, vegetable canning, pulp and paper manufacture — and, in the mouth and delta areas, one of the country's most productive seafood industries. The large flow of fresh water from the Mississippi through the delta flushes the estuarial waters and dilutes the salinity of the tidal area, creating the conditions necessary for the breeding and the harvesting of shellfish.

Due to the vast quantities of water transported by the Mississippi through Louisiana, future expectations are for continued population growth and industrial expansion. The United States Water Resources Council recently conducted a nationwide survey of America's water resources and future requirements, and in viewing the Lower Mississippi Region the council reported in its 1968 summary that this region ". . . occupies a strategic area in the development of the nation's economy. Industry and commerce are expected to become increasingly attracted to the area because of the enormous capacity of the Mississippi River to satisfy water supply, navigation, and waste disposal requirements. Municipal growth and the development of a highly complex and intensive agricultural industry will also contribute to the region's economic growth."

By the time the waters of the Mississippi, in the flow from western New York and the mountains of Montana, reach the major industrial and population area of Louisiana, they contain not only all the water which nature has added in the long journey but also the accumulated wastes and effluents which nature and man, his communities and his industrial activities, have dumped into the river along the way. While the volume of water collected within the Mississippi River Basin and its tributary collection branches has remained constant, human activity along the length of the river has continually multiplied and become more complex. Not only are the wastes which man introduces to the Mississippi drainage ditch constantly increasing with the growth of municipalities and industry, but the effluents are becoming more varied and more complex as modern industry, producing multitudes of synthetic chemicals and sophisticated products, lines the Mississippi River shoreline.

Residents of the Lower Mississippi River area don't need a crystal ball to see what their area will look like if the present trend continues. They need only look to the densely populated New York metropolitan area. There, all that can be done to degrade a river has been done. Only seventy-four years before LaSalle traveled the Mississippi, Henry Hudson sailed his ship *Half Moon* in from the Atlantic through what was to become New York Harbor and 150 miles up the river that bears his name to the point where Albany is now situated. In that year, 1609, the fresh water flow of the Hudson and its main

[285]

tributary, the Mohawk, was relatively clear and uniform in rate throughout the year, the floods were not as great, the low water was not as low, there was less surface run-off and more seepage due to the forest conditions in the watershed, the water was cooler, and the dissolved oxygen content of the waters approached saturation most of the time.

In these waters thrived shad, striped bass, herring, catfish, and carp. Through the late 1800s the abundant sea sturgeon and short-nosed sturgeon provided the basis for a large commercial fishery; sturgeon weighing as much as 300 pounds were reported in the upper stretches of the river and were referred to as "Albany beef." The estuarial waters of the lower Hudson from above the New York City line throughout the lower bay area supported a wide variety of shellfish. Oysters, crabs, and clams could be found in the last miles of the river, and large catches of lobster were made from piers on Staten Island.

In the more than three hundred fifty years since Henry Hudson's trip, this area has grown to be the center of the country's most highly developed urban-commercial complex. At the mouth of the Hudson River over fourteen million people are concentrated in the New York City–Northeastern New Jersey metropolitan area. Clustered in communities along the banks of the upper Hudson are more than a million more people, with a major population center in the Albany-Troy-Rensselaer region.

In the area surrounding the last few miles of the Hudson as it runs along the Palisades into New York Harbor is the nation's leading port and harbor complex, with over 30,000 ships a year arriving and departing, loading and unloading their cargoes at the more than 200 piers along the 650 miles of waterfront. A center for the world's financial and trade transactions, New York–Northeastern New Jersey has developed a tremendous industrial capacity — oil refineries, manufacturing operations, processing plants, and shipyards. More than 50,000 manufacturing plants representing over 90 percent of more than 400 types of manufacturing industries listed by the Federal Bureau of Census employ several million people in this area.

In a Conference on the Pollution of the Interstate Waters of the Hudson River and its Tributaries, New York Governor Nelson A. Rockefeller described the present condition of the river from Albany to the ocean.

The river from Troy to the south of Albany is one great septic tank that has been rendered nearly useless for water supply, for swimming, or to support the rich fish life that once abounded there. The Hudson suffers intermittent contamination as it flows south of Albany, and by the time it reaches New York City it is heavily polluted. In New York Harbor, pollution harms commercial fishing, ruins swimming, spoils boating, impairs the industrial uses of water and presents an ugly affront to the nose and eye.

At the time of the 1965 Conference, New York City was experiencing a serious four-year drought affecting the entire northeastern United States and requiring imposition of emergency measures and water rationing. As this drought reached crisis proportions in the New York metropolitan area, the waters of the Hudson, virtually the only source of fresh water entering the New York Harbor complex, floated mockingly by New York City, dumping a daily average of 11 billion gallons into the ocean. The waters of the lower Hudson could not be used to quench New York City's thirst, primarily because of the level of pollution.

In 1964 several children spied a watermelon floating in the river in New York Harbor at One-twenty-fifth Street. After fishing the watermelon out of the river they took it home, washed it, and ate it. A short time later, eight of these children came down with typhoid fever, which was traced back to the watermelon and to the polluted waters of the Hudson.

[287]

Three years before that incident an outbreak of hepatitis occurred throughout the country. Substantial numbers of hepatitis cases were traced to raw clams taken from Raritan Bay, a triangular-shaped body of water south of Staten Island at the mouth of the Hudson straddling the New York–New Jersey border. On May 1, 1961, the New Jersey State Department of Health issued a press release which stated that,

> Dr. Roscoe P. Kandle, State Commissioner of Health, closed the New Jersey–controlled portions of Raritan Bay and Sandy Hook Bay and also the Navesink and Shrewsbury Rivers to the taking of shellfish.
> Dr. Kandle said of 186 hepatitis cases who had a history of eating raw clams in one or two restaurants, 85 are known to have eaten raw clams traced to Raritan Bay.
> In the face of this and other evidence, I have no alternative except to close the indicated areas to the taking of shellfish until further notice.

The state of New York subsequently closed the shellfish beds in the New York portion of Raritan Bay as a result of studies indicating pollution of the clam-growing beds. A later study disclosed that coliform bacteria concentrations on the order of 20,000 per hundred milliliters and high numbers of fecal coliform and fecal streptococci were pouring out of New York Harbor through the Narrows and into Raritan Bay.

The spread of pollution from the Hudson to the outer harbors and bays has occurred in steady increments over the years. Commercial fishing in the river for shad and other fish has been declining steadily since 1945. Pollution has either killed off the fish populations or tainted their flesh so badly that they are unmarketable. In the lower stretches of the river through the densely populated portions of New Jersey and New York, swimming has been closed because of the fouled water conditions. The last beach that operated just north of the George

Washington Bridge on the New Jersey shore was closed in the 1930s because of pollution. Swimming below that point is not authorized. Local crabs and lobsters have been off the market for years because of tainted flesh and coatings of oil.

From Albany to the ocean the Hudson has been considered an integral part of municipal sewer systems. A 1965 Public Health Service Report indicated that at that time the Hudson received the sewage loading equivalent to the waste from ten million people. In the last 150 miles of the river there were 48 discharges of municipal wastes directly to the stream, and there were 26 discharges to tributaries throughout the entire length which affected the main stream. In 1965 twenty-four communities discharged raw sewage to the Hudson without any treatment at all. New York City alone contributed the raw sewage of four million people to the waters immediately surrounding it to join with the multitude of industrial wastes that swirl back and forth with the tidal currents under the noses of the most densely populated portion of the country, making the lower Hudson the largest cesspool in the country.

Several thousand miles west of New York the population density is a fraction of that in the nation's largest urban area. But the water supply available in the western portion of the United States is also only a fraction of that available on the East Coast.

In Colorado, New Mexico, Arizona, California, Nevada, Wyoming, and Utah the waters of the Colorado River are jealously fought for and coveted. With an economy based upon manufacturing, tourism, irrigated farming and livestock, the dependable water supply in the Lower Colorado region at present is inadequate to satisfy the requirements of the existing economy. In 1968 the United States Water Resources Council reported that in this region groundwater resources were being depleted, that all dependable and readily available surface-water resources were fully utilized, and that projected economic growth indicated that the present water-supply deficiency would increase in the coming years.

During the late 1940s major expansion of the uranium milling industry began and the production peak was reached in the late 1950s and early 1960s. Some of the larger deposits of uranium ore were found in the Colorado River Basin, and at one time twelve uranium processing mills and five uranium concentrators were in operation. At the height of production in 1961 mills and processing plants on the Colorado were producing one-third of the uranium ore processed in the United States.

In the extraction of uranium from its ore quantities of liquid and solid wastes are produced. In the mid fifties, disposal of the liquid and solid wastes from the uranium concentration process was very simple. They were dumped in a convenient nearby stream. In most cases the stream was either the Colorado itself or one of its tributaries.

Subsequently it was discovered that, in addition to creating the more conventional pollution problems associated with the transfer of wastes to the river, about 85 percent of the original radioactivity of the uranium ore was being transferred with the liquid and solid wastes into the waters of the Colorado. Studies conducted at this time showed that radium, the most dangerous radioactive isotope involved, was present in the waters below several uranium mills in concentrations considerably greater than those regarded as safe at that time.

In addition to the dissolved radioactive daughters of uranium, large deposits of radium-bearing uranium mill tailings in solid form were found to be building up along some stream beds. Because of the long period of radioactivity — radium 226 has a half-life of 1,620 years — and the gradual buildup of mill tailings containing radium 226 on stream beds where the flowing waters could leach and dissolve the isotopes, procedures were instituted at the active and operating uranium mills to prevent the liquid and solid wastes containing the radioactive elements from being dumped into the waters. As a result, large piles of solid wastes or tailings began to grow beside the plants and streams as the uranium processors discontinued the dumping into the waters.

The continued production of uranium concentrate produced waste-tailing material in enormous piles ranging in size from several thousand to several million tons. In the 1960s there was a decreased demand for uranium, and as a result production decreased correspondingly. Several individual milling companies began to close down their plants, but even though the active plant operations ceased, the piles of waste uranium tailings remained. By 1966 milling operations had ceased at ten of the seventeen mill sites located in the Colorado Basin; at each of these sites a concentration of radioactivity still remains.

Although direct pollution of the waters of the Colorado with the radioactive wastes from operating uranium mills was put under control, the presence of over twelve million tons of mill tailings piled beside streams in the Colorado Basin and containing a large overall quantity of radium 226 and other radionuclides presents a long-range problem of custodial care to prevent the introduction of these materials into the waters of the Colorado through wind and water erosion, leaching or floods. The long radioactive life of some of the hazardous elements, the quantity of material which must be contained, and the difficulties of providing continual supervision over tailing piles at inactive mills provide a relatively unique and long-range threat to the quality of the waters of the Colorado.

In the midsection of America a less lethal and more unesthetic dumping was occurring. A 1964 study of Omaha, Nebraska, meat-packing wastes showed that the twenty meat-packing houses surrounding Omaha's Union Stockyards were

[291]

slaughtering over 1 million pounds of cattle, hogs, and lamb a day. Eighteen of these meat-packing operations discharged the wastes from their slaughtering operations into the Omaha sewer system, which discharged its effluent into the Missouri River. Over 100,000 pounds of grease, most of it from the meat-packing houses, were being sent through the Omaha sewers each day. In addition to the grease from floor and equipment wash-water, carcass dressing, casing cleaning, intestine cleaning and dressing, the tripe room, and rendering operations, the packers were sending heavy loads of paunch manure and fecal matter from the viscera into Omaha's overloaded sewage system and thence into the Missouri River to be carried downstream. An investigation of the coliform bacteria showed that these large quantities of intestinal waste matter being dumped into the Missouri River at Omaha were creating hazardous water conditions and fouling the waters further downstream.

Representatives of the states of Nebraska, Iowa, Missouri, and Kansas had been meeting since 1957 to discuss their particular pollution problems in the Missouri River — the problem of grease and wastes being dumped into the river by the meat-packing industry at Omaha which still were fouling the water-supply intakes downstream at St. Joseph, Missouri, with balls of grease and bacterial contamination. Subsequent plans for a six-million-dollar packing waste collection and treatment facility specifically designed to handle these problems were then stalled by financial complications.

In the Pacific Northwest the population is burgeoning. One of the most valuable resources of the state of Washington is Puget Sound. Broken up into many bays, channels, and inlets, the Sound is a primary source of commerce, recreation, and beauty for residents and visitors to the Puget Sound Basin area, 3,600 square miles of awesome natural splendor in the extreme northwest corner of the continental United States. Connected to the Pacific Ocean by the straits of Georgia and Juan de Fuca, the Sound is the nearest gateway to the ports of Asia, bringing in great amounts of all sizes and types of shipping, and sending out to world markets crude oils, grains, logs, forest products and paper.

In addition to the commercial shipping which plies the waters of the sound, the boats of a well-developed fishing industry plumb the glacially-formed estuary for the varied and large harvest of fish and shellfish. Between 1950 and 1963 the average annual commercial harvest of all fish and shellfish caught in the sound was over 89 million pounds, with a wholesale value of approximately 11 million dollars. Providing a rich and productive environment for all the organisms in the food chain of commercial and sport fish, the sound yields oysters, crabs, hard-shelled clams, octopus, squid, shrimp, and scallops. Among the prized fish sought by commercial or sport fisherman are the chinook, silver, sockeye, pink and chum species of salmon, and the trout — steelhead, sea-run cutthroat, and dolly varden. Millions of pounds of other varieties of fish are harvested annually for sport or for use in products such as fertilizer and pet foods.

Besides having a distinct beneficial impact upon the economy of the Pacific Northwest through shipping and commercial fishing, Puget Sound is one of the most magnificent bodies of water for natural beauty and recreational use. Framed by the mountains of the Olympic Peninsula, Vancouver Island and the Cascades, the sound provides clear waters in which residents and visitors can boat and swim and skin dive. Beaches, parks, and scenic shoreline help make living in this region much more than mere existence.

In order to maintain the continued existence of Puget Sound as a natural resource of high quality to meet the expected

[293]

growth and development, both economic and social, the state of Washington is committed to prevention and control of pollution of the sound. A cooperative study of the water conditions in Puget Sound issued in March 1967 by the Washington State Pollution Control Commission and the Federal Water Pollution Control Administration investigated the effects of wastes discharged by seven pulp and paper mills which dumped untreated or partially treated wastes into the estuarine waters of the sound.

It was found that the peculiar nature of the wastes of sulfite or sulfate pulp and paper processing which these seven mills dumped in four areas of the sound caused several types of pollution. The high concentrations of toxic wastes close to the mills were found to be injurious to juvenile salmon, thereby damaging the salmon industry, to suppress marine life within the area, and to produce sludge deposits on the bottom which both threatened bottom organisms and made the waters aesthetically unattractive. Even in dilute concentrations, the wastes from the pulp and paper mills degraded the waters and threatened marine life. In particular, these sulfite liquor wastes were found to damage immature forms of indigenous fish and shellfish such as oyster larva, sole eggs, and the young forms of cod, anchovy, herring, smelt, clams, and crabs. These wastes interfered with the marine life, and colored the waters. The sludge deposits produced toxic and odorous gases.

From the Mississippi to the Hudson–New York Harbor waters to Puget Sound the story is the same: the need to dump smelly, ugly, and dirty wastes into streams, rivers, and lakes preempts using the waters for more than open sewers. These three areas, with their concentrations of industry and human beings, have a water pollution problem so intense that attention is continuously focused on the problem. But the difference between them and a myriad of other areas throughout the country is one of size only. Much of the water in the United States, even that of small creeks or rivers, is severely polluted. The problem in the lesser-populated areas is as great for those areas as it is for the densely populated New York area. The pollution occurs in the same way; the effluent discharged into the water is the same; and the threat for the future is as great in the minor areas as in the major areas.

Water resources, limited as they are in this country, continue to be mishandled by man even though the danger of such misuse is clear.

13

DISPOSING OF SOLIDS

In 1942 the historical landmarks of the nation's capital, America's monuments to Washington, Jefferson, and Lincoln, began sharing the late afternoon skyline with a banner of foul black smoke, spreading out from a 125-acre site on the eastern side of the Anacostia River, several miles from the Capitol dome. Known as the Kenilworth Dump, this site was the repository for a substantial portion of the trash and refuse of the District of Columbia. Every day over a period of approximately twenty-five years, approximately six hundred truckloads of garbage, paper, tin cans, bottles, bedding, boxes, rags, junk and other discards from Washington residences and business establishments were carted there.

Until the early part of 1968, the system of disposal of the capital's trash at Kenilworth was elementary. It was an open burning dump. During the day the collection trucks would spread over nine hundred tons of refuse on the ground, leaving it for scavengers, dogs, playing children, flies, mosquitoes and wind to rummage through. In the late afternoon, the trash would be pushed together into a heap and set on fire, sending flames high into the air and billows of oily, black, odiferous smoke into the winds. These rising clouds of soot would spread out from Kenilworth carrying the nauseous matter throughout the metropolitan region, fouling Washington's air and depositing the grit and grime of partially burned trash and garbage on metropolitan homes, automobiles, clothing, furniture and human lung walls.

In the evening, as the fires died to a smolder and the remains were pushed aside to make room for the next day's load of nine hundred tons, the Kenilworth rats and other vermin would impatiently resume their feeding upon the castoffs of human life in the nation's capital.

Kenilworth Dump was recognized during most of its twenty-five years of existence as an eyesore and a public health menace. Air pollution officials continually said that the closing of Kenilworth Dump would keep more pollution out of the Washington air than any other single step. But the fires continued to be lit each afternoon and the smoke poured over the area.

The U.S. Public Health Service noted other health hazards associated with the open burning dump: "Flies, rats, and other disease-carrying pests find large quantities of food, a favored breeding medium, in the piles of exposed refuse. The polluted drainage from open dumps is an additional insult to ground and surface water supplies in the area. The characteristic foul odors, produced by decomposition, together with the smoke created by open burning, are often identifiable for miles." Yet Kenilworth Dump continued to receive daily a dose of nine hundred tons of refuse spread openly on the ground.

A passing motorist observing the daily spectacle at Washington's Kenilworth Dump felt that "Hell must be very much like that, although in Hell there would not be any children playing under the clouds of soot and ashes." But at Kenilworth the children did play among the flames, old bedsprings, and broken bottles, and under the clouds of soot and ashes which became a daily part of the Washington skyline.

On the sixteenth of February, 1968, the daily cycle at Kenilworth began again as usual. Trucks bearing Washington refuse made their deposits on the ground; scavengers combed among the debris; the fires were lit; children played under the clouds of soot and ashes, and the vermin impatiently waited for nightfall. About 5:00 p.m., as Kenilworth belched and crackled, the wind suddenly shifted and four young boys found themselves suddenly surrounded by flames shooting twenty to thirty feet into the air. The four boys started to run for safety. Only three escaped; one seven-year-old neighborhood boy stumbled and fell victim to the trash-consuming fires of the Kenilworth Dump.

The following day, District "Mayor" Walter Washington put an end to twenty-five years of open burning at Kenilworth and instituted a long-delayed plan to cover the daily delivery of trash with dirt, making Kenilworth a sanitary landfill area. One year as a landfill after twenty-five years of open burning would transform Kenilworth Dump into a site for a park along the Anacostia River, which could include a playground, tennis courts, pools, a garden, and a canoeing center. After years of contaminating the air and endangering human health and welfare, Washington refuse would be used to improve the metropolitan environment.

Kenilworth was started as an open burning dump when the District of Columbia found it could not keep pace with the rising piles of refuse its residents were producing. Since 1930 four incinerator plants have been put into operation in the District with a fifth plant planned for 1970. The four operating plants became overloaded in the late 1930s, and the Kenilworth Dump was established to receive what they couldn't handle. Kenilworth, now no longer an open burning area, will be exhausted as a sanitary landfill before 1970. The new incinerator scheduled for 1970 will not be able to disperse the difference. Meanwhile, Washington continues to increase its production of trash.

Washington's problem is the nation's. All along America's main streets, in her alleys and vacant lots, beside her highways, and on the shorelines of her streams lie the discarded bones and wrappings of industrial creation, tossed aside to await the slow but eventual metamorphosis back into the land.

The cigarette packages and the discarded butts and filters join yesterday's newspapers, lunch bags and carry-out coffee cups in the gutter, on the sidewalk, and in the street. A rusting hulk of metal in the vacant lot that once fed on gasoline and pro-pelled a carriage seventy or eighty miles an hour along a con-crete pathway now stands among the carcasses of tires, tired bedsprings and sunbaked Frigidaires. The only life here are the flies and mosquitoes that buzz among the standing puddles, the scurrying rats with their companion fleas scavenging among the empty tin cans and broken bottles, and the slugs and other vermin. Nearby a large concrete ball smashes asunder the bricks and plaster that man one time carefully put together.

In nearly any alley, cardboard boxes and paper bags are carelessly arranged and occasionally burst apart to reveal the ingredients of yesterday's meals for the perusal of the wandering dog bold enough to contest the rat and the flies for the putre-fying matter.

America's rural society and an agricultural economy have given way to the urban life of industrial production built on home consumption. Each day the alarm clock sounds, appetites are stimulated, manufacturing resumes, and the American way of consumption is on its way again.

Waxed or plastic cartons of milk are emptied of their fluid; boxes of cereal pour out their goodness; orange juice is squeezed or reconstructed from the frozen contents of cans; butter is taken out of its paper wrapper; glass jars are relieved of their jelly or jam; cardboard containers are opened and shells are broken to release the egg; ground coffee beans are percolated to give up their aromatic essence; and newspapers are perused for spicy ingredients and the day's bargain sales.

The American breakfast is more than a necessary requirement for revitalization and nutrition. It is the renewal of the relationship between production and consumption which will persist throughout the day. New containers of milk, cereal, orange juice, butter, jelly, eggs, coffee beans, and news must be prepared and purchased. Other appetites will be stimulated and momentarily satisfied throughout this day. New homes, automobiles, appliances, furniture, will become the property of the consumer. Production lines will manufacture and package millions of items, large and small, hard and soft, luxuries and necessities, expensive and inexpensive — all destined for a consumer's purchase.

There is an almost perfect marriage between the producer and the consumer, a continual give and take marred only by an occasional financial lovers' quarrel. Unfortunately, this arrangement is without foresight, and obscures a reality that threatens the future of the relationship. In this case, industrial production and home consumption have united to produce a child which neither wishes to recognize. Our society's bastard offspring is solid waste. While we have been welcoming affluence and increased purchasing power, we have tried to ignore the problem of solid waste.

Very few of the articles purchased by the consumer are totally consumed. Packaging, wrapping, and containers are most often turned into solid waste as soon as the contents are removed. Boxes, jars, plastic wrappers, cartons, cans, containers, paper and bottles are thrown away, never to be used again.

Other consumer items are intentionally engineered to soon become solid waste, such as paper towels, napkins, tissues, and foil and plastic wrappers. And much the same thing occurs with food products, the contents themselves becoming solid waste either as table scraps or trimmings or at the end of the sewage disposal cycle.

Many products are considered solid waste when they become obsolete. Old television and radio sets, furniture, automobiles, appliances and even entire buildings become refuse. Obsolescence is greatly accelerated in an affluent and rapidly changing society. People can afford to buy more new goods, and convenience becomes more important than maintenance. The producer also encourages the consumer to discard the old in favor of the new by continually changing style and adding new features in the same basic product and by building a product which rarely withstands extended use.

In addition to the American home, industry, government, and institutions contribute to the solid wastes of the country. The variety is immense. The American Public Works Association has classified various types of refuse according to point of origin, character, and nature of material. Garbage is defined to include wastes from the preparation, cooking, and serving of food and may originate in the home, institutions, and commercial concerns such as hotels, stores, restaurants, and markets. Classified as rubbish are such items as paper, cardboard, cartons, wood boxes, excelsior, plastics, rags, cloth, bedding, leather, rubber, grass, leaves, and yard trimmings. Noncombustible rubbish would include tin cans, metal foils, dirt, stones, bricks, ceramics, crockery, glass bottles and other mineral refuse. The home, institutions, and commercial concerns also produce ashes or cinders from their heating installations, and discard stoves, refrigerators, old rugs, knick-knacks, and furniture.

[301]

From factories, power plants, and business establishments are thrown away industrial refuse, food-processing wastes, boiler house cinders, wood, plastic, and metal scraps and shavings. This group, along with hospitals, may also discard special wastes: confidential documents, negotiable papers, hospital and laboratory pathological wastes, explosive or radioactive wastes.

Farms and feed lots contribute animal and agricultural wastes, manures and crop residues, while municipal sewage treatment plants and septic tanks produce sludge.

The varied list of unwanted, discarded, and relatively valueless materials that are accumulating daily in the United States is in itself staggering. The rate at which these materials have been increasing, however, is much more ominous. In today's "throw-away" age we are tossing out over 1.65 million tons of solid waste annually. The per capita production of refuse in the United States has been rising steadily since 1920. In 1965 the U.S. Public Health Service estimated that individual refuse production was about 4.5 pounds per day, a substantial rise from the 2.75 pounds per day in 1920. In some urban areas, per capita production of solid wastes had advanced beyond the present 4.5 national average; in the San Francisco Bay area the rate was approximately 8.0 pounds per day, and in Los Angeles it was 6.5.

In 1965 the annual rise in individual solid waste production was increasing at a rate of two percent per year. In addition, total population growth also was increasing at a rate of approximately two percent, resulting in a prediction that the amount of solid waste thrown away annually by all Americans would grow from 165 million tons in 1965 to 260 million tons by 1980.

The composition of solid waste is changing at the same time that it is increasing. For the last ten years, most of the solid waste increase has been in paper, plastics, and other packaging and wrapping materials. The American Public Works Association indicated in their publication *Municipal Refuse Disposal* that in the twenty-year period between 1938 and 1958 the solid wastes of the city of Chicago had changed from 17 percent wet garbage and 21 percent paper to 4.8 percent wet garbage and 56 percent paper.

The change in composition of municipal wastes during the past thirty years has come about because of the nationwide increase in production and prompt discard after use of plastics, bottles and paper. Of the 86 billion pounds of paper and paperboard products consumed in 1963, only about one-third was salvaged for new items. The remainder became a part of the American trash heap. More than 48 billion cans and 26 billion bottles are tossed out annually in this "no deposit–no return" era. More than 8 billion pounds of plastics enter the market each year, but only 10 percent will be recovered. We find the remaining 90 percent in the overflowing waste cans.

Primitive man, in his cave or in his tribal community, had his problems with solid wastes. Every once in a while he had to collect a few bones, skins, entrails, broken tools and shattered pottery and carry them off a distance and deposit them on the ground — an unsophisticated but immediate solution, creating a repository for bones of contention for future archeologists.

Today, with a vastly increased population crowded into urban concentrations and producing waste in growing varieties and amounts, modern man has made little improvement upon the waste collection and disposal methods of his primitive ancestors. Every so often modern man collects his bags, boxes, cartons, cans, bottles, food scraps, bones, dead cats and dogs, plastic wrappers, papers, skins, leaves, old bricks, entrails, lumber, furniture, broken tools, appliances, automobiles, and

[303]

shattered pottery and has someone else carry them off a distance and deposit them on the ground — an unsophisticated but immediate solution.

The final disposal of the unused, unwanted, and discarded wastes of America's affluent production is accomplished in four basic ways: the open dump, sanitary landfill, incineration, and by salvage (which includes composting and hog feeding). The present methods of storage collection and disposal of solid wastes are rudimentary and traditional systems inadequate in the past, incapable of meeting present requirements, and totally unsuited for the future.

The most likely repository of solid wastes in the United States is the open dump. There were 17,500 to 21,300 such dumps found to be operating in this country according to the 1965 survey by the American Public Works Association. The APWA found only 280 to 345 incinerators and 1,000 to 1,250 sanitary landfills. While it is true that the bulk of thousands of open dumps are found in rural communities of under 2,500 population, urban areas still rely upon open dumping as their primary method of disposal.

The open dump is the cheapest and most primitive means of refuse disposal. In essence, a metropolitan area dump operation involves hauling waste and refuse to the dumping site, spreading it on the ground in the morning, sometimes permitting hogs or animals to root out the garbage in the afternoon while scavengers salvage rags, paper, bottles, and metal toward dusk, and then setting fire to the remains in the evening to dispose of the combustibles, reduce the volume, and allow for further metal salvaging. When this is done the remainder is pushed aside to allow for the arrival of the next day's truckloads.

An open dump is a multiple insult to the environment and a danger to man. Degrading the environment aesthetically by its visual and odiferous impact, the dump can pollute the air, the land, and the water in the surrounding region. It is dangerous to man because of the more obvious physical dangers of uncontrolled fire, broken glass and bottles, jagged pieces of wood and metal, old refrigerator coffins, and treacherous footing at the actual dump site. Of greater danger, however, is the capability of a dump to act as a breeding place for the vectors of disease.

Dumps can contaminate water in a number of ways. Surface water and other liquids seep through the wastes and trickle over the land, picking up harmful bacteria and transporting them into creeks, streams, rivers, and reservoirs. Water percolating vertically through refuse piles will carry bacteria and chemicals though the subsoil and into ground water supplies to contaminate well water and springs.

Flies, mosquitoes, roaches, fleas and other insects migrating from the open dump can plague a community by acting as carriers of disease, by threatening the cleanliness and wholesomeness of processed foods, and by becoming extremely annoying pests. The breeding requirements of the common house fly's pre-adult cycle are all present at the dump: food (decaying organic materials), moisture, and a relatively warm temperature. In addition to being a biting and irritating unwanted guest at the backyard barbecue, the fly can act as the traveling host to organisms associated with cholera, polio, tuberculosis, pinkeye, diarrhea, dysentery, anthrax, salmonellosis and hepatitis, among others.

Golueke and Gotaas, writing in the *American Journal of Public Health* on the public health aspects of refuse disposal, reported: "Especially serious are open dumps where flies — flourishing on exposed garbage and breeding countless new generations — are paralleled in numbers only by a well-fed rodent population. Empty tin cans offer breeding places for various mosquitoes, among which are disease vectors such as

Culex tarsalis, responsible for the spread of encephalitis." In addition to encephalitis from mosquito breeding and feeding, the open dump has been associated in the United States with the transmission of malaria by the breeding and nourishing of rats.

Rodents, particularly the rat, have no more exacting requirements for their living conditions than food and shelter. These the rat for ages has found in abundance at the local dump. The rat has a long history of physical and economic attack upon humans — every year thousands of rat bites and damage worth $500 million to $1 billion in goods. But the rat populations supported by dumps are more to be feared for their threat to human health as carriers of disease. The plague, tapeworm, rat-bite fever, Rocky Mountain spotted fever, murine typhus and trichinosis are all associated with the rat, either directly or through the transfer of disease via fleas, ticks and mites to other animals.

The rat is very susceptible to the plague bacillus transmitted and carried by parasitic fleas. Open dumps provide an ideal meeting place for domestic rodents, like the rat, and wild rodents, in whose populations a reservoir of plague is believed to be firmly established. In the dump, fleas from plague-infected wild rodents can easily transmit the disease to rats. Following infection the rat will often die, and thus the parasite fleas on its body go off in search of a new host. This could be either another rat or, in an urban setting, man himself. The greater the rat population, the greater the chance of spreading the plague-carrying fleas brought by wild rodents. The greater the spread of plague among large rat populations, the greater the danger to neighboring human life.

Not all of America's wastes are presently disposed of at open dump sites. The cheapest method of disposal that is entirely satisfactory from both a sanitary and aesthetic viewpoint, when

[306]

properly designed, operated and maintained, is the sanitary land fill. Many operations in this country labeled sanitary landfills, however, are no more than open dumps and are therefore subject to the same degrading influence upon the environment and public health from fires, smoke, odor, physical hazards, insects, rats, vermin, and the contamination of water supplies.

A properly operated sanitary landfill requires a great deal of foresight and direct attention. In metropolitan centers, suitable landfill sites either are not available or are fast disappearing. This is true along the eastern seaboard and around the Great Lakes, where crowded conditions and unfavorable terrain diminish the extent to which sanitary landfills can solve municipal solid waste disposal problems.

And careless or nonexistent supervision of a sanitary landfill project, however well constructed, will result in health and nuisance problems. Inadequate daily compacted cover may allow flies to emerge from eggs or larvae brought in with the raw refuse. Rats may burrow down through to feed and nest.

An uneven or poorly compacted earth cover may crack and allow fires of spontaneous combustion to foul the air with gases and odors and continually present a larger fire danger. Dust raised at the landfill site will pollute the air and soil the neighboring property.

One of the greater problems associated with the sanitary landfill is the danger of polluting ground or surface water supplies. When refuse is deposited on the land, the impact upon water may be significant. An investigation of one sanitary landfill by the California State Water Pollution Control Board proved that ground water in the immediate vicinity was on its way to becoming grossly polluted by continuous or intermittent contact with deposited refuse.

The decomposition of organic matter in sanitary landfill cells can cause the buildup and transfer of volatile gases pre-

[307]

senting danger of explosions and highly obnoxious and sickening odors.

Many metropolitan areas faced with increasing amounts of refuse and fewer and fewer landfill sites at greater and greater distances from the collection points have turned to central incineration as the most desirable method of disposal. Incineration has reduced refuse to between one-fifth and one-tenth its original volume, accordingly decreasing as well the amount of land required for final disposal. The reduction in volume and weight that occurs during burning, however, is merely a transfer into gases discharged into the air. Under optimum conditions these gases would be mostly harmless water vapor and carbon dioxide. However, complete combustion never occurs, and various degrees of air pollution always result. In addition to water vapor and carbon dioxide, soot and smoke, hydrocarbons and aldehydes, sulfur dioxide, hydrogen chloride or the oxides of nitrogen are blown into the air.

Theoretically, all solid matter could be captured in dust collectors before contaminating the air and complete combustion could reduce organic gases to harmless compounds. But the expense for the equipment to do these two things is high, and therefore most municipal incinerators are major polluters of the air.

At one time many municipalities disposed of their garbage by feeding it to swine, either owning and operating their own pig farms or by contracting directly with hog farms or private collectors. This method of garbage disposal has long been under public health scrutiny because of both disease potential to man and animals and aesthetic insults. The feeding of raw garbage to swine always increases the likelihood for trichinosis to be transmitted to man. And because of the fly and stench problems associated with them, hog farms have always been unwelcome neighbors in populated areas.

Composting as a method of solid organic waste disposal and return to the environment has been developed and practiced to a greater extent in Europe than in the United States. This method relies upon the control and accelerated decomposition of moist, solid, organic matter to turn waste into a humus-like material that is useful as a soil conditioner and fertilizer. The success of this method of disposal depends upon a stable interaction of several factors that greatly raise the cost of constructing a composting plant: the separation of inorganic and trash materials such as cans, bottles, and debris from the organic material before composting; a continuing quantity of rapidly degradable organic material; and a steady market for the final product.

Municipal refuse in the United States is becoming more and more a mixed bag of trash — mostly paper, tin cans, bottles and plastic — while the organic matter — food wastes — is being ground into the sewage system. As a result, compost made from municipal refuse has little fertilizer value and can be used only for ground cover or as a soil conditioner much like peat moss. In areas such as Southern California where enormous quantities of agricultural wastes, such as cattle manure, are a staggering problem, and a large farming market is close by, composting for use as agricultural fertilizer may be both feasible and desirable. In other municipal areas, the low-quality end product and the uncertain market have not encouraged the expansion of composting as a common method of solid waste disposal.

As demonstrated by the nation's rising volumes of garbage, rubbish, refuse, and waste, the relationship between production and consumption is not cyclical, for the consumer does not really "consume" the results of production but merely uses a small portion before discarding. One direction for the future successful management of our waste systems, therefore, must

[309]

be an attempt to close the cycle back to manufacturing and turn wastes back into resources. The intent and ability to re-use, recover and recycle our unconsumed discards will assist in preventing the environmental insults of proliferating solid waste. It can also introduce an element of economy and conservation into our management of resources before critical depletion makes this imperative.

However, attitudes and actions relating to solid wastes have remained virtually unchanged for years. The approach is basically one of "sweeping dirt under the rug," preferably some-one else's rug. But while the approach has not varied, the problem has. Solid wastes are increasing. They are changing in character and composition. They are polluting our air, our land, and our water. These increases and changes in solid wastes have been accompanied by increased physical dangers to human safety, a greater potential for transmission of disease, and a deterioration of the aesthetic environment.

Our society has been able to apply its thoughts, creativity, and productivity to the manufacture and distribution of glass bottles which take one hundred years to return to sand, aluminum containers that are virtually indestructible over one thousand years, and plastics that are resistant to fire, chemicals, and microbes. As we pile these monuments to our productive/consumptive age about us in ever greater numbers, we also damage the environment's ability to nurture and sustain mortal life.

III

AWAKENINGS

14

THE CONGRESS ACTS

By mid-twentieth century, rural agricultural America had learned its lessons well and had surpassed England, its teacher, to become *the* urban-industrial society of the world. During the years between 1860 and 1960 little effort was made to understand the changes that were occurring and their effects. Attempts to cope with environmental destruction from population growth, urbanization and industrial expansion were practically nil, and those that were made nearly always came too late. What was done generally was in reaction to a crisis. The nation's environmental ills, when diagnosed at all, were diagnosed superficially, and corrective action, when prescribed, treated the symptoms and not the disease.

The first federal food and drug act was passed in 1906, but it was of dubious effectiveness because it required proof not only that consumers had been poisoned by a product or deceived by its advertised use but also that there had been a deliberate intent to poison or deceive the buyer. With this defense of ignorance written into the law, successful prosecutions were few.

It was not until 1933 that there was an initiative for truly effective protection of the public from contaminated food, dangerous cosmetics, and quack remedies. This initiative stemmed from the efforts of Food and Drug Commissioner Walter G. Campbell, who produced an exhibit of fraudulent drugs, poisonous cosmetics, and contaminated food that was to be dubbed the "Chamber of Horrors." The resulting Federal Food, Drug and Cosmetic Act was not signed into law for another five years. During this time there were four major improvements in the bill, and there was also, in 1937, an episode in which the "Elixir of Sulfanilamide," a patent medicine, caused the deaths of over one hundred persons. Finally on June 25, 1938, Franklin D. Roosevelt signed into law an act to prohibit the introduction for sale or delivery for such introduction across state lines of any food, drug, device, or cosmetic which is adulterated or misbranded.

In 1890, as a result of yellow fever outbreaks, a law for interstate quarantine to prevent the spread of communicable diseases from one state to another was adopted by Congress. That law provided the basis for controlling water hauled across state lines. Then in 1914 the first drinking water standards were enacted to serve as guides for the approval of water supplied on interstate carriers — bus companies, vessels, railroads, and eventually airlines engaged in interstate commerce. These standards, restricted at first to bacteriological contaminants, have been revised several times in the ensuing years as more and more physical, bacteriological, chemical and radiological contaminants have been identified as actual or potential health hazards.

But even today the authority to apply these standards to water supplies still remains limited to interstate carrier water supplies, the same as it was in the early 1900s. For those communities whose water supplies are not used by interstate buses, planes, or trains, the drinking water standards are only a suggested guide. The rapid expansion of interstate travel, particularly of airplanes and buses, coinciding with increased quantities and sophistication of water pollutants, has strained the budget, facilities, and staff of the division of PHS responsible for interstate carrier supplies. While the authority to apply drinking water standards has not expanded, pollution has proliferated.

The only period during which state and local construction of sewage treatment works kept up to needs was during the 1930s, when federal public works programs were assisting local municipal efforts. Before and after the thirties, the number of people served by sewers increased faster than the facilities needed to treat their effluents.

By 1963, over 2700 communities with a total population of nearly 6 million people would be reported by state health authorities as having no sewer systems at all, much less a treatment facility of any kind. Even those cities and towns which had sewer systems and treatment plants could not keep up with obsolescence, insufficient treatment or insufficient capacity. In 1963 another 1500 municipalities with a population of 13 million required new or enlarged facilities.

The efforts of industry to control environmental pollution proved to be inadequate to master the rising tides of effluents. Many industrial firms threatened to relocate and put pressure on local economies to resist local efforts to control their waste effluents. And those firms which had social consciousness experienced difficulty in developing the knowledge and the hardware to treat their own discharges, much less to assist in the construction of community facilities. Surveys and data from the middle 1950s showed that more than 6,000 construction projects would be needed to treat industrial wastes being discharged into the nation's waters.

[315]

In the field of air pollution, the control efforts of state and local governments were minimal. In 1947 California became the first state to adopt legislation authorizing the formation of county air pollution control districts. By 1963, of the thirty-three states and territories which had adopted some kind of air pollution control law, only the states of California and Oregon had established air quality and emission standards for enforcement on a local or statewide basis, and only California had motor vehicle emission standards. Of the 85 local governmental agencies budgeting at least $5000 a year for control programs in 1961, the Los Angeles Air Pollution Control District accounted for almost half of the $8 million expended.

Rising levels of pollutants in the air and mounting untreated municipal and industrial wastes fouling the nation's waterways created concern in the 1950s over the health and welfare of the public and over the damage being inflicted upon physical property and the aesthetic environment. This concern did not give rise in the 1950s to any meaningful plan of action, but it did promote the beginning of a national debate over who should exercise control in the solving of the problems of environmental pollution: the federal government, state or local government, or industry.

The Eightieth Congress of the United States brought the federal government into the water pollution field when it passed the Water Pollution Control Act of 1948. This experimental law was limited to a trial period of five years and basically was aimed at producing data and research on water pollution problems. The act authorized the U.S. Public Health Service to conduct research itself and to make research grants to the states. Although the Public Health Service was authorized also to hold hearings and recommend abatement solutions on interstate waters, there was no enforcement power given to the federal government unless both the polluting state and the affected state consented.

Sewage treatment planning grants were included in the 1948 Water Pollution Control Act, as was an authorization of $22.5 million annually for low-interest construction loans. But because no money ever was appropriated for these loan funds and because federal enforcement on interstate streams required the consent of the polluting state, the 1948 Act actually restricted the federal role to gathering information on water pollution.

When the 1948 Water Pollution Control Act came up for renewal in 1955, the Eisenhower Administration proposed strengthening the enforcement power over interstate waters given to the Public Health Service. In addition to the research role given to the PHS, it was proposed that federal abatement actions could be initiated without the consent of both states involved, as in the 1948 Act, but upon request from the affected state alone. In addition, if the states did not set water quality standards for streams shared with other states, PHS would. With industry knocking out the provision for federal water quality standards in the Senate version of the bill, and stirring up further opposition to any federal enforcement features in the House of Representatives, final passage of the legislation was stalled until the following year.

In 1956 renewal of the 1948 Water Pollution Control Act came before Congressman John Blatnik's Subcommittee on Rivers and Harbors of the House Public Works Committee. The Minnesota Democrat, angered by the bill being stalled and diluted the previous year, drafted a substitute for the Eisenhower bill, returned the pending bill to his committee, and reopened hearings on his own legislation. Blatnik's bill, designed as a strictly Democratic bill, was a strong piece of legislation calling for grants to states and cities to build sewage treatment plants plus the provision for federal abatement power on interstate waters with the consent of the affected state taken from the Senate bill of the previous session.

Helping Blatnik draft his legislation and providing strong testimony in support of its enactment was a coalition of urban representatives, mayors, and conservation groups. Testimony of the American Municipal Association outlined the tremendous backlog in municipal sewage-treatment plant construction. With needs for sewage interception and treatment estimated at more than $5 billion and expenditures of only $200 million annually, the cities were falling farther and farther behind.

The bill which Congressman Blatnik introduced called for $100 million in federal grants to cover up to one-half the cost of a municipal sewage treatment project with a ceiling of $500 thousand for any one project. The final bill, which passed both the Democratic Senate and the House on a voice vote, despite opposition from the Administration and Republicans on the Hill, had been modified in Blatnik's parent committee and in conference with the Senate. When signed into law by the President, The Federal Water Pollution Control Act of 1956 modified and simplified federal abatement procedures on interstate waters and authorized $50 million a year for the construction of municipal sewage treatment plants, with the federal share being 30 percent and the maximum for one project pegged at $250 thousand.

From the passage of the Water Pollution Control Act of 1956 until the presidential election of 1960, Congressman Blatnik and the Congress, supported by the municipalities, state pollution control agencies, conservation groups, and the AFL-CIO, were locked in a head-to-head battle with the Eisenhower Administration, Congressional Republicans and the polluting industries to prevent the demise of the federal grant assistance to municipal sewage-construction projects. In

1957 Democrats in the House had to beat back an attempt to knock out appropriations for the grant program authorized the year before. Also in 1957, as a result of a proposal of President Eisenhower, a joint federal-state action committee suggested turning over sewage treatment grants to the states to be financed by relinquishment to the states of a temporary federal tax on local telephone service.

Congressman Blatnik responded to the joint action committee proposal in 1958 by introducing legislation to increase the grant program authorization to $100 million and to increase the ceiling for individual projects to $500 thousand, the figures of his original 1956 bill. With the added support of the state water pollution control agencies, the bill was reported out of the House Public Works Committee but was not brought to a vote on the floor.

In 1959, Blatnik again introduced legislation to increase the grant program to the level of his original 1956 bill, and this time was successful in the House in overcoming Republican opposition both in committee and on the floor as the Democrats united to pass the bill. It was sent to the President in early 1960. He vetoed it.

The House failed to achieve the two-thirds majority necessary to override the veto, having split on party lines. As the 1950s came to a close, President Eisenhower enunciated the policy of his eight-year Administration and of his party, during this time, with regard to water pollution when in his veto message to Congress on February 23, 1960, he described water pollution as a "uniquely local blight . . . Primary responsibility for solving the problem lies not with the Federal Government but rather must be assumed and exercised, as it had been, by state and local governments . . ." The following year a Democratic Congress would find a Democratic President in the White House.

Early in the first session of President John F. Kennedy's Administration, Congressman John Blatnik renewed his legislative quest for increased federal participation in encouraging and assisting local efforts to control water pollution. With Presidential endorsement of a strong federal water pollution policy, the Congress of the United States enacted and the President signed into law on July 20, 1961, the Federal Water Pollution Control Act Amendments of 1961. These amendments broadened the federal enforcement powers and procedures, and gave authority for abatement of intrastate as well as interstate pollution of interstate or navigable waters, and increased the federal grant for sewage treatment facilities.

In 1955 Congress passed the first identifiable federal program on air pollution. Republican Senator Thomas Kuchel of California, sponsor of the bill, had experienced the decade of difficulties found by his state as it attempted to identify and control air pollution, particularly in Los Angeles. Kuchel's proposal which passed and became Public Law 84–159 was a very modest and limited ". . . act to provide research and technical assistance relating to air pollution control." With an authorized maximum appropriation of but $5 million a year, for research only, Kuchel had produced a law that reflected his view that air pollution control remained a problem for the states, the cities, and the counties to handle.

Three years later, President Eisenhower's Secretary of Health, Education and Welfare, Arthur Fleming, came to the conclusion that federal research was not enough and that the federal government needed to be able to study interstate air pollution problems on its own initiative and to have enforcement powers to abate interstate pollution. His proposals were met with a storm of protest from the Public Health Service within his own department, from the Bureau of the Budget, and from industry spokesmen. Thus the federal role in air pollution remained one of limited research and study in the 1950s.

Four years after the entry of the federal government into a program in air pollution in 1955, the Public Health Service wanted to expand its budget for research and technical assistance activities. Having spent $8.6 million on research activities, PHS wanted specifically to extend their program for an indefinite period of time and to have the ceiling on funds removed. Although Secretary Fleming expressed a desire to expand as well the federal role to include public hearings of specific air pollution problems and the issuance of findings and recommendations, the PHS balked at any expansion of their powers. PHS thought that this expansion would threaten their pet idea of greater research funds.

The Chairman of the Health and Safety Subcommittee of the House Interstate and Foreign Commerce Committee in 1959 was Kenneth A. Roberts, Congressman from Alabama. Roberts's subcommittee, through which all air pollution legislation in the House passed, favored continuance of the PHS research and technical assistance activities at the same level, and when the final version of the law emerged from the Senate-House conference, that was all it did. But also coming out of Chairman Roberts's subcommittee in 1959 and being signed into law the following year was a proposal by Congressman Paul Schenck requiring the Surgeon General to make a study of motor vehicle exhaust and report his findings back to Congress.

In 1960 and 1961 the Senate passed a measure to give the Surgeon General the power to hold hearings on interstate air pollution problems of broad significance. Roberts's subcommittee took no action on this bill either time. Then at the request of the Kennedy Administration Chairman Roberts introduced a bill in the House of Representatives on February 29, 1962.

While the bill recognized an expanded effort to combat air pollution, it also reflected the continuing reluctance of the Public Health Service to add to their research and assistance activities. The bill removed the money and time limits on PHS activities, provided for grants to states and local agencies to study, initiate, or improve control programs, and provided for loans of federal personnel. In addition, the bill allowed the Surgeon General to conduct surveys of interstate pollution and to hold public conferences on problems of nationwide or interstate significance. This modest addition to the federal role would receive one day of committee hearings in June, but would be scrapped by Roberts and the Senate in favor of another extension of the basic 1955 law.

On December 11, 1962, at a National Conference on Air Pollution in Washington with the theme "Let's Clear the Air," attended by over 1,500 participants including 80 of the nation's leaders in health, public administration, industry, education, and air pollution control, Congressman Roberts declared, "In the 1955 legislation setting up a federal research and technical assistance program to combat air pollution, Congress outlined the role the federal government is expected to play in this program.

"It was declared to be the policy of Congress to preserve and protect the primary responsibilities and rights of the states and local governments in controlling air pollution. . . .

". . . Let me say that I do not think the federal government has any business telling the people of, say, Birmingham or Los Angeles how to proceed to meet their air pollution problems. This was made clear in the 1955 Act. Even if Washington attempted to exercise such authority, we would have a hard time writing and enforcing regulations at long range. . . ."

Less than three months after this speech to the National Conference on Air Pollution, Congressman Roberts introduced legislation to provide for federal enforcement of interstate pollution and state enforcement of intrastate pollution.

When Roberts's subcommittee held hearings on his bill on March 19, 1963, the representative of the National Association of Manufacturers, Daniel W. Cannon, called for the deletion of the provisions for federal program grants and for federal enforcement authority and quoted portions of the chairman's December 1962 speech as the best summary of their views. Roberts replied to the industry representative's statement by saying, "Thank you, Mr. Cannon. I want to congratulate you on your statement and say this evidently has been your homework for quite awhile. You certainly quoted me correctly. I would say, however, there are two views about consistency. It has been said, 'consistency, thou art a jewel.' It has also been said that 'consistency is a hobgoblin of little minds.'

"Finally someone said, 'The wise man changes his mind and the fool never does.'

"I might say that it is true that the statements I made with reference to the local aspects of the problem we tried to follow in the provisions of the bill. I do feel, however, that there have been some things that happened, particularly the recent London smog, which make me feel that the federal government does have a responsibility in this field, particularly when it involves the death and health of our people. Now I think there are some of these situations that we cannot reach other than by legislation of this type."

By February 1963, one month before these hearings, Chairman Roberts had achieved greater knowledge and a growing understanding of the increasing magnitude of the air pollution problems in the country, and things had happened which caused him to come to feel that the federal government did indeed have a responsibility in the control and abatement of air pollution. In November of 1961, Roberts had conducted one day of hearings in the smoky steel city of Birmingham, Alabama, next to his congressional district. There he had heard not only the PHS view that the federal role should be limited to research and technical assistance, but also the position of the local municipalities. The Executive Director of the Alabama League of Municipalities, speaking for the American Municipal Association, told Roberts of the local problems in enforcing air pollution control, and suggested that the federal government should be authorized to give enforcement assistance where requested, and afterwards he maintained contact with Roberts to continue to explain the Alabama League's reasoning.

At the December 1962 National Conference on Air Pollution, former President Eisenhower's Secretary of Health, Education and Welfare, Arthur Fleming had proposed increasing the federal role in air pollution control through expanded research and training, a federal grant program, and the authorization of federal enforcement powers similar to those given in water pollution control. While the conference was in progress, London experienced another killing smog, and the deaths of at least 340 were added to the rolls of those killed in air pollution disasters. At this same gathering, two representatives of the American Medical Association drafted a position statement for their organization which called air pollution "one of our most serious environmental health problems," and called for the engagement of the federal government in "enforcement in interstate or interjurisdictional difficulties in the manner of the successfully implemented Water Pollution Act." This statement was then sent in a telegram from the Chicago headquarters of the AMA to the Surgeon General, head of the U.S. Public Health Service, at the conference. Although a later letter, prompted by industry allies of the AMA in their fight against Medicare, qualified the statement in the telegram, the American Medical Association went on record as favoring federal leadership and enforcement in air pollution control.

Between the time of this national conference and February 7, 1963, the day when the President was to speak on health to the Congress, a battle had developed within the Kennedy Administration ranks over the Administration position on the federal role in air pollution control. With the professional bureaucrats, the Public Health Service and the Bureau of the Budget favoring the more conservative position of no federal enforcement, and the Secretary of HEW taking a non-committed position, the fight for a strong federal role and enforcement powers was led by the political activists within the Department: Assistant HEW Secretary of Health, Education and Welfare for Legislation Wilbur Cohen, and his Deputy, Dean Coston. In a two-day meeting with the President in Florida late in December Cohen was able to interest President Kennedy in supporting federal enforcement. Coston set about to press the argument for enforcement in confrontations with the Budget Bureau and PHS, to work with the representatives of the U.S. Conference of Mayors, the American Municipal Association, and the National Association of Counties in drafting strong legislation and in enlisting local and congressional support, and to write a forceful statement for the President to make on the subject.

On February 7, 1963, President Kennedy presented to the Congress a special message on health. He called for the Public Health Service to engage in a more intensive research program, to provide financial stimulation for states and local air pollution control agencies to initiate or improve their control programs, and to take action to abate interstate air pollution, along the general lines of the existing water pollution control enforcement measures.

[325]

The changes that Congressman Roberts underwent in 1962 and 1963 were but one aspect of the larger change which was to give to the Congress of the United States the initiative for leadership in the fight against pollution and the improvement of the environment.

The elevation of Michigan Senator Pat McNamara to chairman of the Senate Public Works Committee, whose first action when Congress reconvened in 1963 was to create the Special Subcommittee for Air and Water Pollution, brought the Senator from Maine, Edmund S. Muskie, to the forefront of the pollution fight. Senator Muskie, as chairman of the subcommittee, brought to it a wealth of knowledge and expertise on the problems of water pollution, developed from his experience as Governor of Maine, during which time he had initiated a program for the upgrading of the quality of water in that state. Muskie also brought to the subcommittee and the Congress an activist philosophy for environmental improvement and an ability to create a climate of bi-partisan cooperation and joint venture.

When at the end of January, 1963, he introduced a measure to improve upon the 1961 Water Pollution Control Act and give to the federal government the authorization to lead a national policy of keeping the country's waters as clean as possible, Muskie soon had 18 Senate co-sponsors joining him.

In addition to calling for a positive national policy of clean waters, Muskie's bill sought to set standards of water quality, establish a program of federal grants for the separation of storm and sanitary sewers, allow the larger municipalities greater participation in sewage-treatment construction grants, and transfer water pollution control out of the Public Health Service and into a new HEW agency where it would be prosecuted more forcefully.

Also before the Muskie subcommittee at this time was a bill

[326]

introduced by committee member Gaylord Nelson of Wisconsin to require synthetic detergents to comply with standards of degradability.

When hearings began on the two bills, opposition to the federal government's enforcement powers and procedures came from the Manufacturing Chemists' Association representative, who testified that there was the feeling that the federal enforcement proceedings had fostered an atmosphere of hostility rather than cooperative effort with the state agencies. Senator Muskie pointed out to the chemists' representatives that of the twenty enforcement actions taken up to that time ten had been upon request of the states, and that only four had needed to go beyond the conference stage to public hearings to be resolved, and only one had to be taken to the last enforcement step and brought before the jurisdiction of the court. The Senator did not feel this record reflected a lack of cooperation between the federal government and the states.

Senator Muskie was more concerned, however, that the federal government and the agency involved in administering and enforcing water pollution abatement should take a more vigorous and forceful attitude about cleaning up the nation's waters. As an example of a lagging enforcement effort in the Public Health Service, Muskie elicited from an Assistant Surgeon General of PHS the admission that a meeting he had held with a representative of the Massachusetts Department of Health had produced a letter from the Massachusetts representative which expressed an understanding that ". . . the Public Health Service will not initiate any enforcement procedures for pollution control in connection with the Merrimack River and its tributaries at this time or until it has been demonstrated that pollution abatement will not be effected within a reasonable time." While admitting that he had no authority to make such a commitment, the Assistant Surgeon General felt that the state of Massachusetts had a right to assume that such a commitment had been made.

When Muskie agreed to incorporate Senator Nelson's proposal on regulation of soap and detergents in the provisions of his bill, the soap industry appeared before the subcommittee and testified against federal regulation. In return for a promise of voluntary compliance, the provision was removed.

The Muskie bill passed the Senate overwhelmingly in 1963, but industry spokesmen stymied the bill in the House until 1965, when finally it was passed in a modified form. The consensus which Muskie had achieved in the Senate in 1963 carried through 1965, and with 31 co-sponsors and one day of hearings, the Muskie bill passed the Senate three weeks after Congress opened in 1965 by a vote greater than that of 1963. Next the House and Senate measures went to conference. With Muskie holding out for interstate federal standards if the states failed to act or if local standards were inadequate, and the House sticking to a larger grant program and transfer of all water pollution functions to a new HEW agency which the Senate also favored, the Water Quality Act of 1965 was born. The House took credit for the compromise, and after the House had notified the Senate it had approved the bill, Senator Muskie commented, "I don't mind retreating into victory."

With a water-pollution control bill on its way to passage in the Senate in 1963, the Muskie subcommittee turned its attention in September to the air pollution legislation which had passed the House in July.

The subcommittee wanted to postpone action until the following year to allow for comprehensive hearings, but prodding by President Kennedy changed Senator Muskie's mind, and by December, Congress saw final enactment of the Clean Air Act of 1963. The Act contained, in addition to research and technical assistance, a federal grant program for air pollution control, the provision for federal enforcement in interstate air pollution, and federal enforcement in intrastate pollution if requested by the governor.

After the passage of the Clean Air Act, the Muskie subcommittee began a series of hearings to make a more detailed inquiry into the complexities of the national air pollution problem. These hearings in various cities across the country and in Washington were summarized in October 1964 in a report entitled "Steps Toward Clean Air." This report cited the exhaust of automobiles as responsible for some 50 percent of the nation's air problems, followed by burning dumps and incinerators and sulfur gases produced by the burning of fossil fuels, coal and gas, and recommended corrective legislation.

In January 1965, Senator Muskie introduced a bill to set standards for exhaust emissions of gasoline-powered vehicles and, taking a step into a new field, called for the establishment of federal grants for solid-waste disposal facilities. At the April 6, 1965, hearing on this legislation, Administration spokesman James M. Quigley, Assistant Secretary of HEW, testifying for the Administration, opposed national automobile standards at that time. ". . . There is still, we think, the important approach through the President meeting with representatives of the automotive industry and exploring what can be done to cope with this problem on a voluntary basis."

Senator Muskie, incredulous, invited Quigley to return to testify in three days, adjourned the hearings in Washington at the end of the first day, and moved for one day of hearings in Detroit with representatives of the automobile industry. At a meeting with the auto-makers before the hearings, Muskie explained to the auto representatives the problems they would face if auto emission standards were left to each of the fifty states and other jurisdictional bodies to determine. The hearing

[329]

which followed produced testimony from the Automobile Manufacturers Association ". . . that the vehicle manufacturers stand ready to pass on the benefit of this extensive research knowledge nationally for the public whenever Congress concludes from its studies that the facts warrant. . . . The vehicle manufacturers, given sufficient time, can do the job."

When the hearings resumed in Washington two days later, Assistant Secretary Quigley came to testify again.

. . . What I thought I said or intended to say in my testimony before the subcommittee on Tuesday was not aimed or intended the way it obviously has been interpreted by some segments of the press, to wit: that the Johnson Administration was somehow unconcerned or uninterested or didn't think this was a serious problem. This is not our position. This is not the position of the President. I think clearly we all recognize from the President on down that this is a serious problem and that corrective action must be taken.

On October 20, 1965, President Johnson signed the Clean Air and Solid Waste Disposal Act of 1965, which called for national auto-emission control standards and the first federal research and demonstration program for solid waste disposal.

In May and June of 1965, the Muskie subcommittee held general, technical, and field hearings throughout the country and in Washington to study the progress and programs of water pollution abatement. In January of 1966 the subcommittee reported finding a continuing backlog of needed municipal sewage-treatment plant construction estimated at nearly $20 billion. That year forty-eight Senators joined with Senator Muskie in sponsoring legislation to increase the federal investment in sewage treatment grants. With minor revisions the Muskie bill passed the Senate 90–0, and after the Senate conferred with the House on their version which had passed by 313–0, the Clean Water Restoration Act of 1966 became law, upgrading the federal grant program, extending water quality standards, and removing the ceiling from individual projects.

Between 1963 and 1966 the Congress of the United States at last emerged to take a firm and leading role in combatting environmental decay and improving the quality of life in the United States. Led by several members who have developed expertise in the field as well as the ability to mold diverse groups together to produce legislation, the Congress has committed the federal government to a primary role in uniting federal, state, local, and private industry effort. The fight to restore the quality of our environment has just begun, however. Several programs are just in the research stage. Others are still underfunded. Many have not yet been touched at all.

The year 1967 saw the Congressional establishment of the first federal authority to create criteria and standards for the control of designated air pollutant emissions. In 1968, the Federal Aviation Administration was given the first authority to establish and enforce regulations to control aircraft noise. By the end of 1969, a House–Senate Conference was underway to resolve their legislative differences and establish a Council on Environmental Quality with a well-staffed office in the Executive branch to provide the President, the Congress and the nation with a thorough and professional review and analysis of matters which pertain to the environment. In 1969, work had also begun in the Muskie subcommittee on new solid waste legislation.

Sulfur fumes still foul the air, and the roar of airplanes is a part of the environment yet. Appropriations of funds in the established air and water pollution programs run behind needs. There is still a long way to go.

[331]

15

THE CHALLENGE

Man *can* avoid a tomorrow of environmental crises. He will have to work at it, for it is easy to accept the conditions we live in as an inevitable concomitant of life. That is what we are doing now. We live with air and water pollution; we tolerate increasing annoyance from noise; with a slight murmur we suffer crowding and congestion; we hardly pay any attention to a host of other environmental abuses that can injure man mentally and physically. We learn little from our past. We do those things that are easiest, and it is easy to ignore environmental pollution. Most Americans have to be reminded continually that there is something wrong with their environment. It's not every day that we come into contact with water pollution. We are not continuously aware of air pollution. Some of the more subtle forms of environmental contamination escape easy detection. The food we eat, the water we drink, the household products which we use most often never appear to be related to problems of health or injury that occur. No one seems to be dying from an attack of the environment. Nor do most people associate any disease with it. If man doesn't like his environment, at least he lives with it. But is no one dying? Certainly man adapts. This history has proved. He emerged in greater numbers than ever before after more than a century of being scourged by infectious diseases. The death rate used to be atrocious, but it was ascribed to the disease and not to the environmental conditions that bred the disease. Death today is even less closely related to the environmental conditions that breed disease. Is no one dying? It only seems that way.

What about the future? It appears now that man is creating more environmental problems for himself than he will be able to solve. But he doesn't have to. He doesn't have to adapt and die in the process.

The challenge to man will not be whether he knows what to do but whether he is able to do what he knows must be done. And before anything he does has any real effect on the quality of air and water or the proper handling of waste, he will have to commit himself to three things:

Establishment of a population policy.

Creation of new towns with built-in standards and safeguards against environmental deterioration.

Spending of substantial public funds to rectify the deterioration that has taken place in our major urban areas.

Imposing a population policy does not mean limiting the number of children any married couple may have; certainly American attitudes will not accept this kind of governmental regulation. Nor would they accept limitations on where individuals could live; the idea that we can establish arbitrary population limits for communities is ludicrous. But certainly population policy must include making family planning information and services available to all Americans. It also means providing options so that those who prefer rural or small-town life will not be forced to tear up roots and move to large urban centers.

[333]

A population policy will have to be built upon the knowledge of what effect varying levels of density and congregation have upon the physical and social environment; based on this knowledge, there could be incentives for dispersal and alternatives to the current urban centers including the redesigning of these centers. Such information is not now available.

New towns must be established so that those who prefer the modern and the planned community can choose that alternative. But new towns must be managed so that those at every economic level can select that option if they so desire.

Existing urban centers cannot be abandoned in a fit of hopelessness, nor should they be left as rotten boroughs for the poor alone to wallow in. City centers in particular must be restored to satisfactory living levels. This will cost much, but the failure to do this will be far costlier in terms of human conflict and despair.

The new towns, the population policy, the massive spending for corrective purposes — all must be followed by a determined government effort at federal, state and local levels to set standards and enforce them so that environmental improvements will not subsequently be broken down.

In making the decision to do these three things we will have to accept the fact that subsidies and financial advantage to private industry are a cost of the political system we have, which must be paid if we are to improve present conditions. Such subsidies are not new; they are rooted in our history. But in spending this money, we shall have to place in proper perspective the use of tools with fancy labels such as cost-benefit ratio, systems analysis, and program planning and budgeting. These are the technicians' tools. These tools can tell us what, from a technical standpoint, can or cannot be done. They can tell how much it costs to do it. But they can only guess at the value of alternatives, because the environment is of importance only as it relates to people. Dealing with the wants and desires of peoples is subjective.

We will also have to destroy the national security mystique that causes us to siphon off the vast majority of the federal budget to perpetuate economic waste in the guise of national defense. It's easier politically to spend money in the interest of protecting the American people from death and destruction at the hands of some human enemy outside our national boundaries than for those goals just outlined. How hollow indeed will be the success of that spending when death and destruction within our boundaries at our own hands leave little worthwhile to be defended. The American people had better come to understand that our national security is threatened rather by a failure to provide the social and physical environment necessary to maintain a strong, growing, independent and thinking population.

Traditionally the nation has dealt with environmental hazards to man's health and welfare as a reaction to crisis. Only when an environmental hazard becomes menacing do we attempt to eliminate or control it. This pattern of environmental protection has failed us.

Avoiding the dangers of the future and correcting the threats of today require that we discard this method of dealing with problems of the environment. We must have a new approach; one based on the idea that impairment of man's health and welfare is nature's last, not first, distress signal of an environmental hazard. This approach to environmental protection must see human illness as a symptom of environmental disease and recognize that environmental health efforts must treat or prevent the disease itself, not the symptom.

We have seen many signs of the need for a new approach for environmental protection. The problem of chronic respiratory illness, for example, must be recognized as a symptom of a diseased environment. Bronchitis, emphysema and lung cancer are associated with both community air pollution and cigarette smoking as well as with occupational hazards, and efforts are being made to bring these environmental causes of respiratory disease under control (or in the case of cigarette smoking, to inform people of a personal environmental hazard which they inflict upon themselves). If medical cures were developed for emphysema, bronchitis and lung cancer, it seems likely that much concern about polluted air would be dissipated.

The first signs are beginning to show that modern man understands that things he does now can have a grave effect on him in the future. In October 1968 the Consolidated Edison Company of New York announced that it was seeking approval of the city to build an underground nuclear generating plant on Welfare Island in the East River almost at the same time that a task force headed by Laurance S. Rockefeller suggested that the electric utility industry, in order to protect the environment, should build nuclear plants underground.

In Pittsburgh, Pennsylvania, the city-county health department put into operation the first fully computerized air pollution detection system in the United States. This monitoring system was expected to provide the county health department with up-to-the-minute information on pollution levels at any point in the county, at any time. Further, striking at the root of the problem, the department proposed a code that would send air pollutors to jail or fine them $1000 a day. In addition, the code proposes to stop pollution before it occurs and to allow close monitoring of industry.

If the nation is going to change, we are going to have to develop a national philosophy about treating our environment. We're going to have to understand that the evidence shows that we are threatening ourselves with an inhospitable environment and that we are increasing this threat at an alarming rate.

Modern man has abused his environment more in the past one hundred years than his predecessors did in thousands of years. And like his predecessors, he is doing so through ignorance — ignorance despite a century of probing and thorough scientific searching to delineate the relationship of man to all that surrounds him. For even with the vast accumulation of the past one hundred years of knowledge, man is only beginning to understand how his health is affected by environmental degradation. He has yet to learn how environmental pollution relates to social pathology. He is hardly able to define the nature of an hospitable environment.

Modern man still assumes that because for thousands of years nature seemed to have the ability to absorb an increasing number and variety of environmental insults it will continue to be able to do so. Man still does not clearly understand that he lives in a delicate equilibrium with the biosphere — upon the precious earth crust, using and re-using the waters, drawing breath from the shallow sea of air. Because he has not understood this, he is now faced with an urgent necessity for defining a hospitable environment. Not just one in which man merely survives, but one in which he flourishes. The need for such urgency was underscored by the Director of the Missouri Botanical Garden, David M. Gates, who wrote, "Mankind has lit the fuse of the environmental bomb. It is not a question of whether or not it will explode, but only a matter of how fast."

It has been a slow and tortuous effort to build a momentum for concern for the environment. The first sanitarians began more than one hundred years ago to identify disease and illness as the backlash of misusing the environment. But only recently have we reached the point in this highly industrialized nation where a concerted effort is being made to determine what a hospitable environment is and how its existence can be ensured. It is doubtful that in the post-industrial era that is upon us we will have the same leisure to determine the answers to these two questions as we have had up to now to examine how our environment has been abused.

If we are to avoid the pathologies that can emerge from overcrowding and congestion, if we are to protect our water resources, if we are to avoid difficulties that could emerge from the use of nuclear energy — then we are going to have to plan more than we have planned ever before, and we are going to have to become able to eliminate environmental degradation with greater speed than we have been able to ever before. We are going to have to do a much better job and a much faster job of developing the information necessary to know how to deal with environmental deterioration. But mostly we are going to have to make decisions rather than simply seek answers.

For fifty years man has been accelerating rapidly his effort to protect his environment from his own onslaughts. We are now beginning to review and reevaluate our national philosophy of growth and expansion — which disregards its effect on the environment — and we are beginning to modify it. But we must develop a new philosophy — one that will assure a concerted effort to enhance the quality of the environment. We must have a national philosophy that concerns itself with both the physical and the mental health of the human being, a philosophy which, in taking both of these factors into account, must concern itself with the aesthetic quality of life.

Our national philosophy must strike a balance between the use of the environment to provide material wants and the preservation of the environment to enhance man's physical and mental well-being. Harold Wolozin of the University of Massachusetts pointed out the necessity of reevaluating some of our terms and goals in light of environmental problems when he reviewed A *Strategy for a Livable Environment*, a report

[338]

prepared in 1967 by a task force appointed by the Secretary of Health, Education and Welfare, John W. Gardner. Wolozin noted that the report set out an ambitious program of research and regulation in the immediate period ahead, but asked whether it went far enough into the future, saying, "Does it recognize the vast sums that will have to be expended and the income that will have to be foregone in order to insure a livable environment? Furthermore, does it face up to the probability that a livable environment will have to be looked upon as a public good in the jargon of the economist?"

The report recommended a system for dealing with environmental problems of today and tomorrow. The one aspect with which the report did not deal was economics.

Wolozin noted that economic growth by the year 2000 may pose a more serious threat to our environment than we are willing to admit.

A Strategy for a Livable Environment said, "American affluence today contaminates the nation's air, water, and land faster than nature and man's present efforts can cleanse them." We are already producing and consuming at levels that create waste products and nuisances which can no longer be cleaned up by the chemistry of nature or by the dispersion into the water and space of the globe. As population and the per capita output increase, the threat to our environment and to life itself will become significantly greater.

As Wolozin put it,

What we have enunciated here is, in a sense, a Malthusian type of forecast: pollution and the general deterioration of the environment will grow at a rate faster than the increase in population and national output. A fundamental problem that we are faced with in trying to eliminate environmental pollution is our inability, given the present state of our knowledge, to estimate the actual or even the potential cost of the damage which environmental pollution is doing. . . . We must face up to the fact that creating a livable environment, devising policies and means to do so, requires soul-searching decisions on resource allocations and public and private control of production and consumption.

It is clear that if we are going to be able to move politically, we are going to have to establish how much we are paying for not cleaning up our environment. We are also going to have to establish just who is making that payment. We have long taken the attitude that the air and water are free and that there is no cost to anybody in dumping wastes into either. This of course is not true. Something is used; someone is paying for that use. A manufacturer can dispose of unwanted materials at no cost to himself. But when he does, someone else has to take on the burden of paying for that disposal. Most of the cost is increased illness and discomfort, and thus a reduction in the value of the resource. As long as the resources were abundant, no one paid much attention. Now we have gone through one hundred years without assessing the cost of using those resources.

There is no better example of the difficulty of establishing cost than in the case of air pollution. Air pollution can be a local problem or a wide-ranging one, depending on the course of winds. It directly affects the physical health of human beings; it damages animals and crops. Its effect can be both chronic and acute. And, unlike water, air, once polluted, is untreatable. But the difficulty of establishing specific damage costs should not stop us from making the effort. Even if the first estimates lack something in their accuracy, a start has to be made someplace. As the estimates are made, more and more efforts will be undertaken to refine them, and ultimately our cost assesssments will become more and more acceptable. Somehow we have got to determine what it will cost in dollars for society to continue contamination of the environment as population and production rise. To determine who is getting the benefit of using the environment as a waste receptacle will be equally as important as determining who is paying the cost for such use. As we make progress in both these areas, which public policies must be adapted will become more evident.

For example, it will be clear that it will be less costly to prevent pollution than to clean it up after it occurs. It will be clear that it will be less costly to re-use wastes than to dispose of them. At this point many people now not only believe in these two statements, but believe they constitute public policy. Yet government dollars are not being spent so as to confirm this, and they won't be, as Wolozin says, until it is recognized that the quality of the environment in which man either flourishes or languishes is related directly to, and is responsible in part for, the state of economic growth. Or until it is recognized that human resources, if not adequately maintained, can be run down and destroyed by a hostile environment just as can physical capital.

No one is now doing any extensive calculations of the costs of environmental deterioration. No one is now making any serious assessment of social distress caused by environmental pollution. Neither in the government nor out of it is there any organization that has the power or the capacity to deal with the environment as a whole. The efforts of government at every level have been too fragmented and have come too late; the efforts of industry have been limited.

The failure to recognize the costs in human resources of polluting the environment, combined with the inadequacies of government and reluctance of industry to come to grips with environmental degradation, portend not a very optimistic view of the future, and will not brighten until the public understands that government must be able to foresee the effects of environmental pollution in order to be able to forestall them.

[341]

To foresee such effects the government must be able to assess the economic consequences of pollution, for which it must have the proper resources and capabilities.

The present level of government spending in the pollution control area is a joke. The Air Pollution Control Administration spends about $80 million a year. The Environmental Control Administration of the Department of HEW, spends about $65 million a year to control rats and noise, to improve water-supply quality, manage waste disposal and eliminate occupational illness and injury and radiological illness. The Food and Drug Administration has about $90 million a year to protect 200 million Americans from illness and death from contaminated foods and dangerous drugs. The economic losses to the nation from air pollution are in the billions, and all the agencies of the federal government combined spend less than one billion dollars a year on environmental protection.

Even with New York's water pollution control program, all fifty states combined spend less than one billion additional dollars a year for environmental protection. Local spending is not significant; local governments are forced to spend most of their environmental money for the collection of garbage and refuse, and so there are few funds left for the other aspects of environmental pollution.

America's sense of priorities is wrong. Tax dollars are not being spent the way they should be.

But tax dollars, as necessary as they are, alone will not solve the problem of environmental pollution. Dollars must support programs that produce knowledge which can be used to avoid pollution and correct what has occurred. Dollars must be supported by programs that will set standards of environmental quality and then enforce those standards.

Responsibility for preventing and correcting pollution will have to be divided between government and industry. Within government, responsibility will have to be shared at each level.

The federal government must undertake extensive research and development and provide technical assistance including substantial funding and must be able to provide leadership in establishing high levels of environmental quality.

Government at all levels must take prime responsibility for setting standards of environmental quality and enforcing them. But this alone is not enough. The Subcommittee on Science, Research and Development of the Committee on Science and Astronautics of the U.S. House of Representatives issued a report entitled *Managing the Environment,* which said:

A systems approach to public health, sanitation, welfare, and environmental quality is needed to get the most benefits from our surroundings, and from program dollars. Pollution abatement measures which are predicted on aesthetic, recreational or ancillary health benefits should be compared with other, similar means to the same or more significant ends. Pollution abatement might prove to be quite effective in some cases. On the other hand the enormous need of the urban, social and natural environment might be served better than by a further incremental improvement in air or water quality. The point is that choices cannot be made if no single coordination group views the total problem.

Congress certainly views the total problem. But its responsibility is set to public policy. And it must deal with much more than the environment. The President certainly views the total problem. But he must deal with much more than the environment.

Industry — particularly those operations that contribute to environmental pollution by the nature of their activities — has a responsibility to accept environmental quality standards and to work with government agencies in a positive manner to establish those standards. We can accept no longer the premise that there is no cost to the indiscriminate disposing of wastes into the environment. If water-quality standards are going to be low enough to foster indiscriminate industrial growth, then those industries feeding from that water should pay for their special benefits. Industry also must undertake research and use its technological know-how to develop ways of preventing environmental damage.

Government responsibility must begin at the local level. Planning for environmental improvement and implementing those plans can best be carried on at the local level, and local government must use its police powers, its tax powers, and its ability to regulate to prevent environmental pollution. Where there are a central city and surrounding suburbs, that planning must be area-wide to be effective, and therefore regional governmental agreements are going to have to be arrived at to deal with air pollution and waste management at the local level.

State government must accept responsibility for providing an adequate legal base for local action programs, for coordination among local areas within a state, for development of compacts with other states, and for funding.

In the 1940s Congress recognized that the economic well-being of the nation was important enough for the President to be provided special capability to enhance economic policy responsibilities and in 1946 authorized the creation of the Council of Economic Advisors.

Certainly the environmental well-being of the nation is as important as the economic well-being. But today, despite the existence of the Department of Health, Education and Welfare, the Department of the Interior, and other agencies with responsibility for environmental management, the Congress should create a Council on Environmental Quality to serve the President in the same manner as his Council of Economic Advisors.

A Council on Environmental Quality would prevent one

executive agency from having to satisfy two constituencies. The Interior Department, for example, would not be left to balance the interests of the oil industry with that of the public's need for water-pollution control. Such a council would serve to prevent the occurrence between executive agencies of conflict now resolved on the basis of who has the greater clout in Congress or is better able to get the ear of the President.

But even with the establishment of a Council on Environmental Quality, one federal agency still must have the capability to operate an environmental protection system. Dealing as is now done with problems of the environment by categories — occupational health, sanitary engineering, solid waste disposal, air pollution — is a hit-or-miss method that invites an insidious overspecialization with government personnel involved in disparate programs, often with conflicting goals. Common concern for overall environmental health objectives too often is crowded out.

The purpose of an environmental protection system is to provide the means of continuously identifying, analyzing and controlling environmental hazards, both old and new, and making certain that environmental protection efforts are comprehensively integrated.

There are four elements to such a protection system. One is constant awareness of what man is doing to air, water, land and space and how what he is doing affects his health and welfare. This is called surveillance and includes research to determine the health effects of pollutants. Currently this is being done in the United States on a piecemeal basis with a few pollutants. Air pollution has some local monitoring systems but needs one nationwide.

The second element is developing performance criteria for detection of pollution-causing elements. But this is a new art, and it is coming along very slowly. By 1968 criteria were being developed only in the air pollution program. But criteria must be developed for elements affecting all aspects of the environment. And it is not enough to set just one standard; that implies that no improvement need be planned for. Actually two standards should be set: one to be adhered to immediately and a second to be achieved within a given number of years.

This leads us then to the third element of the system, developmental research. This means using tax money to get industry to develop the means of achieving the higher standard. Federal appropriations should be used for industrial research for environmental improvement just as it has been for space and defense research.

The fourth element of the system is compliance — getting local government and industry to accept and implement the standards. If voluntary commitment cannot be obtained, government must have the authority to enforce standards.

The primary step in this systems approach is continuous surveillance of the environment for any element that does or may adversely affect man's health and welfare. This could be called an early warning system, and it should identify hazards before man falls victim to their effects. Assessment of physical, social, psychological and economic effects and their significance in increasing human susceptibility to physical, chemical and biological agents is needed. Without this activity it is impossible to define clearly what the problems are that are affecting man as a result of abusing his environment. Yet this is not done today.

The development of criteria for environmental quality should reflect and set forth the best knowledge of the effects of environmental contaminants, singly and in combination, on man's health and welfare. Such criteria would thus be expressed in terms of range of effects, beginning at the level of exposure at which no effect can be detected and extending from that point up — along a spectrum of observable effects.

The setting of criteria and promulgation of standards for any environmental contaminant is to some extent an arbitrary action, a value judgment which in many cases must be made on the basis of insufficient evidence. It is a weighing of risks versus rewards, of cost versus benefits to society. We could, for example, forbid the use of insecticides because of contamination of foodstuffs, but at the cost of a change in agricultural production.

Dr. James Goddard, former Commissioner of the Food and Drug Administration, said that we annually apply 600 million pounds of pesticide chemicals and other organic agricultural chemicals, fungicides and herbicides to the ground and crops. Pointing to a level of five-thousandths of a part per million, which industry believes is a safe residue of aldrin and dieldrin in milk, Dr. Goddard states, "No one knows what the quantal ingestion of three parts per billion of pesticides in milk would do over a long period." The major problem here is that there is a lack of scientific data to support a specific standard. Furthermore, even though toxicological research is vastly accelerated, it may take years to acquire and evaluate the data. Obviously, standards have to be set now in the absence of complete data, because the consumer must be protected. The level of pesticide residue permitted in milk must represent the best judgment that experts can now make concerning the potential hazard. If they are to err they must do so on the side of caution, curtailing the benefit to be derived through the use of pesticides and other chemicals in food production.

In the final analysis, success in dealing with environmental problems can be measured only by the improvement that

[347]

occurs, and to achieve improvement we must create local agencies capable of determining what is causing the environmental deterioration in their areas and taking the steps to bring the deterioration to an end. This requires providing funding to local agencies and developing enough trained persons to do the job. It means doing comprehensive health planning which includes action programs to change the nature of the physical environment. It means including in comprehensive transportation planning, a careful assessment of what the transportation plans will do to the physical environment. Comprehensive planning means shaping the pattern of land use in cities to enhance environmental quality.

This is not done today. Today the king is economic enhancement. And no local government will undertake environmental improvement if it means another area will get a more obvious economic advantage.

Thus if local government is to take the required initiative, the federal government must establish rules that make it impossible for industry to move for economic advantage over environmental protection. Unions must use their bargaining power and consumers their buying power to protect the environment.

René Dubos says the experience of our own period suggests that man's adaptability has remained as effective as it was during the ancient past. Modern man, like his ancestors, can achieve some form of physiological and socio-cultural adjustment to a very wide range of conditions, even when these appear almost incompatible with organic survival. Dubos says, "Because human beings are so likely to become adapted to many undesirable conditions and because they tend at present to make economic growth the most important criteria of social betterment, it will not be easy to create a climate of opinion favorable to the immense effort needed for the control of environmental threats. Yet it is certain that many environmental factors exert a deleterious influence on important aspects of human life."

What needs to be done is to fashion the tools and develop the information necessary to mobilize public support for environmental control. We must find which environmental factors exert deleterious influences and what the effect of the influence is. But we cannot wait until all the scientific evidence is conclusive. We must act on the basis of the knowledge in hand. We must accept that we will err; but the error will be to protect life not endanger it.

We cannot wait until the future proves that crowding and congestion cause severe social pathology and disruption. We cannot let economics weaken our resolve to restore the quality of polluted waters, particularly when the economics do not take into consideration human values. We cannot chance that nuclear technicians ever will be perfect. We cannot trust industry to police itself against selling dangerous goods.

We can use regulation and taxation so as to provide alternatives and incentives to keep population centers from demanding more of the physical environment than it can give. We can use a host of tools and public policies to restore and maintain a quality of environment as high as we want it. If we are to avoid a future of environmental crises we must do these things.

EPILOGUE

The air is clear as the plane approaches the airport, and the New York skyline stands out sharply against the horizon. It is an electrifying sight. Below is a panorama of boats in both the lower and upper parts of the bay. It has become a pleasure to sail on the blue-green waters fed by a Hudson River where fishing and swimming are enjoyed.

There are two ways into Manhattan from the airport: a quick underground journey in sleek, clean subway trains or a twenty-minute surface trip in a cab or bus.

The streets are clean in Manhattan. Private cars are restricted to underground throughways, and commercial traffic moves at a steady pace. Moving-belt sidewalks are wide enough to accommodate both walkers and stationary riders. Crowds are large, but there is no sense of jamming.

The situation is the same in all major cities. Growth rates are managed, and new towns are created when necessary. Air and water quality is rigidly maintained at levels that make it a pleasure to live. Land is used to serve human needs. Waste disposal problems have been conquered, and nuclear power, carefully monitored, is bringing a bonanza to life.

This is the U.S.A. of tomorrow.

Utopia? Perhaps. But one thing is certain; the choice between the confused society and the clean one lies completely with man.

AUTHOR'S NOTE

Professor Ian McTaggart Cowan, ecologist and dean of graduate studies at the University of British Columbia, made this statement in remarks at the Conference on the Future Environments of North America:

It is our thesis that as man expands his occupancy and varies his use of the North American continent, he can do so heedlessly, and so contribute to the further degradation of landscape, the pollution of the air, the land, the water, or he can do so with sensitivity and enlightenment, with a determination to conserve around him the greatest possible combination of the biological treasures that are end products of the eons of evolution that have preceded the present.

It is that thesis so simply yet eloquently stated which with slight modification I have used in fashioning this book. That modification is that man *has* heedlessly contributed to degradation of his environment and that he *must* in the future use sensitivity and enlightenment to avoid causing himself unnecessary illness and death. This position is not new or unique. While much of what I have written here has been recorded

[352]

by others, many of them scientists who have made invaluable assessments of environmental problems, I have attempted to reveal as simply as possible a view of the physical environment as it affects man.

If I have been successful in retelling this story of the danger man poses to himself by the way he lives, I will have excited the interest of the reader sufficiently to compel him to read for himself the works of the experts upon whom I relied in order that he may understand in more depth the problems we face. Many of those to whom I am indebted for their work in studying the environment are listed in the text. Others are listed in the bibliography.

Two men mentioned briefly in the text — while they bear no responsibility for what I have said in this book — are most responsible for my writing it. I am deeply indebted to United States Senator Edmund S. Muskie of Maine, whose probing mind and insatiable interest in solving man's problems stimulated, while I was working for him, my own interest in environmental problems and forced me to learn. I am also indebted to John W. Gardner, who as Secretary of Health, Education and Welfare in 1967 assigned me a task that intensified my need to learn about environmental problems and set performance standards so high that I had to know what I was talking about when I reported to him.

There are others who have helped me a great deal, and I wish I could mention them all here as well. Some others have been so involved, however, that I must mention them. I am grateful to Ralph Lapp for his suggestions. I must share credit for this work with my assistants David E. Osterhout and Ann Harlan. I could not have done without Sam Smith's editing advice. And I must thank my long-suffering secretaries, Mary Terpak, Jacqueline Weldon and Susan Bloom. Finally I must

[353]

express my gratitude to the Ford Foundation, who made it possible for me to complete the book.

Washington, D.C.
1969

RON M. LINTON

BIBLIOGRAPHY

GOVERNMENT PUBLICATIONS

Air Pollution. Hearings before the Subcommittee on Health and Safety, 88th Congress, 1st Session. U.S. House of Representatives, Committee on Interstate and Foreign Commerce. Washington, D.C.: U.S. Government Printing Office, 1963.

Air Pollution Control. Hearings before the Special Subcommittee on Air and Water Pollution, 88th Congress, 1st Session. U.S. Senate, Committee on Public Works. Washington, D.C.: U.S. Government Printing Office, 1963.

Air Pollution Control. Hearings before the Special Subcommittee on Air and Water Pollution, 89th Congress, 1st Session. U.S. Senate, Committee on Public Works. Washington, D.C.: U.S. Government Printing Office, 1965.

Air Pollution — A National Sample. U.S. Department of Health, Education, and Welfare. Washington, D.C.: U.S. Government Printing Office, 1966.

Atomic Fuel. U.S. Atomic Energy Commission, Division of Technical Information. Washington, D.C., 1967.

Clean Air. Field hearings before the Subcommittee on Air and Water Pollution, 88th Congress, 2nd Session. U.S. Senate, Committee on Public Works.

Clean Air Act Amendments and Solid Waste Disposal Act. Report No. 192 to accompany S. 306, 89th Congress, 1st Session. U.S. Senate, Committee on Public Works. Washington, D.C.: U.S. Government Printing Office, 1965.

The Cost of Clean Water. U.S. Department of the Interior. Washington, D.C.: U.S. Government Printing Office, 1968.

Electronic Products Radiation Control. Hearings before the Subcommittee on Public Health and Welfare, 90th Congress, 1st Session. U.S. House of Representatives, Committee on Interstate and Foreign Commerce. Washington, D.C.: U.S. Government Printing Office, 1967.

FDA Papers. "Special Issue — The Thirtieth Anniversary of the Food, Drug, and Cosmetic Act." Washington, D.C.: U.S. Government Printing Office, June 1968.

Historical Statistics of the United States, Colonial Times to 1957. U.S. Department of Commerce. Washington, D.C.: U.S. Government Printing Office, 1960.

Historical Statistics of the United States, Continuation to 1962 and Revisions. U.S. Department of Commerce. Washington, D.C.: U.S. Government Printing Office, 1965.

An Industrial Waste Guide to the Synthetic Textile Industry. U.S. Department of Health, Education, and Welfare, Public Health Service Publication No. 1320. Washington, D.C.: U.S. Government Printing Office, 1965.

Interstate Air Pollution Study — Phase II Project Report IV Odors — Results of Surveys. U.S. Department of Health, Education, and Welfare, Robert A. Taft Sanitary Engineering Center. Cincinnati, Ohio, June 1966.

Investigation of the Use of Chemicals in Foods and Cosmetics (H. Rept. 2356, 82nd Congress, 2nd Session) U.S. House of Representatives. Washington, D.C.: U.S. Government Printing Office, 1952.

Lake Erie Report, A Plan for Water Pollution Control. U.S. Department of Interior, Federal Water Pollution Control Administration (Great Lakes Region), August 1968.

The Nation's Water Resources — Summary Report. U.S. Water Resources Council, Washington, D.C.: U.S. Government Printing Office, 1968.

Nuclear Power Plants. U.S. Atomic Energy Commission, Division of Technical Information, Washington, D.C., 1966.

Nuclear Reactors. U.S. Atomic Energy Commission, Division of Technical Information, Washington, D.C., 1965.

An Odor Survey of the Two Kansas Cities, A Cooperative Study by the Cities of Kansas City, Kansas, and Kansas City, Missouri, and the Public Health Service of the U.S. Department of Health, Education, and Welfare, U.S. Department of Health, Education, and Welfare, July 1965.

Pollutional Effects of Pulp and Paper Mill Wastes in Puget Sound. A Report on Studies Conducted by the Washington State Enforcement Project, Federal Water Pollution Control Administration, Northwest Regional Office, Portland, Oregon. U.S. Department of the Interior, March 1967.

Public Health Service Drinking Water Standards. Revised. Public Health Service 956. Washington, D.C.: U.S. Government Printing Office, 1962.

Preliminary Results of 5263 X-Ray Protection Surveys of Facilities with Medical X-Ray Equipment . . . (1962–1967). Fess, Lawrence R., and LaVert C. Seaborn, Rockville, Md.: U.S. Department of Health, Education, and Welfare, National Center for Radiological Health, April 1968.

Proceedings, Volume 1 — Conference in the Matter of the Interstate Waters of the Hudson River and its Tributaries — New York and New Jersey. Waldorf-Astoria Hotel, New York, September 28, 1965. U.S. Department of Health, Education, and Welfare.

Proceedings, Volumes 1–4 — Conference in the Matter of Pollution of the Interstate Waters of the Lower Mississippi River. New Orleans, May 5–6, 1964. U.S. Department of Health, Education, and Welfare.

Proceedings, Surgeon General's Conference on Solid Waste Management for Metropolitan Washington, July 19–20, 1967. U.S. Department of Health, Education, and Welfare. Washington, D.C.: U.S. Government Printing Office, 1967.

Radiation Control for Health and Safety Act of 1967. Hearings before the Commerce Committee, 90th Congress, 2nd Session. U.S. Senate, Committee on Commerce. Washington, D.C.: U.S. Government Printing Office, 1968.

Radiation Protection in Educational Institutions, National Council on Radiation Protection and Measurements, NCRP Report No. 32. Washington, D.C., July 1966.

Radioactive Wastes. U.S. Atomic Energy Commission, Division of Technical Information. Washington, D.C., 1965.

Recommendations for the Safe Operation of Particle Accelerators. Gundaker, Walter E., and Richard F. Boggs. U.S. Department of Health, Education, and Welfare, National Center for Radiological Health, Rockville, Md., February 1968.

Report of the Medical X-Ray Advisory Committee on Public Health Considerations in Medical Diagnostic Radiology (X-Rays). U.S. Department of Health, Education, and Welfare. Washington, D.C.: U.S. Government Printing Office, October 1967.

Report on Pollution of Lake Erie and Its Tributaries. U.S. Department of Health, Education, and Welfare, Public Health Service, Division of Water Supply and Pollution Control, July 1965.

Restoring the Quality of Our Environment. President's Science Advisory Committee, Environmental Pollution Panel, Washington, The White House, 1965.

SL–1 Accident. Atomic Energy Commission Investigation Board Report, 87th Congress, 1st Session, U.S. Congress, Joint Committee on Atomic Energy. Washington, D.C.: U.S. Government Printing Office, 1965.

Solid Waste/Disease Relationships — A Literature Survey. U.S. Department of Health, Education, and Welfare. Washington, D.C.: U.S. Government Printing Office, 1967.

Status Report No. 2, Nuclear Fuel Services — Spent Fuel Processing Plant. U.S. Department of Health, Education, and Welfare, Division of Radiological Health. Washington, D.C., December 31, 1964.

Steps Toward Clean Air. Report from the Special Subcommittee on Air and Water Pollution, 88th Congress, 2nd Session, U.S. Senate, Committee on Public Works. Washington, D.C.: U.S. Government Printing Office, 1964.

A *Strategy for a Livable Environment.* A report to the Secretary of Health, Education, and Welfare. Task Force on Environmental Health and Related Problems. Washington, D.C.: U.S. Government Printing Office, 1967.

A *Study of Pollution — Air.* Staff Study, 88th Congress, 1st Session. U.S. Senate, Committee on Public Works. Washington, D.C.: U.S. Government Printing Office, 1963.

Study of Nebraska Meat-Packing Wastes. U.S. Department of Health, Education, and Welfare. Robert A. Taft Sanitary Engineering Center. Cincinnati, Ohio, February 1965.

A *Study of Pollution — Water.* Staff Study, 88th Congress, 1st Session. U.S. Senate, Committee on Public Works. Washington, D.C.: U.S. Government Printing Office, 1963.

Summary Report on Pollution of the Niagara River. International Joint Commission Advisory Board, October 1967.

Water Pollution. Hearings before the Special Subcommittee on Air and Water Pollution, Parts 1–3, 89th Congress, 1st Session. U.S. Senate, Committee on Public Works. Washington, D.C.: U.S. Government Printing Office, 1965.

Water Pollution Control. Hearings before the Special Subcommittee on Air and Water Pollution, 88th Congress, 1st Session. U.S. Senate, Committee on Public Works. Washington, D.C.: U.S. Government Printing Office, 1963.

ARTICLES

"Aircraft Noise — Unrelenting, Unremitting, Intolerable," *Environmental Science and Technology,* December 1967.

"Air Pollution — A Special Report," *Power,* December 1960.

Angelotti, Robert, and Keith H. Lewis. "Salmonellosis and the Meat Industry," *Proceedings of the Meat Industry Research Conference,* March 24–25, 1966. Chicago: American Meat Institute Foundation, 1966.

Archambault, La Salle. "The Effect of Noise on the Nervous System: A Plea for Official Action by This Society Toward Abatement of This Damaging Nuisance," *N.Y. State Journal of Medicine,* October 1, 1932.

Baron, Robert Alex. "Noise . . . Abatement Problems," *Hearing and Speech News,* May 1967.

Bartsch, Alfred F. "Stream Life and the Pollution Environment," *Public Works Publications,* July 1959, 104.

Browning, Glen, and James Mankin. "Gastroenteritis Epidemic Owing to Sewage Contamination of Public Water Supply," *Journal of the American Water Works Association,* November 1966.

[358]

Calhoun, John. "Population Density and Social Pathology," *Scientific American,* February 1962.

"The Case for Clean Air — Special Report," *Mill & Factory,* 1967.

Cohen, Alexander. "Location-Design Control of Transportation Noise," *Journal of the Urban Planning and Development Division — American Society of Civil Engineers,* December 1967.

Cralley, L. J., R. G. Keenan and J. R. Lynch. "Exposure to Metals in the Manufacture of Asbestos Textile Products," *American Industrial Hygiene Journal,* September-October 1967.

"Deskbook Issue — Environmental Engineering — A Complete Guide to Pollution Control," *Chemical Engineering,* October 14, 1968.

Dougherty, John D., and Oliver L. Welsh. "Environmental Hazards — Community Noise and Hearing Loss," *New England Journal of Medicine,* October 6, 1966.

"The Effective Use of X-Ray Radiation in Dentistry," *Oral Surgery, Oral Medicine and Oral Pathology,* March 1963.

Ferris, Benjamin G., and James L. Whittenberger. "Environmental Hazards — Effect of Community Air Pollution on Prevalence of Respiratory Disease," *New England Journal of Medicine,* December 22, 1966.

"The 500 Largest U.S. Industrial Corporations," *Fortune,* June 15, 1968.

Grimm, Roger C., and Howard L. Kusnetz. "The Plasma Torch," *Archives of Environmental Health,* March 1962.

Hoagland, Hudson. "Cybernetics of Population Control," *Bulletin of the Atomic Scientists,* February 1964.

"Industrial Air Pollution," *Factory,* October, 1965.

Jones, Herbert H., and Alexander Cohen. "Noise as a Health Hazard at Work, in the Community, and in the Home," *Public Health Reports,* July 1968.

Kryter, Karl D. "Effect of Noise on Man," *Journal of Speech and Hearing Disorders,* Monograph Supplement No. 1, September, 1950.

Lee, G. Fred, and E. Gus Fruh. "The Aging of Lakes," *Industrial Water Engineering,* February 1966.

Molos, Jerome E. "Control of Odors from a Continuous Soap Making Process," *Journal of the Air Pollution Control Association,* January 1961.

"Noise — Still Another Environmental Pollutant; Will All Remaining Havens of Silence Disappear?" *Conservation Foundation Letter,* December 29, 1967.

Novick, Sheldon. "Breeding Nuclear Power," *Scientist and Citizen,* June-July 1967.

Penfil, Richard L., and Morton L. Brown. "Genetically Significant Dose to the United States Population from Diagnostic Medical Roentgenology, 1964," *Radiology,* February 1968.

"The Polluted Air," *Time,* January 27, 1967.

Press, Edward. "Chemical Contaminants and Additives in Food and Water," Presentation to the Section Committee on Allergy of the American Academy of Pediatrics, October 20, 1968, Chicago.

Ripley, Randall B. "Congress and Clean Air: The Issue of Enforcement,

1963," *Congress and Urban Affairs*, F. N. Cleaveland, ed. Washington, D.C.: The Brookings Institution, 1968.

Ross, Everett C., K. W. Campbell and H. J. Ongerth. "Salmonella Typhimurium Contamination of Riverside, California, Supply," *Journal of the American Water Works Association*, February 1966.

"Solid Wastes — the Job Ahead," *APWA Reporter*, August 1966.

Strauss, W. "Odor Control for the Process Industries," *Chemical and Process Engineering*, March 1965.

Taylor, Floyd B., James Eagen, H.F.D. Smith, Jr., and Ronald Coene. "The Case for Water-Borne Infectious Hepatitis," *American Journal of Public Health*, December 1966.

Taylor, Floyd B. "Emergency Service on Poisons in Drinking Water," *Water & Sewage Works*, Annual Reference Number, 1965.

——— "Significance of Trace Elements in Public, Finished Water Supplies," *Journal American Water Works Association*, May 1963.

Weibel, S. R., F. R. Dixon, R. B. Weidner, and L. J. McCabe. "Waterborne-Disease Outbreaks, 1946–60," *Journal of the American Water Works Association*, August 1964.

Welch, Henry. "Problem of Antibiotics in Foods," *The Journal of the American Medical Association*, August 22, 1959.

BOOKS AND PAMPHLETS

American City Publishing Company. *The American City*: Vol. I, September–November 1909. New York.

American Public Works Association, Committee on Refuse Disposal. *Municipal Refuse Disposal*. American Public Works Association Research Foundation, Project No. 104. Chicago: Public Administration Service, 1961.

American Public Works Association, *Committee on Refuse Disposal. Refuse Collection Practice*. American Public Works Association Research Foundation, Project No. 101. Chicago: Public Administration Service, 1958.

Ayres, J. C., A. A. Kraft, H. E. Snyder, H. W. Walker, eds. *Chemical and Biological Hazards in Food*. Ames, Iowa: Iowa State University Press, 1962.

Bell, Alan. *Noise: An Occupational Hazard and Public Nuisance*. Geneva: World Health Organization, 1966.

Blake, John B. *Public Health in the Town of Boston 1630–1822*. Cambridge, Mass.: Harvard University Press, 1959.

Brown, Harrison. *The Challenge of Man's Future*. New York: Viking, 1954.

Buer, M. C. *Health, Wealth, and Population in the Early Days of the Industrial Revolution*. New York: Howard Fertig, 1968.

Cassedy, James H. *Charles V. Chapin and the Public Health Movement.* Cambridge, Mass.: Harvard University Press, 1962.

Chemicals Used in Food Processing. Publication 1274, National Academy of Sciences — National Research Council. Washington, D.C., 1965.

The Control of Noises. National Physical Laboratory, Symposium No. 12. London: Her Majesty's Stationery Office, 1961.

Diamond, Sigmund, ed. *The Nation Transformed — The Creation of an Industrial Society.* New York: Braziller, 1963.

Dubos, René. *Man Adapting.* New Haven: Yale University Press, 1965.

Duhl, Leonard J., ed. *The Urban Condition: People and Policy in the Metropolis.* New York: Basic Books, 1963.

Edelson, Edward. *The Battle for Clean Air.* Public Affairs Pamphlet No. 403. New York: Public Affairs Committee, 1967.

Eisenbud, Merril. *Environmental Radioactivity.* New York: McGraw-Hill, 1963.

An Evaluation of Public Health Hazards from Microbiological Contamination of Foods. Publication 1195, National Academy of Sciences — National Research Council. Washington, D.C., 1964.

Frye, Alton. *The Hazards of Atomic Wastes: Perspectives and Proposals on Oceanic Disposal.* Washington, D.C.: Public Affairs Press, 1962.

Gordon, Mitchell. *Sick Cities.* Baltimore: Penguin, 1966.

Green, Constance McLaughlin. *American Cities in the Growth of the Nation.* Great Britain: Broadwater Press, 1957.

Hall, Edwart T. *The Hidden Dimension.* Garden City, N.Y.: Doubleday, 1966.

Hatt, Paul K., Albert J. Reiss, Jr., eds. *Reader in Urban Sociology.* Glencoe, Ill. Free Press, 1951.

Herber, Lewis. *Crisis in Our Cities.* Englewood Cliffs, N.J.: Prentice-Hall, 1965.

———— *Our Synthetic Environment.* New York: Knopf, 1962.

Hormonal Relationships and Applications in the Production of Meats, Milk, and Eggs. Publication 714, National Academy of Sciences — National Research Council. Washington, D.C., 1959.

Jennings, Burgess H., and John E. Murphy, eds. *Interactions of Man and His Environment.* New York: Plenum, 1966.

Keep Our City Clean. Issued by the Civic Improvement League. St. Louis, 1902.

Lake Erie Bathing Beach Water Quality. Report to the Lake Erie Enforcement Conferees. June, 1968.

Lewis, Howard R. *With Every Breath You Take.* New York: Crown, 1965.

Longgood, William. *The Poisons in Your Food.* New York: Simon & Schuster, 1960.

McCabe, Louis, ed. *Air Pollution: Proceedings of the United States Technical Conference on Air Pollution.* New York: McGraw-Hill, 1952.

Mooney, Booth. *The Hidden Assassins.* Chicago: Follett, 1966.

Mumford, Louis. *City in History.* New York: Harcourt, Brace and World, 1961.

[361]

National Conference on Air Pollution, Proceedings. Washington, D.C., December 1962.

Nevins, Allan. *The Emergence of Modern America, 1865–1878.* New York: Macmillan, 1927.

New Developments and Problems in the Use of Pesticides. Publication 1082, National Academy of Sciences — National Research Council. Washington, D.C., 1963.

Report of the Lake Erie Enforcement Conference Technical Committee. Made to the Lake Erie Enforcement Conferees, March, 1967.

Rogers, Edward S. *Human Ecology and Health.* New York: Macmillan, 1960.

Rosen, George. *A History of Public Health.* New York: MD Publications, 1958.

Schlesinger, Arthur M. *The Rise of the City, 1878–1898.* New York: Macmillan, 1933.

Schubert, Jack, and Ralph E. Lapp. *Radiation: What It Is and How It Affects You,* New York: Viking, 1957.

Sheps, Mindel, and Jeanne Claire Ridley, eds. *Public Health and Population Change.* Product of a Symposium on Research Issues in Public Health and Population Change sponsored by the Graduate School of Public Health, University of Pittsburgh, 1964. Pittsburgh: University of Pittsburgh Press, 1965.

Smillie, Wilson G. *Public Health Administration in the United States.* New York: Macmillan, 1940.

Stewart, George R. *Not So Rich As You Think.* Boston: Houghton Mifflin, 1968.

Sundquist, James L. *Politics and Policy — The Eisenhower, Kennedy, and Johnson Years.* Washington, D.C.: The Brookings Institution, 1968.

Sydenstricker, Edgar. *Health and Environment.* New York: McGraw-Hill, 1933.

Tobey, James A. *The National Government and Public Health.* Baltimore: Johns Hopkins Press, 1926.

University of Michigan School of Public Health and the Institute of Industrial Health. *Noise: Causes, Effects, Measurement, Costs, Control.* Ann Arbor: University of Michigan Press, 1952.

Vaughan, Richard D., and Ralph J. Black. *The Federal Solid Wastes Program — A Progress Report.* In Proceedings of National Incinerator Conference. New York: American Society of Mechanical Engineers, 1968.

Waste Management and Control: A Report to the Federal Council for Science and Technology. Publication 1400, National Academy of Science — National Research Council. Washington, D.C., 1966.

Winslow, C. E. A. *Man and Epidemics.* Princeton: Princeton University Press, 1952.

Woods, Robert A., W. T. Elsing, Jacob A. Riis, et al. *The Poor in Great Cities.* New York: Scribner's, 1895.

World Health Organization. *Air Pollution.* Monograph Series No. 46. Geneva, 1961.

[362]

INDEX

Acids, 60, 124, 167, 168, 186, 216, 218, 221, 223
Acoustical Society of America, 98
Adrenal hormones, 26
AFL–CIO, 218
Agriculture; use of pesticides in, 134–136, 347; use of antibiotics, 139; use of chemicals, 218; near nuclear plants, 235–236; projected future, 252; diseases from, 272. *See also* Air pollution: effect on agriculture; Meat; Waste
Air pollution, 37–71; by industry, 34, 39–42, 45, 49, 50, 51, 52, 53, 55–57, 59–60, 68–69, 71, 79–80, 215–216, 218–221; examples, in specific areas, 37–48, 52–59, 67–71; ingredients, 39, 42, 44, 51, 54, 60–61, 68; man-made causes, 39, 42, 49, 51, 54, 60, 62, 329; property damage from, 40, 48, 53, 60, 81, 214; meteorological and geographic causes, 42–43, 45, 57, 68, 83; by automobiles, 43, 45–46, 51–56, 58, 60–61, 69–71, 86, 268, 270, 316, 321, 329–330; definition, 44, 203, 340; by air traffic, 45; effect on agriculture and animals, 46–51; effect on humans, 47–49, 51–52, 54, 75–78, 80–81; conferences and studies on, 48–49, 51, 53–54, 57–59, 61–67; photochemical (smog), 48–50, 54, 67–71; effect on trees, 49–50; and urban areas, 51–52, 62, 64; and visibility, 52, 55, 58–59; art and book damage, 53, 55; relation to health and disease, 56, 60–67, 75–78, 81, 83, 268–270, 336; effect on breathing, 66; relation to psychic disorders, 76, 93; classifications, 60; cost, 53, 60, 70, 340, 342; and economic deterioration, 74; control, 69–70, 316, 320–326, 328–331, 336, 345–346; in early America, 51, 197–198; from radioactive gases,

230; from nuclear wastes and accidents, 233, 235, 238, 242, 248; from metallic compounds, 268–270, 277; from plasma torch, 276; from waste disposal, 297, 304, 308, 310; future projection, 253; mentioned, 19, 34, 35. *See also* Odor pollution
Air Pollution Control Administration, 342
Air traffic: as air pollutant, 45; endangered by air pollution, 52, 55, 58–59; noise from, 103–105, 113–118, 331
Airplanes, 210, 266. *See also* Air traffic
Akron, O., 191, 192
Alabama, 56–57, 218, 324
Albany, N.Y., 285–287, 289
Albany County, N.Y., 163–164
Alcoholism, 27
Aldehydes, 39, 60, 167
Algae, 175, 179–185, 238–239
Allergies, 29, 140, 254, 267–270, 273
Allied Chemical, 188
American International Refining Co., 220
American Journal of Public Health, 305
American Medical Association, 104, 140, 165, 324–325
American Municipal Association, 324, 325
American Public Health Association, 98
American Public Works Association, 301, 303
Ammonia, 39, 168, 186, 190, 217
Anacostia River, 296, 298
Animals, 91–92, 166–167, 201, 219. *See also* Cattle; Meat; Waste: animal
Antibiotics, 136, 139–144
Antioxidants, 146
Appalachian Mountains, 56
Archambault, LaSalle, 119–120

[363]